*Rod and Staff Books*

(Milestone Ministries)
800-761-0234 or 541-466-3231
www.RodandStaffBooks.com

# Mathematics for Christian Living Series

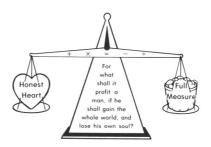

Honest Heart

Full Measure

For what shall it profit a man, if he shall gain the whole world, and lose his own soul?

# Mathematics for Christian Living Series

## Working Arithmetic

## Grade 2

### Teacher's Manual
Units 1, 2

*Rod and Staff Publishers, Inc.*
Hwy. 172, Crockett, Kentucky 41413
Telephone: (606) 522-4348

# Acknowledgments

We are indebted to God for the vision of the need for a *Mathematics for Christian Living Series* and for His enabling grace. Charitable contributions from many churches have helped to cover the expenses for research and development.

This revision was written by Sisters Miriam Rudolph and Marla Martin. The brethren Marvin Eicher, Jerry Kreider, and Luke Sensenig served as editors. Most of the illustrations were drawn by Lois Myer. The work was evaluated by a panel of reviewers and tested by teachers in the classroom. Much effort was devoted to the production of the book. We are grateful for all who helped to make this book possible.

—The Publishers

This book is part of a course for grade 2 arithmetic and will be most effective if used with the other parts of the course. *Working Arithmetic* includes the following items:

Teacher's Manual, part 1 (Units 1, 2)
Teacher's Manual, part 2 (Units 3–5)
Pupil's Workbook, Unit 1
Pupil's Workbook, Unit 2
Pupil's Workbook, Unit 3
Pupil's Workbook, Unit 4
Pupil's Workbook, Unit 5
Blacklines

Copyright, 1992

by

*Rod and Staff Publishers, Inc.*

**Hwy. 172, Crockett, Kentucky 41413**

Printed in U.S.A

ISBN 978-07399-0460-2
Catalog no. 13291.3

# CONTENTS

## Materials for This Course

### Books and Worksheets

5 Pupil's Workbooks

2 Teacher's Manuals

Blacklines

### Teaching Aids

Addition and Subtraction Flash Cards 1–18

Individual Student Flash Cards 11–18

\* Boat Poster

\* Clover Patch Poster

\* Blossom Charts

\* 1,000 Book

Number Line 0–100

Large coins

Large clock

Cup, pint, quart, gallon

\* See pages 12–14 for further instructions.

# An Overview of This Course

## Understanding the Teacher's Manual

In the Teacher's Manual, each lesson is outlined under three main headings: *Before Class, Class Time,* and *After Class.*

*Before Class* lists the things to do before school in the morning.

(1) Gather the materials that are listed.

(2) Put your chalkboard samples and exercises on the board.

*Class Time* is the second heading. *Class Time* tells you what to do during your teaching session. This section contains the core of the lesson. Begin with number 1 and proceed step by step to the last point. Bold type indicates what is spoken or recited. An ellipsis ( . . . ) usually means to continue with more of this same drill. The last point always reads: Assign Lesson (number)

SAMPLE (Lesson 5)

**Get your arithmetic book. Tear out Lesson 5.** Pause until the books have been put away again.

**Begin with the first whole and parts. Trace and write the first facts. Then move on to the next whole and parts, and facts.**

**We understand how to do the second page. Tell me what you will do at the top of the third page. Tell me what you will do at the water lilies.**

**When you have completed and checked over these three pages, you may do the Extra Activity. How many rows will you fill today?**

We will fill all the rows that have equal lines.

Your teaching session does not include doing the workbook lesson. Your teaching and chalkboard samples prepared the children to work. They are eager to begin. The exercises are repetitive. A running look at each page is sufficient.

However, if the children ought to be more particular in number formation or rechecking their work, tell them before they begin the day's work.

*After Class* is the last heading. These exercises are like the gravy on the potatoes. They add flavor for today and savor for tomorrow.

*After Class* gives further practice with new material, and it also previews concepts that are taught in succeeding lessons. Thus, new material is introduced by stages: first in *After Class,* then in *Class Time,* and finally in the pupil's lesson. A pupil is usually exposed to a new concept several times before he actually uses it in a written assignment.

When should you use *After Class*? Near the end of your arithmetic period or in the afternoon. Try to cover each point. Some individual drills can be done in other free time, such as lunch time.

## The Pupil's Workbook

Each workbook lesson has two perforated sheets. Allow the children to keep the books inside their desks. They can tear out one lesson each day.

Tear-out pages will make checking more convenient for you. It will help to keep the parent abreast with his child's daily performance because the child will take arithmetic work home every day, not just when the book is completed.

The first three pages of a lesson contain the core of the child's seatwork for that lesson. The fourth page is an Extra Activity or a Speed Drill.

Use the Extra Activity *only* after the rest of the lesson is completed. If you need to choose between Extra Activity and Blacklines, choose Extra Activity.

Many pages have a line of fine print at the bottom. Use these thoughts as is suitable for your class, to develop an atmosphere of God-consciousness in relation to the lesson. The line can be read and discussed at the beginning of the assignment. Able students can be encouraged to look up the references and read the account after the assignment is finished. When there is not time to discuss the bottom line in class, it can be a silent influence to think of God in the sphere of arithmetic class.

## Grading Arithmetic

Since the arithmetic lesson is the core of the child's work, his arithmetic grade should be derived from the lesson. The number of answers will vary from one lesson to another. But the total value of each lesson will not vary.

The total value of each lesson has been established as 50 points. Therefore, if you use an E-Z Grader, always set it at 50 to determine the child's score.

In most lessons the actual number of answers is more than 50. But each lesson has some review exercises. With the E-Z Grader set at 50, the child will lose more points if he gets a review exercise wrong. This is realistic, for the child should have a thorough mastery of that exercise.

## Speed Drills

This course has 81 Speed Drills in the pupil's workbooks. Speed Drills appear on the fourth page of Lessons 6, 8, and 10. They begin again in Lesson 16 and continue every two lessons through Lesson 170.

Give the Drill right after the teaching session before the children begin the workbook lesson.

(1) Their minds will be fresh.

(2) They will not have had an opportunity to mentally answer the Drill beforehand.

Administering the Speed Drill:

**Tear out the two pages for today's lesson.** Pause until the books have been put away again. **Find the Speed Drill. Look at me. Pencils up!** Each child will raise his pencil above his head. **Ready, set, go!**

After 1 minute: **If you are not finished, circle the problem you are working on, and then finish.**

Check the completed Drills immediately. The child will write the number of correct answers inside the bee. If he has any fact wrong, he will write it correctly in the boxes below.

## Extra Activity

This course has Extra Activity pages in the pupil's workbook. Extra Activity appears on the fourth page of Lessons 1-5, 7, 9, 11-15, 17, 19; and continues every two lessons through Lesson 169.

Extra Activity is not a part of the lesson core. Use Extra Activity *only* after the core of the lesson is done. The children should complete the Extra Activity before they work on the Blacklines for a particular lesson.

The type of work on the Extra Activity page will vary throughout the year.

*Rocky Bluff*

In Lesson 1-40 the Extra Activity is a rocky bluff where the facts are written. The child begins at the top.

In Lesson 1 he fills two rows.

In Lesson 2 he fills three rows.

In Lesson 3 he fills four rows.

In each lesson the screened equal lines show the child how far to write the facts.

The illustrations below show in what order the facts will be written. Facts with 0 are not written.

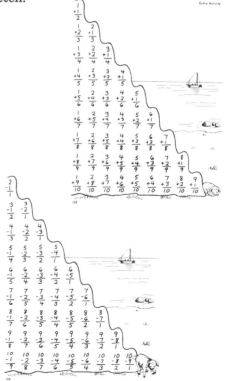

*Beehive*

In Lessons 41–159 the Extra Activity is a skep (straw hive).

When there is one triplet, fill all the clovers and bees with that triplet.

When there are two or more triplets, make the triplets take turns as you fill the clovers and bees.

The small bee inside a skep ring shows which facts shall be written in this ring.

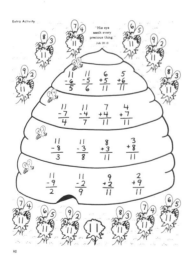

*Miniature Blossom Charts*

In Lessons 161–169 the Extra Activity is a review of Blossom Charts 11–18. The whole number will be written in the blossom. The parts will be written in the bees.

## Blacklines

Since the amount of work a class needs will vary from year to year, this course includes Blacklines. These Blacklines may be reproduced as needed in teaching the course.

The Teacher's Manual lists the Blacklines that correlate with each lesson. The Blacklines are listed in order of importance. For example, Lesson 8:

Blacklines
    Number Facts #2
    Form B
    Missing Numbers #4

Select Number Facts #2 before Form B. Use the Blacklines as masters. Make as many copies as you need for your class.

A lesson number is in the upper righthand corner of most Blacklines.

 means use in Lessons 8, 9, and 10.

 means this is a form. There are four forms in all: A, B, C, and D. They will be used in many lessons.

 means this is a fact form. There are twelve fact forms in all: I–XII. They will be used in many lessons.

You may ask, "Why the same worksheet again and again?" This is the way second graders learn. "Line upon line, line upon line." (Isaiah 28:10).

The Blacklines are not confined to these specific lessons. For example, your children may need drill in writing numbers in sequence for Lesson 3, but Form A is not listed with Blacklines in Lesson 3. You may copy Form A and give it to your children again.

A handy way to file your Blackline masters is to put them in a 1½" D-Ring Binder. Since the forms will be used often, put those at the front of your notebook. Keep each skill set together. *Multiply and Divide* is optional; put this set at the back of the notebook. File the other sets in alphabetical order as they are in the box or in the order they are introduced in the course.

(This order is listed below.)
- Forms A–D
- Forms I–XII
1. Missing Numbers
2. Number Facts
3. 2-Place Computation
4. Skip Counting
5. Money
6. Reading Problems
7. Fact Hives
8. Missing Whole or Parts
9. Triplets With Facts
10. Number Triplets
11. Number Words
12. Mixed Computation
13. Equations
14. Multiply and Divide

## Directions for Blackline Forms

**Form A——** *Number Grid.* Turn the paper sideways to write numbers in the rows. Use this form to make a blank copy of *My 1,000 Book* for each child. Have the children fill in the numbers to write their own 1,000 books as they are able in spare time.

**Form B——** *Addition and Subtraction Facts.* Write the facts up to the family currently being studied.

**Form C——** *Flash Card Drill.* Use the pictures in the left margin to identify which row you are working on. As you flash a fact card, the children will write the answer in a box.

**Form D——** *Blank Fact Form.* Use this form for special drill on problem combinations. Prepare the sheet by filling it with facts for the combination that needs to be drilled.

**Fact Forms**—Use these sheets often as progress checks and refresher drills.

## Directions for Blacklines

**Equations**—Complete each equation. The word box on the right will help the child to spell his words correctly.

**Fact Hives**—The triplet at the first skep in each row tells which facts shall be written in that row. Write the facts in order.

**Missing Numbers**—Write the numbers that are missing.

**Missing Whole or Parts**—Fill in the missing whole number or the missing part.

**Mixed Computation**—Figure the answer to the first two numbers; then add or subtract the third number. Write the answer.

**Money Identification**—Write the name of the coin on the blank and the value in the box.

**Number Facts**—Answer the facts.

**Number Triplets**—Write the whole number on the clover blossom. Write the parts on the bee's wings.

**Number Words**—Write the numerals for the number words.

**Reading Problems**
- #1 Read the story. Write the numbers in the beehive. Write the label words on the lines.
- #4 Read the sentence. Write the problem in the box.

**Skip Counting**—Read the directions. Start with that number in the first blank and continue counting until the blanks are full. Have the children use *My 1,000 Book* for help.
- #3 Count 25–100 again and again.

**Triplets With Facts**—What triplet must the child think of to complete the fact? Write the whole number in the clover; write the parts on the bee's wings. Complete the fact.

**2-Place Computation**—Answer the problems.

**Multiply/Divide** (Optional)
*Multiply Form.* Copy a multiplication table from a key four times.
*Divide Form.* Copy a division table from a key four times.
- #1 Each child will use his multiplication key to answer the facts.
- #2 Each child will use his division key to answer the facts.

## The Whole Number and Its Two Parts

In Grade 1, the child learned that addition is putting two or more numbers together to see how many there are in all. He learned that subtraction is taking a part away, then discovering how many are left. Addition and subtraction facts were learned by families.

In Grade 2 Lessons 1–40 are basically review.

Addition—Lessons 1–10
Subtraction—Lessons 11–20
Addition—Lessons 21–30
Subtraction—Lessons 31–40

In this review the child sees that each number fact has a whole number and two parts. The whole and parts are illustrated with sailboats on a poster.

After Lesson 40 new addition and subtraction facts are introduced in the same lesson. They are introduced by the whole number and its two parts. They are illustrated with clover blossoms and bees on a poster.

The whole number and two parts are called a triplet. Example: (11) 6 5. This method of introducing facts is valuable for these eight reasons:

1. The whole number is seen first.
2. The two parts are seen second.
3. Memorizing the triplet (11) 6 5 helps the child to know four facts:
   $11-6=5$, $11-5=6$, $6+5=11$, $5+6=11$.
4. The triplet helps the child realize that no matter if he adds or subtracts, (11) 6 5 must stay together.
5. The child can clearly understand the interrelationship of addition and subtraction.
6. It helps the child comprehend reading problems. He determines which is missing, the whole or a part. If the whole is missing, he adds. If the part is missing, he subtracts.
7. It breaks the crutch of tapping out answers with the fingers.
   The child sees $5+6=\_\_$.
   He taps 6, 7, 8, 9, 10, **11**.
   He sees $11-5=\_\_$.
   He taps 10, 9, 8, 7, **6**.

With the "whole number and two parts" method *the child does not tap at all*.

8. When a child knows the triplet (11) 6 5, he can quickly answer all these combinations:

| | | |
|---|---|---|
| $5+6=\_\_$ | $6+\_\_=11$ | $11-\_\_=5$ |
| $6+5=\_\_$ | $5+\_\_=11$ | $11-\_\_=6$ |
| $\_\_+5=11$ | $11-5=\_\_$ | $\_\_-5=6$ |
| $\_\_+6=11$ | $11-6=\_\_$ | $\_\_-6=5$ |

## Hand Signals

Develop a healthy combination of verbal and visual teaching. It helps a teacher and a group of children to count and recite with one voice because everyone starts together, stays together, and stops together.

The first day, introduce a few hand signals.

1. One downward sweep of your hand means "begin together or answer together."
2. A cupped hand at your ear means "speak up."
3. A wide-spread hand means "stop."

Following are illustrations of other hand signals you will find sprinkled through the Teacher's Manual.

The teacher will motion and say:

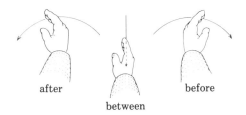

after          between          before

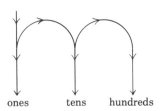

ones          tens          hundreds

Since the children are facing you, their motions will mirror yours. When you motion to your right, they will motion to their left. This is why the ones, tens, hundreds motion proceeds from left to right for you.

## Scheduling Arithmetic Class

Arithmetic is one of the basic subjects in second grade. A basic subject should be taught in the morning when a child is most alert. Aim to have each child complete the day's assignment. Reading, English, and recess will also need to be scheduled during these morning hours. You may circle back in the afternoon and complete unfinished seatwork or *After Class* activities.

A suggested order:
1. Conduct *Class Time* period.
2. Do the Speed Drill—if the lesson has one.
3. Assign the lesson.
4. Work on Extra Activity—if the lesson has one.
5. Do *After Class* activities.
6. As children finish their seatwork, some may have time to do a Blackline copy.

## Multiplication and Division

Multiplication and division are optional in Grade 2. If you teach them, begin no earlier than Lesson 124. You may begin later than Lesson 124. The outline below shows the scope of multiplication and division in this course. Each table is used for nine lessons, six lessons with multiplication and three lessons with division.

### Multiply and divide by 2

*Lessons*        *Activities*
124, 125, 126—Copy the multiplication facts.
127, 128, 129—Answer the multiplication facts.
130, 131, 132—Copy and answer the division facts.

### Multiply and divide by 10

133, 134, 135—Copy the multiplication facts.
136, 137, 138—Answer the multiplication facts.
139, 140, 141—Copy and answer the division facts.

### Multiply and divide by 5

142, 143, 144—Copy the multiplication facts.
145, 146, 147—Answer the multiplication facts.
148, 149, 150—Copy and answer the division facts.

### Multiply and divide by 1

151, 152, 153—Copy the multiplication facts.
154, 155, 156—Answer the multiplication facts.
157, 158, 159—Copy and answer the division facts.

In Grade 2, Multiplication and Division are optional because
- the Addition and Subtraction facts are to be taught, drilled, or reviewed daily.
- some children need all their time for Addition and Subtraction facts.
- Multiplication and Division are taught as new concepts in Grade 3.

Therefore
- the *Class Time* will continue to center around Addition and Subtraction.
- the children will continue to carry their Addition and Subtraction flash cards home each evening to practice.
- the ring of keys with Multiplication and Division tables will not be carried home to practice.
- no Multiplication or Division exercises are in the workbook. They are on Blacklines.
- the keys will introduce the children to the signs ($\times$ $\sqrt{\phantom{x}}$) and operations.
- the children will learn to read and copy the facts. They will not master the facts until Grade 3.

### Multiplication and Division Keys
**Making the Keys**
Materials
Heavy paper, file-folder weight is ideal
1 metal ring that opens and closes for each child (Look for them in a bookstore or office supply store.)
Key patterns can be found in the Multiply/Divide set of the Blacklines.
1. Copy the keys onto heavy paper.
2. You may have each child cut out his own key.
3. Fasten the key to the ring.

**Using the keys**
1. Use them during *After Class* activities.
2. Use them for referral during seatwork.

# TEACHING AIDS

## My 1,000 Book

In the set of Blacklines for this course are masters for *My 1,000 Book*. Before the school term opens, copy a 1,000 book for each child in second grade. A clear plastic report cover with a backbone spine will make a nice book.

The book will be used during *Class Time* for counting beyond 100. It will be used during seatwork for writing beyond 100. It will be used for counting by 1's, 2's, 5's, and 10's.

The book will be used first in Lesson 3 during *Class Time* and seatwork.

## Number Line

A Number Line is a long runner-type chart showing large, clear, easy-to-read numbers. You will find a Number Line with numbers 0–100 very helpful in second grade.

Mount the Number Line high on the wall before the school year begins. If you do not have space to put it in one continuous line, divide the line at number 50. Mount 1–50 above and 51–100 beneath.

You may purchase a Number Line at a local school supply store or order it from

Kurtz Bros.
Clearfield, PA 16830
PA: 800-252-3811
Other States: 800-441-8223

## Money

In second grade, pennies, nickels, dimes, and quarters are reviewed, and half dollars are introduced. Counting different kinds of coins is directly related to different kinds of rote counting.

- Count by 1's for pennies
- Count by 5's for nickels
- Count by 10's for dimes
- Count by 25's for quarters

The children will count and add money. They will learn how to change 115¢ to $1.15.

Real coins will be used during *After Class*. Giant coins will be used to drill and review money. You may purchase giant coins at a local school supply store or order them from the address above.

## Boat Poster

In lessons 1–40 you will use this poster to illustrate the "whole and parts" concept.

**Making the poster**
Materials:
   41" × 22" blue poster board
   Blue crayon
   White poster board
   Black construction paper
   Patterns—See Appendix, page 212.

1. Lay the bottom edge of the wave pattern flush with the bottom edge of the blue poster board. Trace the waves. Flip the pattern end for end. Trace more waves. Continue to flip and trace until you have 10 "dips."
2. Outline the waves with blue crayon.
3. Cut a 2½" slit in the "dip" of each wave.
4. Trace 10 sailboats on white poster board. Paste black construction paper on the back of the white poster board. Cut out the boats. When the boats are finished, they will be black on one side and white on the other side.
5. Optional: Add a cloud and birds.
6. Optional: The sailboats may be laminated to make sliding in and out of slots easier. When cutting out the boats, be careful to keep a sealed edge around the paper.

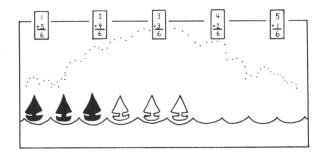

### Mounting the poster

Mount the poster on the wall with E-Z Clips. E-Z Clips will hold the poster away from the wall, making it easier to slide the boats in and out of the slots.

### Using the poster

1. *Always* place the first boat in the first wave on the left.
2. *Always* have the dark boats first and the light boats last. Never mix the dark and light boats.
3. When you want to exchange a dark boat for a light boat, pull the dark boat out, flip it over and slide it back into the same slot.
4. Tack your flash cards above the poster with E-Z Clips.
5. Follow these rules for addition and subtraction.

## Clover Patch Poster

In Lessons 41–159 you will use this poster to illustrate the whole and parts concept.

### Making the poster

Materials:

44¼″ × 14″ light green poster board
White poster board
Patterns—See Appendix, page 212
Ruler      Crayons
Pencil      Scissors
Razor blade      Paste

1. Draw a light horizontal line 5 inches above the bottom of the green poster board.
2. Begin at the left end of the line and mark ¾″, 1½″, ¾″, 1½″ . . . until you reach the right end of the line.
3. With the green marker, draw a tall grass clump in every ¾″ section. Draw a short grass clump in every 1½″ section.
4. Cut a horizontal slit through each 1½″ (short grass) section.

### Making the blossoms

1. Use pink. Color 10 blossoms without bees. Paste these blossoms on white poster board.
2. Use pink. Color 9 blossoms with bees. Paste these on the back of 9 blossoms that you made in point 1.
3. Use red-violet. Color 8 blossoms without bees. Paste these blossoms on white poster board.
4. Cut out the blossoms. Slide them into the slots in the grass.
5. Optional: Add treetops and more grass.
6. Optional: The clover blossoms may be laminated to make sliding in and out of slots easier. When you cut out the blossoms, be careful to keep a sealed edge around the paper.

### Mounting the poster

Mount the poster on the wall with E-Z clips when you are ready for Lesson 41. Preceding Lesson 41 is an explanation on using the Clover Patch Poster, page 148.

## Blossom Charts

In lessons 47–170 you will use Blossom Charts to drill the triplets.

**Making the charts**

Materials:

8 (13″ × 16″) pieces of posterboard

8 large clover blossoms—See Appendix page 217.

20 bees—See Appendix, page 216.

Black marker (broad-tipped)

Green marker (broad-tipped)

Crayons

1. Color the clover blossoms pink, red, purple, white, red-violet, or yellow.
2. Color the bees yellow and brown. Do not color the wings.
3. Use the black marker to write the *whole* numbers on the clover blossoms.
4. Use the green marker to write the *parts* on the bees' wings.

| | | | |
|---|---|---|---|
| (11)  9  2 | (12)  9  3 | | |
| (11)  8  3 | (12)  8  4 | (13)  9  4 | (14)  9  5 |
| (11)  7  4 | (12)  7  5 | (13)  8  5 | (14)  8  6 |
| (11)  6  5 | (12)  6  6 | (13)  7  6 | (14)  7  7 |

  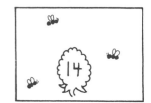

| | | | |
|---|---|---|---|
| (15)  9  6 | (16)  9  7 | | |
| (15)  8  7 | (16)  8  8 | (17)  9  8 | (18)  9  9 |

Why are subtraction facts first? The (11) 9 2 facts are taught, drilled, and written in this order:

$$
\begin{array}{cccc}
11 & 11 & 9 & 2 \\
-9 & -2 & +2 & +9 \\
\hline
2 & 9 & 11 & 11
\end{array}
$$

We begin with $11-9=2$ because

- the numbers in the problem are in the same order as the triplet.
- we say the *whole* number first—11.
- we say the greater *part* next—9.
- the clover patch poster illustrates the greater *part* and then the lesser *part*.

**Using the Blossom Charts**

1. Blossom 11 Chart is first used in Lesson 47.
2. The Teacher's Manual tells you when to add each new bee.
3. The Teacher's Manual tells you when to mount a new Blossom Chart.
4. *Drill, drill, drill the triplets.* Always say the *whole* number first, the greater *part* second, the smaller *part* last: (11) 9 2.
5. Add bee after bee to a Blossom Chart. Add chart after chart to the wall until Blossom Charts 11–18 are all displayed.

# New Skills Listed by Lessons

| | Teacher's Manual | | Pupil's Book |
|---|---|---|---|
| **Lesson Number** | **New Skills** | **Lesson Number** | **New Skills** |
| 1 | Addition Families 2 and 3<br>Whole and parts concept<br>Largest number<br>Counting by 1's | 1 | Addition Families 2 and 3<br>Whole and parts concept<br>After numbers<br>Counting by 1's |
| 2 | Addition Family 4 | 2 | Addition Family 4 |
| 3 | Addition Family 5<br>After numbers | 3 | Addition Family 5<br>Largest numbers |
| 4 | Addition Family 6<br>Before numbers | 4 | Addition Family 6 |
| 5 | Place value: 1's, 10's, 100's | 5 | |
| 6 | Reading Problem: key word—in all<br>2 digits + 2 digits | 6 | Place value: 1's, 10's, 100's<br>Before numbers |
| 7 | Addition Family 7<br>Penny | 7 | Addition Family 7 |
| 8 | 2 digits + 1 digit | 8 | 2 digits + 2 digits<br>Reading Problem: key word—in all<br>Penny |
| 9 | Skip counting by 10's | 9 | |
| 10 | | 10 | 2 digits + 1 digit |
| 11 | Subtraction families 2 and 3<br>Smallest number | 11 | Subtraction Families 2 and 3<br>Skip counting by 10's |
| 12 | Subtraction Family 4<br>Before and After numbers | 12 | Subtraction Family 4 |
| 13 | Subtraction Family 5<br>2 digits − 2 digits | 13 | Subtraction Family 5<br>Smallest number |

# New Skills Listed by Lessons

## Teacher's Manual

| Lesson Number | New Skills |
|---|---|
| 14 | Subtraction Family 6<br>Reading Problem: key word—left<br>Dime |
| 15 | 2 digits − 1 digit |
| 16 | |
| 17 | Subtraction Family 7 |
| 18 | |
| 19 | Dimes + pennies<br>Before and After numbers by 10's |
| 20 | |
| 21 | Addition Family 8<br>Skip counting by 5's |
| 22 | Nickel |
| 23 | Reading Problem: key word—altogether |
| 24 | Addition Family 9 |
| 25 | 3 digits + 3 digits |
| 26 | |

## Pupil's Book

| Lesson Number | New Skills |
|---|---|
| 14 | Subtraction Family 6 |
| 15 | 2 digits − 2 digits |
| 16 | Dime |
| 17 | Subtraction Family 7<br>2 digits − 1 digit |
| 18 | |
| 19 | Dimes + pennies<br>Reading Problem: key word—left |
| 20 | |
| 21 | Addition Family 8<br>Before and After numbers by 10's |
| 22 | |
| 23 | Skip counting by 5's |
| 24 | Addition Family 9<br>Nickel |
| 25 | |
| 26 | |

# New Skills Listed by Lessons

## Teacher's Manual

| Lesson Number | New Skills |
|---|---|
| 27 | Addition Family 10<br>Nickels + pennies |
| 28 | 3 digits + 2 digits |
| 29 | |
| 30 | Reading Problem: key word—both |
| 31 | Subtraction Family 8<br>Skip counting by 25's<br>Before and After numbers by 5's |
| 32 | Quarter |
| 33 | Reading Problem: no key word |
| 34 | Subtraction Family 9 |
| 35 | 3 digits − 3 digits |
| 36 | Quarters + pennies |
| 37 | Subtraction Family 10<br>3 digits − 2 digits |
| 38 | 1 digit + 1 digit + 1 digit<br>Find total cents |
| 39 | Skip counting by 2's |

## Pupil's Book

| Lesson Number | New Skills |
|---|---|
| 27 | Addition Family 10<br>3 digits + 3 digits |
| 28 | |
| 29 | Nickels + pennies<br>3 digits + 2 digits |
| 30 | |
| 31 | Subtraction Family 8<br>Before and After numbers by 5's |
| 32 | |
| 33 | Skip counting by 25's |
| 34 | Subtraction Family 9<br>Quarter |
| 35 | |
| 36 | 3 digits − 3 digits |
| 37 | Subtraction Family 10<br>Quarters + pennies |
| 38 | 3 digits − 2 digits |
| 39 | |

# New Skills Listed by Lessons

| Teacher's Manual | | Pupil's Book | |
|---|---|---|---|
| **Lesson Number** | **New Skills** | **Lesson Number** | **New Skills** |
| 40 | | 40 | |
| | | | |
| 41 | (11)  9  2  triplet and facts | 41 | (11)  9  2  triplet and facts<br>Skip counting by 2's |
| 42 | Before and After numbers by 2's | 42 | |
| 43 | Clocks—:00<br>Missing whole or part | 43 | Find total cents |
| 44 | Reading Problem: missing part | 44 | 1 digit + 1 digit + 1 digit<br>Missing whole or part<br>Clocks—:00 |
| 45 | | 45 | Before and After numbers by 2's |
| 46 | (11)  8  3  triplet and facts | 46 | (11)  8  3  triplet and facts |
| 47 | | 47 | |
| 48 | Equation: 60 minutes = 1 hour | 48 | |
| 49 | Dimes + nickels | 49 | |
| 50 | | 50 | Reading Problem: no key word<br>Dimes + nickels |
| 51 | (11)  7  4  triplet and facts | 51 | (11)  7  4  triplet and facts |

# New Skills Listed by Lessons

## Teacher's Manual

| Lesson Number | New Skills |
|---|---|
| 52 | |
| 53 | 2 digits + 2 digits + 2 digits |
| 54 | |
| 55 | Equation: 30 minutes = ½ hour |
| 56 | (11)  6  5  triplet and facts<br>Clocks—:30<br>2 digits + 2 digits + 1 digit |
| 57 | |
| 58 | Missing Signs |
| 59 | |
| 60 | |
| | |
| 61 | (12)  9  3  triplet and facts<br>Skip Counting by 100's<br>Mental arithmetic |
| 62 | Place value: 1's, 10's, 100's, 1,000's |
| 63 | |

## Pupil's Book

| Lesson Number | New Skills |
|---|---|
| 52 | Reading Problem: key word—altogether |
| 53 | |
| 54 | |
| 55 | 2 digits + 2 digits + 2 digits |
| 56 | (11)  6  5  triplet and facts |
| 57 | Clocks—:30 |
| 58 | |
| 59 | |
| 60 | |
| | |
| 61 | (12)  9  3  triplet and facts<br>2 digits + 2 digits + 1 digit |
| 62 | |
| 63 | |

# New Skills Listed by Lessons

| | Teacher's Manual | | | Pupil's Book | |
|---|---|---|---|---|---|
| **Lesson Number** | **New Skills** | | **Lesson Number** | **New Skills** | |
| 64 | Reading Problem: 2-digit computation<br>Reading Problem: ¢ | | 64 | Place value: 1's, 10's, 100's, 1,000's | |
| 65 | Carrying: 2 digits + 2 digits | | 65 | | |
| 66 | (12)  8  4  triplet and facts | | 66 | (12)  8  4  triplet and facts | |
| 67 | | | 67 | Carrying: 2 digits + 2 digits | |
| 68 | | | 68 | | |
| 69 | | | 69 | | |
| 70 | | | 70 | | |
| 71 | (12)  7  5  triplet and facts | | 71 | (12)  7  5  triplet and facts | |
| 72 | Clocks—:15 | | 72 | | |
| 73 | | | 73 | | |
| 74 | | | 74 | Clocks—:15 | |
| 75 | | | 75 | | |
| 76 | (12)  6  6  triplet and facts | | 76 | (12)  6  6  triplet and facts | |
| 77 | | | 77 | | |

# New Skills Listed by Lessons

## Teacher's Manual

| Lesson Number | New Skills |
|---|---|
| 78 | |
| 79 | (13)  9  4  triplet and facts<br>Clocks—:45 |
| 80 | |
| 81 | |
| 82 | |
| 83 | Shapes: circle, square |
| 84 | Column addition—carrying<br>Shape: triangle |
| 85 | |
| 86 | |
| 87 | (13)  8  5  triplet and facts<br>Shape: rectangle |
| 88 | Borrowing: 2 digits — 2 digits |
| 89 | |
| 90 | |
| 91 | |

## Pupil's Book

| Lesson Number | New Skills |
|---|---|
| 78 | Reading Problem: key word—both |
| 79 | (13)  9  4  triplet and facts |
| 80 | |
| 81 | Clocks—:45 |
| 82 | |
| 83 | |
| 84 | Column addition—carrying<br>Shapes: circle, square |
| 85 | Shape: triangle |
| 86 | |
| 87 | (13)  8  5  triplet and facts<br>Shape: rectangle |
| 88 | |
| 89 | |
| 90 | Borrowing: 2 digits — 2 digits |
| 91 | |

# New Skills Listed by Lessons

## Teacher's Manual

| Lesson Number | New Skills |
|---|---|
| 92 | |
| 93 | |
| 94 | |
| 95 | (13)  7  6  triplet and facts |
| 96 | |
| 97 | $ sign and decimal point |
| 98 | Fraction: ½ |
| 99 | |
| 100 | Reading Problem: how much more |
| 101 | |
| 102 | |
| | |
| 103 | (14)  9  5  triplet and facts |
| 104 | |

## Pupil's Book

| Lesson Number | New Skills |
|---|---|
| 92 | |
| 93 | |
| 94 | |
| 95 | (13)  7  6  triplets and facts |
| 96 | |
| 97 | |
| 98 | $ sign and decimal point |
| 99 | |
| 100 | Fraction: ½<br>Reading Problem: missing part |
| 101 | |
| 102 | |
| | |
| 103 | (14)  9  5  triplet and facts |
| 104 | |

# New Skills Listed by Lessons

## Teacher's Manual

| Lesson Number | New Skills |
|---|---|
| 105 | |
| 106 | Fraction: ¼ |
| 107 | |
| 108 | ½ of a number |
| 109 | |
| 110 | |
| 111 | (14)  8  6  triplet and facts |
| 112 | |
| 113 | Reading Problem: how much less |
| 114 | Carrying twice: 3 digits + 3 digits |
| 115 | Equation: 12 things = 1 dozen<br>Equation:  6 things = ½ dozen |
| 116 | |
| 117 | Reading Problem: 1 dozen<br>Equation: 7 days = 1 week |
| 118 | |

## Pupil's Book

| Lesson Number | New Skills |
|---|---|
| 105 | |
| 106 | |
| 107 | |
| 108 | Fraction: ¼ |
| 109 | |
| 110 | |
| 111 | (14)  8  6  triplet and facts |
| 112 | Reading Problem: 2-digit computation |
| 113 | |
| 114 | |
| 115 | Carrying twice: 3 digits + 3 digits |
| 116 | Reading Problem: ¢ |
| 117 | Equation: 12 things = 1 dozen<br>Equation:  6 things = ½ dozen |
| 118 | |

# New Skills Listed by Lessons

| Teacher's Manual | | Pupil's Book | |
|---|---|---|---|
| Lesson Number | New Skills | Lesson Number | New Skills |
| 119 | (14)  7  7  triplet and facts<br>Equation: 12 months = 1 year | 119 | (14)  7  7  triplet and facts |
| 120 | | 120 | |
| 121 | | 121 | |
| 122 | (15)  9  6  triplet and facts | 122 | (15)  9  6  triplet and facts |
| 123 | Reading Problem: ½ dozen | 123 | |
| 124 | 2 × table (optional) | 124 | |
| 125 | Equation: 12 inches = 1 foot | 125 | |
| 126 | | 126 | |
| 127 | | 127 | Reading Problem: 1 dozen<br>Equation: 12 inches = 1 foot |
| 128 | Even and odd numbers<br>Equation: 3 feet = 1 yard | 128 | |
| 129 | | 129 | Equation: 3 feet = 1 yard |
| 130 | (15)  8  7  triplet and facts<br>Divide by 2 (optional) | 130 | (15)  8  7  triplet and facts |
| 131 | | 131 | |
| 132 | Skip Counting by 50's | 132 | |

# New Skills Listed by Lessons

## Teacher's Manual

| Lesson Number | New Skills |
|---|---|
| 133 | Half dollar<br>10× table (optional) |
| 134 | Half dollar + dimes |
| 135 | |
| 136 | |
| 137 | |
| | |
| 138 | (16) 9 7 triplet and facts<br>Half dollar + pennies |
| 139 | Divide by 10 (optional) |
| 140 | Fraction: ⅓ |
| 141 | |
| 142 | Finding the sum<br>5× table (optional) |
| 143 | |
| 144 | |
| 145 | |
| 146 | (16) 8 8 triplet and facts |

## Pupil's Book

| Lesson Number | New Skills |
|---|---|
| 133 | |
| 134 | |
| 135 | Half dollar + dimes |
| 136 | |
| 137 | |
| | |
| 138 | (16) 9 7 triplet and facts<br>Half dollar + pennies |
| 139 | |
| 140 | |
| 141 | Fraction: ⅓ |
| 142 | |
| 143 | |
| 144 | |
| 145 | |
| 146 | (16) 8 8 triplet and facts |

# New Skills Listed by Lessons

## Teacher's Manual

| Lesson Number | New Skills |
|---|---|
| 147 | Equation: 2 cups = 1 pint |
| 148 | Divide by 5 (optional) |
| 149 | (17)  9  8  triplet and facts |
| 150 | Equation: 2 pints = 1 quart |
| 151 | 1× table (optional) |
| 152 | |
| 153 | Reading Problem: difference<br>Equation: 4 quarts = 1 gallon |
| 154 | |
| 155 | |
| 156 | |
| 157 | (18)  9  9  triplet and facts<br>Equation: 16 ounces = 1 pound |
| 158 | |
| 159 | |
| 160-170 | Review |

## Pupil's Book

| Lesson Number | New Skills |
|---|---|
| 147 | |
| 148 | |
| 149 | (17)  9  8  triplet and facts<br>Equation: 2 cups = 1 pint |
| 150 | |
| 151 | Equation: 2 pints = 1 quart |
| 152 | |
| 153 | |
| 154 | |
| 155 | Equation: 4 quarts = 1 gallon |
| 156 | |
| 157 | (18)  9  9  triplet and facts |
| 158 | Equation: 16 ounces = 1 pound |
| 159 | |
| 160-170 | Review |

# Unit 1

## Lessons 1–40

Trace the *whole* and *parts*.
Trace and write the facts.

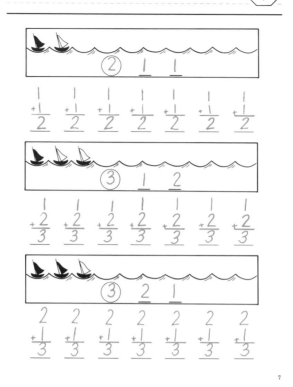

## Before Class

Tack Addition 2 and 3 flash cards above the waves in this order:

$$\begin{array}{r} 1 \\ +1 \\ \hline 2 \end{array} \qquad \begin{array}{r} 1 \\ +2 \\ \hline 3 \end{array} \qquad \begin{array}{r} 2 \\ +1 \\ \hline 3 \end{array}$$

**Materials** (Use italicized items in *After Class*)
  2, 3 sailboats
  *Addition 2 and 3 flash cards*

**Chalkboard**

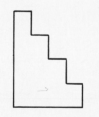

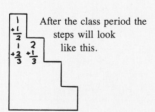

After the class period the steps will look like this.

## Class Time

1. Call the children to the Number Line. Point to 0.
   **Count 0–50 with me.**

2. a. Motion: **After, after, after.**
   b. **Answer together. What comes after 9, 36, 12, 48, 19, 43, 21, 30, 25, 49, 17?**

3. Have the children stand near the Boats and Waves Chart.

   | 1 dark boat, 1 light boat |
   | --- |

   Circle the boats with your finger.
   **2 boats in the sea;**
   **2 is the whole number.**
   **What part of the 2 has dark sails?** 1
   **What part of the 2 has light sails?** 1
   **2 is the whole number.**
   **Its parts are 1 and 1.**
   a. Fill in ②  1  1  on the board as everyone repeats: **2 is the whole number. Its parts are 1 and 1.**
   b. Point to the flash card: **1 + 1 = 2 . . .**

Answer these facts.

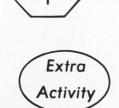

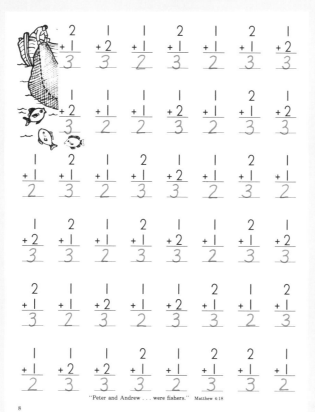

$$\begin{array}{ccccccc} 2 & 1 & 1 & 2 & 1 & 2 & 1 \\ +1 & +2 & +1 & +1 & +1 & +1 & +2 \\ \hline 3 & 3 & 2 & 3 & 2 & 3 & 3 \end{array}$$

$$\begin{array}{ccccccc} 1 & 1 & 1 & 1 & 1 & 2 & 1 \\ +2 & +1 & +1 & +2 & +1 & +1 & +2 \\ \hline 3 & 2 & 2 & 3 & 2 & 3 & 3 \end{array}$$

$$\begin{array}{cccccccc} 1 & 2 & 1 & 2 & 1 & 1 & 2 & 1 \\ +1 & +1 & +1 & +1 & +2 & +1 & +1 & +1 \\ \hline 2 & 3 & 2 & 3 & 3 & 2 & 3 & 2 \end{array}$$

$$\begin{array}{cccccccc} 1 & 2 & 1 & 2 & 1 & 1 & 2 & 1 \\ +2 & +1 & +1 & +1 & +2 & +1 & +1 & +2 \\ \hline 3 & 3 & 2 & 3 & 3 & 2 & 3 & 3 \end{array}$$

$$\begin{array}{cccccccc} 2 & 1 & 1 & 1 & 1 & 2 & 1 & 2 \\ +1 & +1 & +2 & +1 & +2 & +1 & +1 & +1 \\ \hline 3 & 2 & 3 & 2 & 3 & 3 & 2 & 3 \end{array}$$

$$\begin{array}{cccccccc} 1 & 1 & 1 & 2 & 1 & 2 & 2 & 1 \\ +1 & +2 & +2 & +1 & +1 & +1 & +1 & +1 \\ \hline 2 & 3 & 3 & 3 & 2 & 3 & 3 & 2 \end{array}$$

"Peter and Andrew . . . were fishers."   Matthew 4:18

8

---

4. | 1 dark boat, 2 light boats |

   Circle the boats with your finger.

   **3 boats in the sea;**

   **3 is the whole number.**

   **What part of the 3 has dark sails?** 1

   **What part of the 3 has light sails?** 2

   **3 is the whole number.**

   **Its parts are 1 and 2.**

   a. Fill in ③ 1 2 on the board as everyone

      repeats: **3 is the whole number. Its parts**
      **are 1 and 2.**

   b. Point to the flash card: **1 + 2 = 3** . . .

5. | 2 dark boats, 1 light boat |

   Circle the boats with your finger.

   **3 boats in the sea;**

   **3 is the whole number.**

   **What part of the 3 has dark sails?** 2

   **What part of the 3 has light sails?** 1

   **3 is the whole number.**

   **Its parts are 2 and 1.**

   a. Fill in ③ 2 1 on the board as everyone

      repeats: **3 is the whole number. Its parts**
      **are 2 and 1.**

   b. Point to the flash card: **2 + 1 = 3** . . .

6. Stand near the steps on the board.

   Write **1 + 1 = 2, 1 + 2 = 3, 2 + 1 = 3.**

7. Assign Lesson 1.

*Note:* Facts with zero, such as 0 + 0, 0 + 1, and
1 + 0, are not tacked above the waves. Include the zero facts with the flash cards that
you use for individual and class drill, as in *After
Class* #1.

30

Fill in the missing numbers.

| 0 | 1 | 2 | 3 | 4 | 5 | 6 | 7 | 8 | 9 |
|---|---|---|---|---|---|---|---|---|---|
| 10 | 11 | 12 | 13 | 14 | 15 | 16 | 17 | 18 | 19 |
| 20 | 21 | 22 | 23 | 24 | 25 | 26 | 27 | 28 | 29 |
| 30 | 31 | 32 | 33 | 34 | 35 | 36 | 37 | 38 | 39 |
| 40 | 41 | 42 | 43 | 44 | 45 | 46 | 47 | 48 | 49 |

Write the numbers that come after.

**Blackline**

Missing Numbers #1

| 7 | 8 | 9 | 13 | 14 | 15 |
|---|---|---|----|----|----|
| 45 | 46 | 47 | 26 | 27 | 28 |
| 29 | 30 | 31 | 9 | 10 | 11 |
| 35 | 36 | 37 | 38 | 39 | 40 |
| 47 | 48 | 49 | 19 | 20 | 21 |

9

## After Class

```
              12  18  19
              48  45  47
              17  37  27
23  43  13    25  35  45
40  20  30    21  12  22
```

1. Drill each child with Addition 2 and 3 flash cards.

2. Call the children to the water lily.

   **Near the edge of the sea where the water is still, God makes water lilies grow. The lily buds push up through the water. Then the petals unfold to make a beautiful, large flower.**

   **Buzz-z! A thirsty bee darts down to get a drink from the largest lily.**

   Have the children circle the largest number.

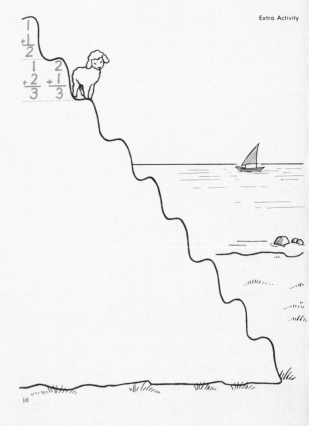

Extra Activity

$\frac{1}{+\frac{1}{2}}$

$\frac{1}{+\frac{2}{3}}$  $\frac{2}{+\frac{1}{3}}$

10

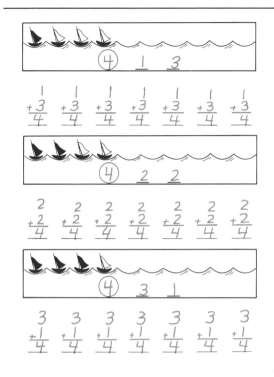

Trace the *whole* and *parts*.
Trace and write the facts.

$$\text{④} \quad 1 \quad 3$$

$$\begin{array}{c}1\\+3\\\hline 4\end{array}\quad\begin{array}{c}1\\+3\\\hline 4\end{array}\quad\begin{array}{c}1\\+3\\\hline 4\end{array}\quad\begin{array}{c}1\\+3\\\hline 4\end{array}\quad\begin{array}{c}1\\+3\\\hline 4\end{array}\quad\begin{array}{c}1\\+3\\\hline 4\end{array}\quad\begin{array}{c}1\\+3\\\hline 4\end{array}$$

$$\text{④} \quad 2 \quad 2$$

$$\begin{array}{c}2\\+2\\\hline 4\end{array}\quad\begin{array}{c}2\\+2\\\hline 4\end{array}\quad\begin{array}{c}2\\+2\\\hline 4\end{array}\quad\begin{array}{c}2\\+2\\\hline 4\end{array}\quad\begin{array}{c}2\\+2\\\hline 4\end{array}\quad\begin{array}{c}2\\+2\\\hline 4\end{array}\quad\begin{array}{c}2\\+2\\\hline 4\end{array}$$

$$\text{④} \quad 3 \quad 1$$

$$\begin{array}{c}3\\+1\\\hline 4\end{array}\quad\begin{array}{c}3\\+1\\\hline 4\end{array}\quad\begin{array}{c}3\\+1\\\hline 4\end{array}\quad\begin{array}{c}3\\+1\\\hline 4\end{array}\quad\begin{array}{c}3\\+1\\\hline 4\end{array}\quad\begin{array}{c}3\\+1\\\hline 4\end{array}\quad\begin{array}{c}3\\+1\\\hline 4\end{array}$$

11

## Before Class

Tack Addition 4 flash cards above the waves in
  this order:

$$\begin{array}{c}1\\+3\\\hline 4\end{array}\qquad\begin{array}{c}2\\+2\\\hline 4\end{array}\qquad\begin{array}{c}3\\+1\\\hline 4\end{array}$$

Materials (Use italicized items in *After Class*.)

4 sailboats
*Addition 2–4 flash cards*

Chalkboard

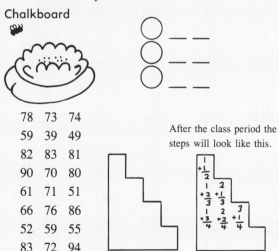

| | | |
|---|---|---|
| 78 | 73 | 74 |
| 59 | 39 | 49 |
| 82 | 83 | 81 |
| 90 | 70 | 80 |
| 61 | 71 | 51 |
| 66 | 76 | 86 |
| 52 | 59 | 55 |
| 83 | 72 | 94 |

After the class period the
steps will look like this.

## Class Time

1. Call the children to the Number Line. Point to 0.
   **Count 0–100 with me.**

2. **When I pause, tell me the answer.**
   **The teens begin with ____.** 1
   **The 20's begin with ____.** 2
   Continue to **The 90's begin . . .**

3. **The bee buzzes to the large lily.** Have the
   children circle the largest number.

4. Stand near the boats and waves.

   | 1 dark boat, 3 light boats |

   Circle the boats with your finger.
   **4 boats in the sea;**
   **4 is the whole number.**
   **What part of the 4 has dark sails?** 1
   **What part of the 4 has light sails?** 3
   **4 is the whole number.**
   **Its parts are 1 and 3.**

   a. Fill in the whole and parts on the board as
      everyone repeats; **4 is the whole number.**
      **Its parts are 1 and 3.**

2

Answer these facts.

| | | | | | | |
|---|---|---|---|---|---|---|
| 1 +3 = 4 | 3 +1 = 4 | 1 +1 = 2 | 1 +3 = 4 | 2 +1 = 3 | 2 +2 = 4 | 3 +1 = 4 |
| 1 +3 = 4 | 3 +1 = 4 | 1 +2 = 3 | 3 +1 = 4 | 1 +1 = 2 | 3 +1 = 4 | 2 +2 = 4 |
| 1 +2 = 3 | 1 +3 = 4 | 1 +2 = 3 | 2 +1 = 3 | 2 +2 = 4 | 1 +2 = 3 | 1 +3 = 4 | 2 +1 = 3 |
| 3 +1 = 4 | 1 +1 = 2 | 1 +3 = 4 | 3 +1 = 4 | 1 +2 = 3 | 3 +1 = 4 | 1 +1 = 2 | 2 +2 = 4 |
| 1 +3 = 4 | 1 +2 = 3 | 1 +3 = 4 | 3 +1 = 4 | 2 +2 = 4 | 1 +3 = 4 | 1 +2 = 3 | 3 +1 = 4 |
| 2 +2 = 4 | 1 +3 = 4 | 2 +1 = 3 | 3 +1 = 4 | 1 +3 = 4 | 2 +1 = 3 | 2 +2 = 4 | 1 +3 = 4 |

"Peter and Andrew . . . were fishers." Matthew 4:18

12

b. Point to the flash card: 1+3=4 . . .

5. ⬚ 2 dark boats, 2 light boats

Circle the boats with your finger.
**4 boats in the sea;**
**4 is the whole number.**
**What part of the 4 has dark sails?** 2
**What part of the 4 has light sails?** 2
**4 is the whole number.**
**Its parts are 2 and 2.**

   a. Fill in the whole and parts on the board as everyone repeats: **4 is the . . . Its parts are . . .**

   b. Point to the flash card: 2+2=4 . . .

6. ⬚ 3 dark boats, 1 light boat

Circle the boats with your finger.
**4 boats in the sea;**
**4 is the whole number.**
**What part of the 4 has dark sails?** 3
**What part of the 4 has light sails?** 1
**4 is the whole number.**
**Its parts are 3 and 1.**

a. Fill in the whole and parts on the board as everyone repeats: **4 is the . . . Its parts are . . .**

b. Point to the flash card: 3+1=4 . . .

7. **Can you name one of Jesus' disciples who had a fishing boat?**
Peter (Luke 5:3)

8. **Say the facts as I fill the steps. 1+1=2, 1+2=3, 2+1=3, 1+3=4, 2+2=4, 3+1=4.**

9. Assign Lesson 2.

*Note:* Be prepared to give each child a copy of *My 1,000 Book* in Lesson 3. See page 12 for an explanation. Patterns can be found in the blacklines packet for this course.

Fill in the missing numbers.

| 50 | 51 | 52 | 53 | 54 | 55 | 56 | 57 | 58 | 59 |
|----|----|----|----|----|----|----|----|----|----|
| 60 | 61 | 62 | 63 | 64 | 65 | 66 | 67 | 68 | 69 |
| 70 | 71 | 72 | 73 | 74 | 75 | 76 | 77 | 78 | 79 |
| 80 | 81 | 82 | 83 | 84 | 85 | 86 | 87 | 88 | 89 |
| 90 | 91 | 92 | 93 | 94 | 95 | 96 | 97 | 98 | 99 |

Write the numbers that come after.

| 57 | 58 | 59 | 69 | 70 | 71 |
|----|----|----|----|----|----|
| 63 | 64 | 65 | 74 | 75 | 76 |
| 95 | 96 | 97 | 62 | 63 | 64 |
| 79 | 80 | 81 | 56 | 57 | 58 |
| 88 | 89 | 90 | 97 | 98 | 99 |

**Blacklines**

Form A: 0–99

Missing Numbers #1

13

## After Class

1. Drill individuals with Addition 2–4 flash cards.

2. | Chalkboard Drill |  Have the children stand at the board with chalk and an eraser. **Write these three numbers:**

   24, (pause) **85,** (pause) **36. Erase.**

   **70**   **51**   **19. Erase.**

   **43**   **67**   **92. Erase.**

   **58**   **35**   **86. Erase.**

Extra Activity

### Note . . .

The students have not had much practice with the subtraction facts they learned near the end of first grade. To strengthen subtraction skills, hang up the subtraction flash cards (with answers showing) that correspond to the addition families you are currently teaching. Recite them with the class a few times a day.

14

**3**

Trace the *whole* and *parts*.
Trace and write the facts.

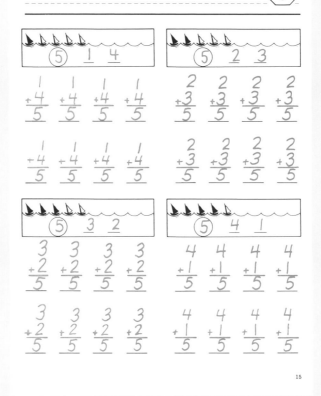

15

## Before Class

Tack Addition 5 flash cards above the waves in this order:

| 1<br>+4<br>5 | 2<br>+3<br>5 | 3<br>+2<br>5 | 4<br>+1<br>5 |

**Materials** (Use italicized items in *After Class*.)
A copy of *My 1,000 Book* for each child.
5 sailboats
Addition 2–5 flash cards
*Addition 2–5 flash cards*

**Chalkboard**

| 86 | 56 | 96 |
| 72 | 79 | 75 |
| 104 | 108 | 107 |
| 125 | 123 | 126 |
| 116 | 113 | 112 |
| 143 | 133 | 123 |

## Class Time

1. Call the children to the teaching corner. Give each child his 1,000 book. **Count 50–149 with me.**

2. **God sees the busy bee buzz toward the large lily. Yes, God's eye sees every precious thing. Can you see the largest number in each row?** Circle it.

3. Stand near the boats and waves.

   | 1 dark boat, 4 light boats |

   Circle the boats with your finger.
   **5 boats in the sea;**
   **5 is the whole number.**
   **What part of the 5 has dark sails? 1**
   **What part of the 5 has light sails? 4**
   **5 is the whole number.**
   **Its parts are 1 and 4.**
   a. Ask a child to fill in the whole and parts on the board as everyone repeats: **5 is the . . . Its parts are . . .**
   b. Point to the flash card: **1+4=5 . . .**

Answer these facts.

3   1   2   2   3   3   2

| $\frac{+2}{5}$ | $\frac{+2}{3}$ | $\frac{+2}{4}$ | $\frac{+3}{5}$ | $\frac{+2}{5}$ | $\frac{+2}{5}$ | $\frac{+3}{5}$ |
|---|---|---|---|---|---|---|

3
Extra Activity

| $2$ | $2$ | $1$ | $3$ | $2$ | $3$ | $1$ |
|---|---|---|---|---|---|---|
| $\frac{+1}{3}$ | $\frac{+3}{5}$ | $\frac{+4}{5}$ | $\frac{+1}{4}$ | $\frac{+3}{5}$ | $\frac{+2}{5}$ | $\frac{+4}{5}$ |

| $2$ | $1$ | $3$ | $2$ | $3$ | $1$ | $2$ | $4$ |
|---|---|---|---|---|---|---|---|
| $\frac{+3}{5}$ | $\frac{+3}{4}$ | $\frac{+2}{5}$ | $\frac{+1}{3}$ | $\frac{+2}{5}$ | $\frac{+4}{5}$ | $\frac{+3}{5}$ | $\frac{+1}{5}$ |

| $2$ | $2$ | $2$ | $4$ | $3$ | $1$ | $3$ | $1$ |
|---|---|---|---|---|---|---|---|
| $\frac{+3}{5}$ | $\frac{+2}{4}$ | $\frac{+3}{5}$ | $\frac{+1}{5}$ | $\frac{+2}{5}$ | $\frac{+2}{3}$ | $\frac{+2}{5}$ | $\frac{+4}{5}$ |

| $1$ | $2$ | $1$ | $1$ | $3$ | $1$ | $2$ | $1$ |
|---|---|---|---|---|---|---|---|
| $\frac{+3}{4}$ | $\frac{+3}{5}$ | $\frac{+4}{5}$ | $\frac{+3}{4}$ | $\frac{+2}{5}$ | $\frac{+3}{4}$ | $\frac{+3}{5}$ | $\frac{+3}{4}$ |

| $3$ | $4$ | $2$ | $3$ | $4$ | $1$ | $2$ | $1$ |
|---|---|---|---|---|---|---|---|
| $\frac{+2}{5}$ | $\frac{+1}{5}$ | $\frac{+2}{4}$ | $\frac{+1}{4}$ | $\frac{+1}{5}$ | $\frac{+3}{4}$ | $\frac{+2}{4}$ | $\frac{+4}{5}$ |

"Peter and Andrew . . . were fishers." Matthew 4:18

16

4. 2 dark boats, 3 light boats

Circle the boats . . .

**5 boats in the sea;**
**5 is the whole number.**
**What part of the 5 has dark sails?** 2
**What part of the 5 has light sails?** 3
**5 is the whole number.**
**Its parts are 2 and 3.**

a. Ask a child to fill in the whole and parts as everyone repeats: **5 is the . . . Its parts are . . .**

b. Point to the flash card: **2+3=5** . . .

5. 3 dark boats, 2 light boats

Circle the boats . . .

**5 boats in the sea;**
**5 is the whole number.**
**What part of the 5 has dark sails?** 3
**What part of the 5 has light sails?** 2
**5 is the whole number.**
**Its parts are 3 and 2.**

a. Ask a child to fill in the whole and parts as everyone repeats: **5 is the . . . Its parts are . . .**

b. Point to the flash card: **3+2=5** . . .

6. 4 dark boats, 1 light boat

Circle the boats . . .

**5 boats in the sea;**
**5 is the whole number.**
**What part of the 5 has dark sails?** 4
**What part of the 5 has light sails?** 1
**5 is the whole number.**
**Its parts are 4 and 1.**

a. Ask a child to fill in the whole and parts as everyone repeats: **5 is the . . . Its parts are . . .**

b. Point to the flash card: **4+1=5** . . .

7. **Say the addition facts as I fill the steps.**
Continue to the 5 Family.

8. Flash Addition 2-5 flash cards. **Answer together.**

9. Assign Lesson 3.

Fill in the missing numbers. The child may refer to his 1,000 book for exercises like this.

| 100 | 101 | 102 | 103 | 104 | 105 | 106 | 107 | 108 | 109 |
| 110 | 111 | 112 | 113 | 114 | 115 | 116 | 117 | 118 | 119 |
| 120 | 121 | 122 | 123 | 124 | 125 | 126 | 127 | 128 | 129 |
| 130 | 131 | 132 | 133 | 134 | 135 | 136 | 137 | 138 | 139 |
| 140 | 141 | 142 | 143 | 144 | 145 | 146 | 147 | 148 | 149 |

**Blackline**

Missing Numbers #2

Circle the largest number.

31 (78) 20

| 52 | 39 | 51 |
| 82 | (92) | 72 |

| (60) | 59 | 50 | 51 | 56 | (65) |
| (32) | 12 | 22 | 18 | (81) | 78 |
| (58) | 38 | 54 | 28 | (36) | 34 |
| 38 | 48 | (58) | (98) | 88 | 68 |

17

## After Class

1. Drill each child with Addition 2–5 flash cards.

2. Motion: **After, after, after. Answer together. What comes after 74, 79, 85, 96, 99, 111, 145, 130, 119, 100, 129?**

3. Stand near the chalkboard. Pick up a piece of chalk. **Give me some**
   **1-digit numbers**
   **2-digit numbers**
   **3-digit numbers**

Extra Activity

$\begin{array}{r}1\\+1\\\hline2\end{array}$

$\begin{array}{r}1\\+2\\\hline3\end{array}$ $\begin{array}{r}2\\+1\\\hline3\end{array}$

$\begin{array}{r}1\\+3\\\hline4\end{array}$ $\begin{array}{r}2\\+2\\\hline4\end{array}$ $\begin{array}{r}3\\+1\\\hline4\end{array}$

$\begin{array}{r}1\\+4\\\hline5\end{array}$ $\begin{array}{r}2\\+3\\\hline5\end{array}$ $\begin{array}{r}3\\+2\\\hline5\end{array}$ $\begin{array}{r}4\\+1\\\hline5\end{array}$

18

Trace the *whole*.
Fill in the *parts*.
Trace and write the facts.

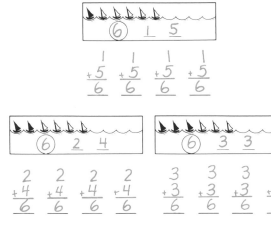

19

## Before Class

Tack Addition 6 flash cards above the waves in this order:

| 1 | 2 | 3 | 4 | 5 |
|---|---|---|---|---|
| +5 | +4 | +3 | +2 | +1 |
| 6 | 6 | 6 | 6 | 6 |

**Materials** (Use italicized items in *After Class*.)
  6 sailboats
  *Addition 4–6 flash cards*

### Chalkboard

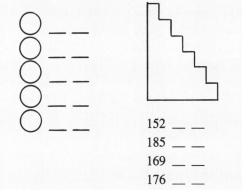

152 __ __
185 __ __
169 __ __
176 __ __
158 __ __

## Class Time

1. Have the children stand in a circle with you. **Count 100–199.**

2. Call the children to the board samples.
   a. Motion: **After, after, after.**
   b. Do the samples.

3. Stand near the boats and waves.

   [ 1 dark boat, 5 light boats ]

   Circle the boats with your finger.
   **6 boats in the sea;**
   **6 is the whole number.**
   **What part of the 6 has dark sails?** 1
   **What part of the 6 has light sails?** 5
   **6 is the whole number.**
   **Its parts are 1 and 5.**
   a. Ask a child to fill in the whole and parts as everyone repeats: **6 is the . . . Its parts are . . .**
   b. Point to the flash card: **1+5=6 . . .**

4. [ 2 dark boats, 4 light boats ]

   Circle the boats . . .

## 4

Answer these facts.

| | | | | | | |
|---|---|---|---|---|---|---|
| 4 +2 = 6 | 1 +5 = 6 | 2 +4 = 6 | 2 +3 = 5 | 4 +2 = 6 | 2 +2 = 4 | 5 +1 = 6 |
| 5 +1 = 6 | 2 +4 = 6 | 2 +3 = 5 | 2 +4 = 6 | 1 +5 = 6 | 1 +3 = 4 | 3 +3 = 6 |

| | | | | | | | |
|---|---|---|---|---|---|---|---|
| 2 +4 = 6 | 3 +2 = 5 | 3 +3 = 6 | 4 +2 = 6 | 4 +1 = 5 | 5 +1 = 6 | 1 +1 = 2 | 2 +4 = 6 |
| 4 +2 = 6 | 1 +5 = 6 | 1 +4 = 5 | 4 +2 = 6 | 3 +3 = 6 | 1 +1 = 2 | 1 +5 = 6 | 3 +2 = 5 |
| 1 +2 = 3 | 5 +1 = 6 | 2 +4 = 6 | 3 +2 = 5 | 1 +5 = 6 | 2 +3 = 5 | 4 +2 = 6 | 2 +4 = 6 |
| 1 +4 = 5 | 5 +1 = 6 | 4 +2 = 6 | 2 +1 = 3 | 2 +4 = 6 | 2 +4 = 6 | 3 +2 = 5 | 3 +3 = 6 |

"Peter and Andrew . . . were fishers." Matthew 4:18

20

---

**6 boats in the sea;**
**6 is the whole number.**
**What part of the 6 has dark sails?** 2
**What part of the 6 has light sails?** 4
**6 is the whole number.**
**Its parts are 2 and 4.**
  a. Ask a child to fill in the whole and parts as everyone repeats: **6 is the . . . Its parts are . . .**
  b. Point to the flash card: **2+4=6 . . .**

5. ☐ 3 dark boats, 3 light boats ☐
Circle the boats.
**6 boats in the sea;**
**6 is the whole number.**
**What part of the 6 has dark sails?** 3
**What part of the 6 has light sails?** 3
**6 is the whole number.**
**Its parts are 3 and 3.**
  a. Ask a child to fill in the whole and parts as everyone repeats: **6 is the . . . Its parts are . . .**
  b. Point to the flash card: **3+3=6 . . .**

6. ☐ 4 dark boats, 2 light boats ☐
Circle the boats . . .

**6 boats in the sea;**
**6 is the whole number.**
**What part of the 6 has dark sails?** 4
**What part of the 6 has light sails?** 2
**6 is the whole number.**
**Its parts are 4 and 2.**
  a. Ask a child to fill in the whole and parts as everyone repeats: **6 is the . . . Its parts are . . .**
  b. Point to the flash card: **4+2=6 . . .**

7. ☐ 5 dark boats, 1 light boat ☐
**6 boats in the sea;**
**6 is the whole number.**
**What part of the 6 has dark sails?** 5
**What part of the 6 has light sails?** 1
**6 is the whole number.**
**Its parts are 5 and 1.**
  a. Ask a child to fill in the whole and parts as everyone repeats: **6 is the . . . Its parts are . . .**
  b. Point to the flash card: **5+1=6 . . .**

8. **Say the addition facts as I fill the steps.**
Continue to the 6 Family.

9. Assign Lesson 4.

Fill in the missing numbers.

| 150 | 151 | 152 | 153 | 154 | 155 | 156 | 157 | 158 | 159 |
| --- | --- | --- | --- | --- | --- | --- | --- | --- | --- |
| 160 | 161 | 162 | 163 | 164 | 165 | 166 | 167 | 168 | 169 |
| 170 | 171 | 172 | 173 | 174 | 175 | 176 | 177 | 178 | 179 |
| 180 | 181 | 182 | 183 | 184 | 185 | 186 | 187 | 188 | 189 |
| 190 | 191 | 192 | 193 | 194 | 195 | 196 | 197 | 198 | 199 |

31 (78) 20

Circle the largest number.

| (87) | 57 | 80 |
| --- | --- | --- |
| (54) | 47 | 34 |

| (31) | 11 | 13 | 57 | 70 | (97) |
| --- | --- | --- | --- | --- | --- |
| 14 | (33) | 24 | 39 | 48 | (50) |
| 22 | 21 | (23) | (20) | 15 | 16 |
| 19 | 37 | (53) | (63) | 61 | 36 |

**Blacklines**

*Form A: 100–199

Missing Numbers #2

*The child may refer to his 1,000 book for exercises like this.

21

## After Class

| | | | |
| --- | --- | --- | --- |
| ____ | 76 | ____ | 49 |
| ____ | 94 | ____ | 83 |
| ____ | 51 | ____ | 62 |
| ____ | 25 | ____ | 30 |

1. Drill individuals with Addition 4–6 flash cards.
2. Call the children to the board samples.
   a. Motion: **Before, before . . .**
   b. Do the samples.
3. Review *digits*.
   a. **Give me a 1-digit number.** Write it.
   b. **How could I change it to a 2-digit number?**
   c. **How could I change it to a 3-digit number?**

Extra Activity

22

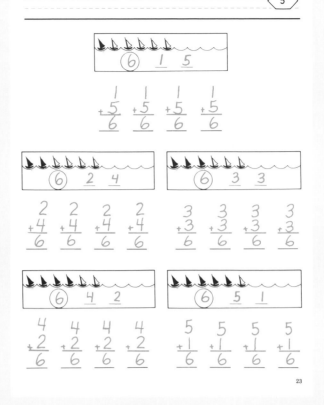

Trace the *whole*.
Fill in the *parts*.
Trace and write the facts.

---

## Before Class

**Materials** (Use italicized items in *After Class*.)
   5, 6 sailboats
   *Addition 2–6 flash cards*

### Chalkboard

| | |
|---|---|
| _____ 80 | _____ 131 |
| _____ 93 | _____ 175 |
| _____ 56 | _____ 148 |
| _____ 40 | _____ 114 |
| _____ 70 | _____ 169 |

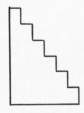

## Class Time

1. Have each child bring *My 1,000 Book* to the teaching corner. **Count 150–249.**

2. a. Motion: **Before, before . . .**
   b. Do the samples.

3. Stand near the boats and waves.

   | 2 dark boats, 3 light boats |

   Circle the boats with your finger.
   **5 boats in the sea;**
   **5 is the whole number.**
   **What part of the 5 has dark sails?** 2
   **What part of the 5 has light sails?** 3
   **5 is the whole number.**
   **Its parts are 2 and 3.**
   a. Ask a child to fill in the whole and parts as everyone repeats: **5 is the . . . Its parts are . . .**
   • b. **Say the fact with me. 2+3=5.**

4. | 3 dark boats, 2 light boats |

   Circle the boats . . .
   **5 boats in the sea;**
   **5 is the whole number.**

Answer these facts.

Extra Activity

| | | | | | | |
|---|---|---|---|---|---|---|
| 5 | 1 | 2 | 4 | 2 | 4 | 4 |
| +1 | +5 | +3 | +2 | +2 | +2 | +2 |
| 6 | 6 | 5 | 6 | 4 | 6 | 6 |

| | | | | | | |
|---|---|---|---|---|---|---|
| 2 | 2 | 5 | 2 | 1 | 1 | 3 |
| +3 | +4 | +1 | +4 | +3 | +5 | +3 |
| 5 | 6 | 6 | 6 | 4 | 6 | 6 |

| | | | | | | | |
|---|---|---|---|---|---|---|---|
| 3 | 1 | 2 | 4 | 4 | 5 | 3 | 2 |
| +3 | +1 | +4 | +2 | +1 | +1 | +1 | +4 |
| 6 | 2 | 6 | 6 | 5 | 6 | 4 | 6 |

| | | | | | | | |
|---|---|---|---|---|---|---|---|
| 4 | 1 | 1 | 4 | 3 | 5 | 3 | 1 |
| +2 | +1 | +5 | +2 | +2 | +1 | +3 | +3 |
| 6 | 2 | 6 | 6 | 5 | 6 | 6 | 4 |

| | | | | | | | |
|---|---|---|---|---|---|---|---|
| 1 | 2 | 2 | 3 | 1 | 1 | 4 | 2 |
| +5 | +1 | +4 | +2 | +5 | +4 | +2 | +4 |
| 6 | 3 | 6 | 5 | 6 | 5 | 6 | 6 |

| | | | | | | | |
|---|---|---|---|---|---|---|---|
| 2 | 5 | 2 | 5 | 3 | 2 | 1 | 3 |
| +4 | +1 | +3 | +1 | +2 | +4 | +2 | +3 |
| 6 | 6 | 5 | 6 | 5 | 6 | 3 | 6 |

"Peter and Andrew . . . were fishers." Matthew 4:18

24

What part of the 5 has dark sails? 3
What part of the 5 has light sails? 2
**5 is the whole number.**
**Its parts are 3 and 2.**
a. Ask a child to fill in the whole and parts as everyone repeats: **5 is the . . . Its parts are . . .**
b. **Say the fact with me. 3+2=5.**

5. ☐ 2 dark boats, 4 light boats
Circle the boats . . .
**6 boats in the sea;**
**6 is the whole number.**
What part of the 6 has dark sails? 2
What part of the 6 has light sails? 4
**6 is the whole number.**
**Its parts are 2 and 4.**
a. Ask a child to fill in the whole and parts as everyone repeats: **6 is the . . . Its parts are . . .**
b. **Say the fact with me. 2+4=6.**

6. ☐ 4 dark boats, 2 light boats
Circle the boats . . .
**6 boats in the sea;**

**6 is the whole number.**
What part of the 6 has dark sails? 4
What part of the 6 has light sails? 2
**6 is the whole number.**
**Its parts are 4 and 2.**
a. Ask a child to fill in the whole and parts as everyone repeats: **6 is the . . . Its parts are . . .**
b. **Say the fact with me. 4+2=6.**

7. Stand near the boat on the chalkboard.
a. Circle 2+3=5. **Close your eyes.** **Say it 3 times: 2+3, 5;   2+3, 5;   2+3, 5.** (Eliminate equals.)
b. Drill each fact.

8. **Say the addition facts as I fill the steps.** Continue to the 6 Family.

9. Assign Lesson 5.

*Note:* Keep the recitation crisp and concise. Eliminate *equals* during oral drill: 2+3, (pause) 5.

5

Fill in the missing numbers.

| 200 | 201 | 202 | 203 | 204 | 205 | 206 | 207 | 208 | 209 |
|-----|-----|-----|-----|-----|-----|-----|-----|-----|-----|
| 210 | 211 | 212 | 213 | 214 | 215 | 216 | 217 | 218 | 219 |
| 220 | 221 | 222 | 223 | 224 | 225 | 226 | 227 | 228 | 229 |
| 230 | 231 | 232 | 233 | 234 | 235 | 236 | 237 | 238 | 239 |
| 240 | 241 | 242 | 243 | 244 | 245 | 246 | 247 | 248 | 249 |

31  78  20

Circle the largest number.

| 140 | (150) | 105 |
|-----|-----|-----|
| 103 | (123) | 113 |

| 141 | (142) | 140 | (136) | 126 | 129 |
|-----|-----|-----|-----|-----|-----|
| 119 | (125) | 115 | (124) | 114 | 116 |
| (144) | 132 | 134 | 102 | 110 | (112) |
| 159 | 149 | (169) | 114 | (124) | 104 |

Blacklines

Number Facts (+) #1

Missing Numbers #3

25

***After Class***

| | hundreds | tens | ones |
|-----|-----|-----|-----|
| 75 | | | |
| 143 | | | |
| 209 | | | |
| 177 | | | |
| 101 | | | |
| 246 | | | |
| 232 | | | |

1. Point to the grid on the chalkboard.
   **The lamb is in ones' place.**
   **The pig is in tens' place.**
   **The pony is in hundreds' place.**
   a. Motion: **Ones' place, tens' place, hundreds' place . . .**
   b. Have the children fill in the grid.

2. Flash Addition 2–6 flash cards. **Answer together.**

3. **5 is a ____.**  1-digit number
   **35 is a ____.**  2-digit number
   **145 is a ____.**  3-digit number

Extra Activity

$\begin{array}{r} 1 \\ +1 \\ \hline 2 \end{array}$

$\begin{array}{r} 1 \\ +2 \\ \hline 3 \end{array}$ $\begin{array}{r} 2 \\ +1 \\ \hline 3 \end{array}$

$\begin{array}{r} 1 \\ +3 \\ \hline 4 \end{array}$ $\begin{array}{r} 2 \\ +2 \\ \hline 4 \end{array}$ $\begin{array}{r} 3 \\ +1 \\ \hline 4 \end{array}$

$\begin{array}{r} 1 \\ +4 \\ \hline 5 \end{array}$ $\begin{array}{r} 2 \\ +3 \\ \hline 5 \end{array}$ $\begin{array}{r} 3 \\ +2 \\ \hline 5 \end{array}$ $\begin{array}{r} 4 \\ +1 \\ \hline 5 \end{array}$

$\begin{array}{r} 1 \\ +5 \\ \hline 6 \end{array}$ $\begin{array}{r} 2 \\ +4 \\ \hline 6 \end{array}$ $\begin{array}{r} 3 \\ +3 \\ \hline 6 \end{array}$ $\begin{array}{r} 4 \\ +2 \\ \hline 6 \end{array}$ $\begin{array}{r} 5 \\ +1 \\ \hline 6 \end{array}$

26

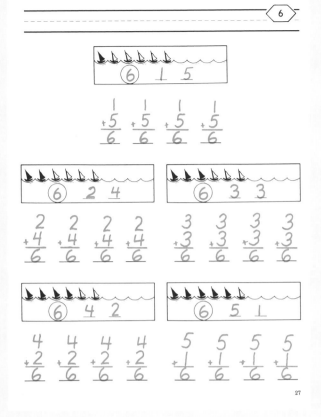

Trace the *whole*.
Fill in the *parts*.
Trace and write the facts.

⑥ 1 5

$$\begin{array}{r}1\\+5\\\hline 6\end{array}\quad\begin{array}{r}1\\+5\\\hline 6\end{array}\quad\begin{array}{r}1\\+5\\\hline 6\end{array}\quad\begin{array}{r}1\\+5\\\hline 6\end{array}$$

⑥ 2 4     ⑥ 3 3

$$\begin{array}{r}2\\+4\\\hline 6\end{array}\quad\begin{array}{r}2\\+4\\\hline 6\end{array}\quad\begin{array}{r}2\\+4\\\hline 6\end{array}\quad\begin{array}{r}2\\+4\\\hline 6\end{array}\qquad\begin{array}{r}3\\+3\\\hline 6\end{array}\quad\begin{array}{r}3\\+3\\\hline 6\end{array}\quad\begin{array}{r}3\\+3\\\hline 6\end{array}\quad\begin{array}{r}3\\+3\\\hline 6\end{array}$$

⑥ 4 2     ⑥ 5 1

$$\begin{array}{r}4\\+2\\\hline 6\end{array}\quad\begin{array}{r}4\\+2\\\hline 6\end{array}\quad\begin{array}{r}4\\+2\\\hline 6\end{array}\quad\begin{array}{r}4\\+2\\\hline 6\end{array}\qquad\begin{array}{r}5\\+1\\\hline 6\end{array}\quad\begin{array}{r}5\\+1\\\hline 6\end{array}\quad\begin{array}{r}5\\+1\\\hline 6\end{array}\quad\begin{array}{r}5\\+1\\\hline 6\end{array}$$

27

## Before Class

**Materials**

5, 6 sailboats

**Chalkboard**

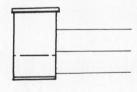

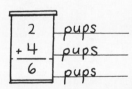

For 7a the beehive will look like this.

## Class Time

1. Stand near the boats and waves.

   2 dark boats, 3 light boats

   Circle the boats with your finger.
   **The whole number is __.**
   **Its parts are __ and __.**
   **The addition fact is __.** 2+3=5

2. 3 dark boats, 2 light boats

   Circle the boats . . .
   **The whole number is __.**
   **Its parts are __ and __.**
   **The addition fact is __.** 3+2=5

3. 2 dark boats, 4 light boats

   Circle the boats . . .
   **The whole number is __.**
   **Its parts are __ and __.**
   **The addition fact is __.** 2+4=6

4. 3 dark boats, 3 light boats

   Circle the boats . . .
   **The whole number is __.**

## 6

Answer these facts.

Speed Drill

$$\begin{array}{ccccccc} 4 & 2 & 1 & 2 & 5 & 4 & 2 \\ +2 & +4 & +5 & +3 & +1 & +2 & +3 \\ \hline 6 & 6 & 6 & 5 & 6 & 6 & 5 \end{array}$$

$$\begin{array}{ccccccc} 1 & 2 & 5 & 2 & 1 & 5 & 3 \\ +4 & +4 & +1 & +3 & +5 & +1 & +3 \\ \hline 5 & 6 & 6 & 5 & 6 & 6 & 6 \end{array}$$

$$\begin{array}{cccccccc} 2 & 1 & 3 & 5 & 4 & 4 & 1 & 2 \\ +4 & +1 & +3 & +1 & +1 & +2 & +1 & +4 \\ \hline 6 & 2 & 6 & 6 & 5 & 6 & 2 & 6 \end{array}$$

$$\begin{array}{cccccccc} 1 & 3 & 1 & 3 & 3 & 5 & 2 & 4 \\ +5 & +1 & +5 & +2 & +3 & +1 & +2 & +2 \\ \hline 6 & 4 & 6 & 5 & 6 & 6 & 4 & 6 \end{array}$$

$$\begin{array}{cccccccc} 1 & 5 & 3 & 4 & 1 & 2 & 4 & 2 \\ +5 & +1 & +2 & +2 & +2 & +3 & +2 & +4 \\ \hline 6 & 6 & 5 & 6 & 3 & 5 & 6 & 6 \end{array}$$

$$\begin{array}{cccccccc} 4 & 1 & 3 & 2 & 2 & 2 & 3 & 3 \\ +2 & +4 & +3 & +1 & +4 & +4 & +2 & +3 \\ \hline 6 & 5 & 6 & 3 & 6 & 6 & 5 & 6 \end{array}$$

"Peter and Andrew . . . were fishers." Matthew 4:18

28

---

Its parts are __ and __.
The addition fact is __. 3+3=6

5. 4 dark boats, 2 light boats

Circle the boats . . .
The whole number is __.
Its parts are __ and __.
The addition fact is __. 4+2=6

6. **Who sat in a boat to teach a crowd of people?** Jesus (Luke 5:3)

7. Stand near the beehive on the board.
   a. **Paul has __.** Write *2 pups.*
   **Mark has __.** Write *4 pups.*
   **How many pups is that in all?**
   Write *6 pups.* Erase.
   b. **Listen! Mother picked 3 apples and Jane picked 2 apples. How many is that in all? Tell me what to write in the beehive.**
   3 apples+2 apples=5 apples.

8. **The teens begin with __.**
   **The 20's begin with __.**

Continue to the 90's.

9. **I will count 190–239. But I will stop many, many times. When I stop, you say the next number.**

10. Do the Speed Drill in Lesson 6. See Overview: Speed Drills, page 7.

11. Assign Lesson 6.

*Note:* While reviewing facts 1–10 in Lessons 1–40, you need not make individual flash cards for your children unless you feel they need them.

**6**

Write the numbers in the correct places.

| | hundreds | tens | ones | | hundreds | tens | ones |
|---|---|---|---|---|---|---|---|
| 237 | 2 | 3 | 7 | 234 | 2 | 3 | 4 |
| 153 | 1 | 5 | 3 | 85 | | 8 | 5 |
| 6 | | | 6 | 203 | 2 | 0 | 3 |
| 249 | 2 | 4 | 9 | 176 | 1 | 7 | 6 |
| 210 | 2 | 1 | 0 | 94 | | 9 | 4 |

Write the number that comes before.

| 31 | 32 | 29 | 30 | 85 | 86 |
|---|---|---|---|---|---|
| 72 | 73 | 58 | 59 | 23 | 24 |
| 17 | 18 | 79 | 80 | 40 | 41 |
| 66 | 67 | 94 | 95 | 76 | 77 |

**Blacklines**

Number Facts (+) #1

Form B

Missing Numbers #3

29

---

## After Class

| ↓ | ↓ | ↓ | ↓ | ↓ | ↓ | ↓ | ↓ |
|---|---|---|---|---|---|---|---|
| 43 | 24 | 26 | 35 | 14 | 53 | 34 | 21 |
| +12 | +32 | +40 | +20 | +41 | +13 | +22 | +45 |

1. Motion: **Ones' place, tens' place, hundreds' place . . .**
   a. Trace the arrows at the 2-digit samples. **Ones' place first, ones' place first . . .**
   b. Have each child say: **ones' place first,** then answer a problem.

2. Chalkboard Drill: **Write 146. Change it to 143. (Erase 1 digit.)** Continue with **243, 203, 103, 113, 213, 219, 249, 209, 200, 210.**

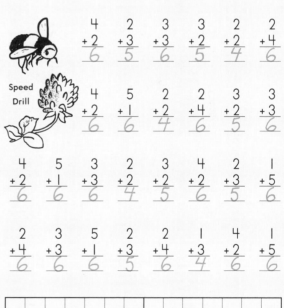

Speed Drill

$$\begin{array}{cccccc} 4 & 2 & 3 & 3 & 2 & 2 \\ +2 & +3 & +3 & +2 & +2 & +4 \\ \hline 6 & 5 & 6 & 5 & 4 & 6 \end{array}$$

$$\begin{array}{cccccc} 4 & 5 & 2 & 2 & 3 & 3 \\ +2 & +1 & +2 & +4 & +2 & +3 \\ \hline 6 & 6 & 4 & 6 & 5 & 6 \end{array}$$

$$\begin{array}{ccccccc} 4 & 5 & 3 & 2 & 3 & 4 & 2 & 1 \\ +2 & +1 & +3 & +2 & +2 & +2 & +3 & +5 \\ \hline 6 & 6 & 6 & 4 & 5 & 6 & 5 & 6 \end{array}$$

$$\begin{array}{ccccccc} 2 & 3 & 5 & 2 & 2 & 1 & 4 & 1 \\ +4 & +3 & +1 & +3 & +4 & +3 & +2 & +5 \\ \hline 6 & 6 & 6 & 5 & 6 & 4 & 6 & 6 \end{array}$$

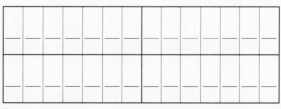

30

Fill in the whole and parts.
Trace and write the facts.

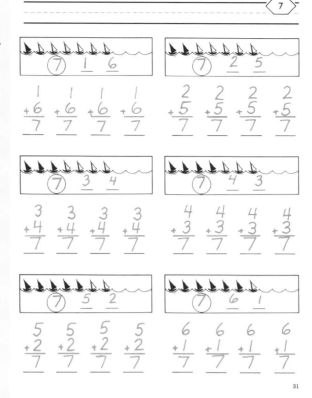

31

## Before Class

Tack Addition 7 flash cards above the waves in this order:

| 1 +6 7 | 2 +5 7 | 3 +4 7 | 4 +3 7 | 5 +2 7 | 6 +1 7 |

### Materials

7 sailboats

*1 penny for each child*

*Addition 2–7 flash cards*

### Chalkboard

| 43 | 52 | 22 | 30 | 14 | 34 | 23 |
|-----|-----|-----|-----|-----|-----|-----|
| +13 | +14 | +34 | +25 | +42 | +21 | +43 |

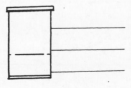

Mother made 4 big pies and 2 little pies. How many pies is that in all?

## Class Time

1. Stand near the boats and waves.

   1 dark boat, 6 light boats

   Circle the boats with your finger.

   **7 boats in the sea;**

   **7 is the whole number.**

   **What part of the 7 has dark sails?** 1

   **What part of the 7 has light sails?** 6

   **7 is the whole number.**

   **Its parts are 1 and 6.**

   a. Ask a child to fill in the whole and parts as everyone repeats: **7 is the . . . Its parts are . . .**

   b. Point to the flash card: **1+6=7 . . .**

2. 2 dark boats, 5 light boats

   Circle the boats . . .

   **7 boats in the sea;**

   **7 is the whole number.**

   **What part of the 7 has dark sails?** 2

   **What part of the 7 has light sails?** 5

   **7 is the whole number.**

Answer these facts.

$7$

Extra Activity

| | | | | | | |
|---|---|---|---|---|---|---|
| 3<br>+4<br>7 | 5<br>+1<br>6 | 2<br>+1<br>3 | 4<br>+3<br>7 | 4<br>+2<br>6 | 3<br>+4<br>7 | 6<br>+1<br>7 |
| 2<br>+5<br>7 | 4<br>+3<br>7 | 2<br>+4<br>6 | 2<br>+5<br>7 | 1<br>+2<br>3 | 1<br>+5<br>6 | 3<br>+4<br>7 |

| | | | | | | | |
|---|---|---|---|---|---|---|---|
| 5<br>+2<br>7 | 2<br>+3<br>5 | 1<br>+3<br>4 | 3<br>+3<br>6 | 4<br>+3<br>7 | 2<br>+2<br>4 | 3<br>+2<br>5 | 4<br>+3<br>7 |
| 1<br>+6<br>7 | 4<br>+3<br>7 | 2<br>+5<br>7 | 4<br>+3<br>7 | 4<br>+2<br>6 | 3<br>+4<br>7 | 5<br>+2<br>7 | 4<br>+3<br>7 |
| 3<br>+4<br>7 | 2<br>+4<br>6 | 5<br>+2<br>7 | 3<br>+2<br>5 | 2<br>+5<br>7 | 3<br>+4<br>7 | 2<br>+4<br>6 | 6<br>+1<br>7 |
| 3<br>+4<br>7 | 5<br>+2<br>7 | 4<br>+2<br>6 | 2<br>+5<br>7 | 4<br>+1<br>5 | 2<br>+4<br>6 | 5<br>+2<br>7 | 3<br>+4<br>7 |

"Peter and Andrew . . . were fishers."   Matthew 4:18

32

**Its parts are 2 and 5.**

a. Ask a child to fill in the whole and parts as everyone repeats: **7 is the . . . Its parts are . . .**

b. Point to the flash card: **2+5=7** . . .

3. ‖ 3 dark boats, 4 light boats ‖

Circle the boats . . .

**7 boats in the sea;**

**7 is the whole number.**

**What part of the 7 has dark sails?** 3

**What part of the 7 has light sails?** 4

**7 is the whole number.**

**Its parts are 3 and 4.**

a. Ask a child to fill in the whole and parts as everyone repeats: **7 is the . . . Its parts are . . .**

b. Point to the flash card: **3+4=7** . . .

4. Proceed step by step through

‖ 4 dark boats, 3 light boats ‖

‖ 5 dark boats, 2 light boats ‖

‖ 6 dark boats, 1 light boat ‖

5. **Read the story problem with me.** Ask a child to fill in the beehive.

6. Motion: **Ones, tens, hundreds . . .** Do the 2-digit samples.

7. Assign Lesson 7.

*Note:* Does your pack of flash cards include the facts with 0?   7+0, 0+7, 6+0, 0+6 . . .

48

Write the numbers in the correct places.

| | hundreds | tens | ones | | | hundreds | tens | ones |
|---|---|---|---|---|---|---|---|---|
| 140 | 1 | 4 | 0 | | 243 | 2 | 4 | 3 |
| 239 | 2 | 3 | 9 | | 35 | | 3 | 5 |
| 70 | | 7 | 0 | | 123 | 1 | 2 | 3 |
| 285 | 2 | 8 | 5 | | 236 | 2 | 3 | 6 |
| 42 | | 4 | 2 | | 164 | 1 | 6 | 4 |

Write the number that comes before.

The child may refer to his 1,000 book for exercises like this.

| 135 | 136 | 194 | 195 | 157 | 158 |
|---|---|---|---|---|---|
| 178 | 179 | 183 | 184 | 112 | 113 |
| 103 | 104 | 120 | 121 | 166 | 167 |
| 129 | 130 | 141 | 142 | 107 | 108 |

**Blacklines**

Number Facts (+) #1

Missing Numbers #4

33

## After Class

1. Drill each child with Addition 2–7 flash cards.
2. Give each child one penny.
   a. **What coin is this? Whose picture is on the coin? How much is a penny worth? We count pennies by __.** 1's
   b. **Hold up your penny. Say "penny, 1¢; penny, 1¢ . . ."**
   c. **Let's count each child's penny to see how many cents we have. 1¢, 2¢, 3¢ . . .**

Extra Activity

34

Fill in the whole and parts.
Trace and write the facts.

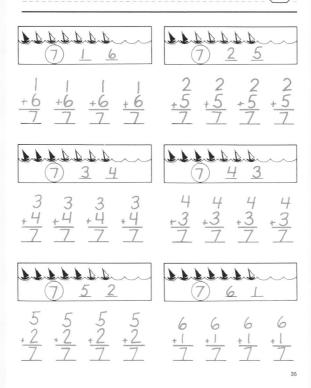

35

## Before Class

**Materials**

    7 sailboats

    Addition 5–7 flash cards

    *Addition 5–7 flash cards*

**Chalkboard**

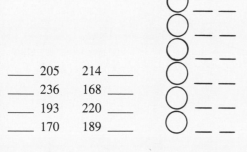

| | |
|---|---|
| ___ 205 | 214 ___ |
| ___ 236 | 168 ___ |
| ___ 193 | 220 ___ |
| ___ 170 | 189 ___ |

Lee's father has 3 black cows and 4 brown cows. How many cows is that in all?

## Class Time

1. Have each child bring *My 1,000 Book* to the teaching corner. **Count 150–249.**

2. a. Motion: **Before, before . . . After, after . . .**

    b. Do the samples.

3. **Read the story problem with me.** Ask a child to fill in the beehive.

4. Stand near the boats and waves.

    | 1 dark boat, 6 light boats |

    Circle the boats with your finger.

    **7 boats in the sea;**

    **7 is the whole number.**

    **What part of the 7 has dark sails?** 1

    **What part of the 7 has light sails?** 6

    **7 is the whole number.**

    **Its parts are 1 and 6.**

    a. Ask a child to fill in the whole and parts as everyone repeats: **7 is the . . . Its parts are . . .**

    b. Point to the flash card: **1+6=7 . . .**

50

< 8 >

Answer these facts.

| | | | | | | |
|---|---|---|---|---|---|---|
| 6 +1 = 7 | 4 +3 = 7 | 5 +1 = 6 | 4 +3 = 7 | 4 +2 = 6 | 3 +4 = 7 | 3 +4 = 7 |
| 4 +3 = 7 | 4 +2 = 6 | 3 +4 = 7 | 2 +5 = 7 | 3 +4 = 7 | 2 +4 = 6 | 2 +5 = 7 |
| 4 +3 = 7 | 1 +5 = 6 | 3 +1 = 4 | 2 +5 = 7 | 2 +4 = 6 | 5 +2 = 7 | 3 +4 = 7 | 5 +2 = 7 |
| 5 +2 = 7 | 2 +3 = 5 | 2 +5 = 7 | 1 +3 = 4 | 2 +3 = 5 | 3 +4 = 7 | 1 +6 = 7 | 4 +3 = 7 |
| 4 +1 = 5 | 2 +2 = 4 | 5 +2 = 7 | 4 +3 = 7 | 1 +3 = 4 | 3 +4 = 7 | 3 +3 = 6 | 6 +1 = 7 |
| 4 +3 = 7 | 1 +2 = 3 | 3 +4 = 7 | 2 +5 = 7 | 2 +1 = 3 | 2 +4 = 6 | 2 +5 = 7 | 3 +2 = 5 |

"Peter and Andrew . . . were fishers."  Matthew 4:18

36

5. 2 dark boats, 5 light boats

Circle the boats . . .

**7 boats in the sea;**

**7 is the whole number.**

**What part of the 7 has dark sails?** 2

**What part of the 7 has light sails?** 5

**7 is the whole number.**

**Its parts are 2 and 5.**

a. Ask a child to fill in the whole and parts as everyone repeats: **7 is the . . . Its parts are . . .**

b. Point to the flash card: **2+5=7** . . .

6. 3 dark boats, 4 light boats

Circle the boats . . .

**7 boats in the sea;**

**7 is the whole number.**

**What part of the 7 has dark sails?** 3

**What part of the 7 has light sails?** 4

**7 is the whole number.**

**Its parts are 3 and 4.**

a. Ask a child to fill in the whole and parts as everyone repeats: **7 is the . . . Its parts are . . .**

b. Point to the flash card: **3+4=7** . . .

7. Proceed step by step through

4 dark boats, 3 light boats

5 dark boats, 2 light boats

6 dark boats, 1 light boat

8. Flash Addition 5–7 flash cards for one minute.

9. Do the Speed Drill in Lesson 8.

10. Assign Lesson 8.

Answer these problems.

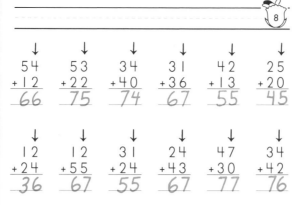

| ↓ | ↓ | ↓ | ↓ | ↓ | ↓ |
|---|---|---|---|---|---|
| 54 | 53 | 34 | 31 | 42 | 25 |
| +12 | +22 | +40 | +36 | +13 | +20 |
| 66 | 75 | 74 | 67 | 55 | 45 |

| ↓ | ↓ | ↓ | ↓ | ↓ | ↓ |
|---|---|---|---|---|---|
| 12 | 12 | 31 | 24 | 47 | 34 |
| +24 | +55 | +24 | +43 | +30 | +42 |
| 36 | 67 | 55 | 67 | 77 | 76 |

Count the pennies.
Write the amount.
   Remember the cent sign.

5¢

7¢

### Blacklines

Number Facts (+) #2

Form B

Missing Numbers #4

Read the story.
Write the numbers
   in the beehive.
Write the label words
   on the lines.
Answer the problem.

Ray and Jay gave Mother a gift. Ray gave 3 cups. Jay gave 3 cups. How many cups was that **in all**?

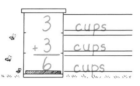

      3   cups
    + 3   cups
      6   cups

37

---

## *After Class*

| ↓ | ↓ | ↓ | ↓ | ↓ | ↓ |
|---|---|---|---|---|---|
| 32 | 43 | 31 | 14 | 61 | 24 |
| + 5 | + 2 | + 3 | + 2 | + 4 | + 3 |

Use white chalk for ones' place numbers.
Use green chalk for the tens' place numbers.

1. Drill each child with Addition 5–7 flash cards.

2. Stand near the Addition samples.

   a. Trace the arrows. **Ones' place, first; ones' place first . . .**

   b. **2+5=__.** Write 7.
      **3+nothing=__.** Write 3.

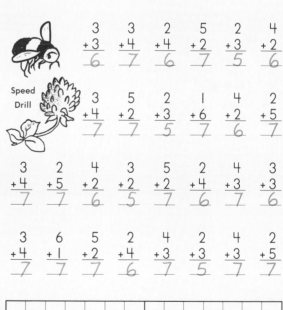

Speed
Drill

| 3 | 3 | 2 | 5 | 2 | 4 |
|---|---|---|---|---|---|
| +3 | +4 | +4 | +2 | +3 | +2 |
| 6 | 7 | 6 | 7 | 5 | 6 |

| 3 | 5 | 2 | 1 | 4 | 2 |
|---|---|---|---|---|---|
| +4 | +2 | +3 | +6 | +2 | +5 |
| 7 | 7 | 5 | 7 | 6 | 7 |

| 3 | 2 | 4 | 3 | 5 | 2 | 4 | 3 |
|---|---|---|---|---|---|---|---|
| +4 | +5 | +2 | +2 | +2 | +4 | +3 | +3 |
| 7 | 7 | 6 | 5 | 7 | 6 | 7 | 6 |

| 3 | 6 | 5 | 2 | 4 | 2 | 4 | 2 |
|---|---|---|---|---|---|---|---|
| +4 | +1 | +2 | +4 | +3 | +3 | +3 | +5 |
| 7 | 7 | 7 | 6 | 7 | 5 | 7 | 7 |

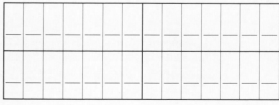

38

52

Fill in the whole and parts.
Trace and write the facts.

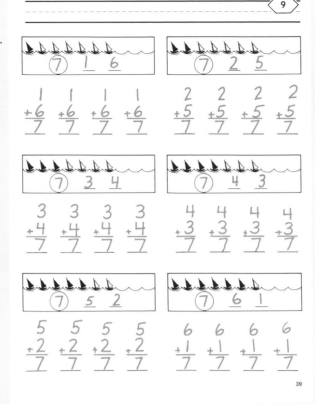

Boat boxes with whole and parts:

⑦ 1 6     ⑦ 2 5

```
 1    1    1    1        2    2    2    2
+6   +6   +6   +6       +5   +5   +5   +5
 7    7    7    7        7    7    7    7
```

⑦ 3 4     ⑦ 4 3

```
 3    3    3    3        4    4    4    4
+4   +4   +4   +4       +3   +3   +3   +3
 7    7    7    7        7    7    7    7
```

⑦ 5 2     ⑦ 6 1

```
 5    5    5    5        6    6    6    6
+2   +2   +2   +2       +1   +1   +1   +1
 7    7    7    7        7    7    7    7
```

39

## Before Class

Mark the 10's on the Number Line. See
Patterns, page 213.

### Materials

Addition 2–7 flash cards
Large penny

### Chalkboard

| 42 | 23 | 35 | 22 | 43 | 25 | 12 | 54 |
|----|----|----|----|----|----|----|----|
| + 4 | + 4 | + 2 | + 5 | + 4 | + 2 | + 4 | + 3 |

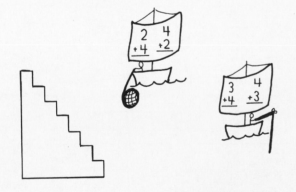

## Class Time

1. Call the children to the steps on the board. **Say
   the addition facts as I fill the steps.** Continue to the 7 Family.

2. Stand near the boats on the board.
   a. **Boys, say each fact once.**
   b. **Girls, say each fact once.**
   c. **Everyone say the facts.**
   d. **Did you catch the answers with the
      fishing net and rod?** (The net is a 6; the
      rod is a 7.)

3. Double Drill Addition 2–7 flash cards. You
   hold the flash cards. Have the children stand
   before you in two straight rows. The child at the
   head of each row will try to answer your flash
   card first. Whoever answers first may go to the
   back of his row. If they both answer correctly at
   the same time, flash more cards until one of them
   may go to the back. Drill until each child has
   gone to the back five times.

Answer these facts.

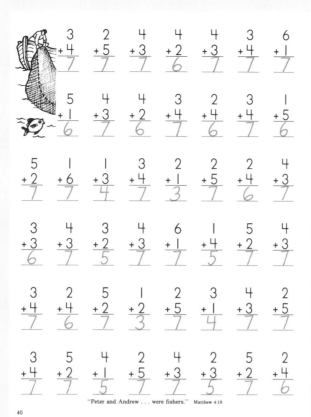

9

Extra Activity

| | | | | | | |
|---|---|---|---|---|---|---|
| 3<br>+4<br>7 | 2<br>+5<br>7 | 4<br>+3<br>7 | 4<br>+2<br>6 | 4<br>+3<br>7 | 3<br>+4<br>7 | 6<br>+1<br>7 |
| 5<br>+1<br>6 | 4<br>+3<br>7 | 4<br>+2<br>6 | 3<br>+4<br>7 | 2<br>+4<br>6 | 3<br>+4<br>7 | 1<br>+5<br>6 |

| | | | | | | | |
|---|---|---|---|---|---|---|---|
| 5<br>+2<br>7 | 1<br>+6<br>7 | 1<br>+3<br>4 | 3<br>+4<br>7 | 2<br>+1<br>3 | 2<br>+5<br>7 | 2<br>+4<br>6 | 4<br>+3<br>7 |
| 3<br>+3<br>6 | 4<br>+3<br>7 | 3<br>+2<br>5 | 4<br>+3<br>7 | 6<br>+1<br>7 | 1<br>+4<br>5 | 5<br>+2<br>7 | 4<br>+3<br>7 |
| 3<br>+4<br>7 | 2<br>+4<br>6 | 5<br>+2<br>7 | 1<br>+2<br>3 | 2<br>+5<br>7 | 3<br>+1<br>4 | 4<br>+3<br>7 | 2<br>+5<br>7 |
| 3<br>+4<br>7 | 5<br>+2<br>7 | 4<br>+1<br>5 | 2<br>+5<br>7 | 4<br>+3<br>7 | 2<br>+3<br>5 | 5<br>+2<br>7 | 2<br>+4<br>6 |

"Peter and Andrew . . . were fishers." Matthew 4:18

40

4. Hold the large penny.
   a. **This coin is a __.**
      **It is worth __.**
      **We count pennies by __.**
      **Whose picture is on the penny?**
   b. **If Stephen has 7 pennies in his pocket,**
      **he has __.** Continue with

      | | |
      |---|---|
      | **5 pennies** | **6 pennies** |
      | **3 pennies** | **14 pennies** |
      | **9 pennies** | **11 pennies** |

5. Motion: **Ones, tens, hundreds . . .**
   a. **Which animal comes first?**
      **Which place comes first?**
   b. Do the Addition samples.

6. **Answer together. What comes before 143,**
   **199, 110, 218, 246, 207, 168, 235, 112, 181,**
   **124?**

7. Assign Lesson 9.

**Reminder . . .**

Are you remembering to also review the subtraction facts as you teach the addition facts? By this time, you should have been reviewing Subtraction Families 2–7. Simple recitation of facts that are posted with the answers showing will help to make them familiar.

In Lessons 11–20, as you teach Subtraction Families 2–7, occasionally review the addition facts in this manner.

**9**

Answer these problems.

| | | | | | |
|---|---|---|---|---|---|
| ↓ | ↓ | ↓ | ↓ | ↓ | ↓ |
| 13 | 34 | 56 | 22 | 14 | 24 |
| +44 | +30 | +20 | +25 | +52 | +33 |
| 57 | 64 | 76 | 47 | 66 | 57 |

| | | | | | |
|---|---|---|---|---|---|
| ↓ | ↓ | ↓ | ↓ | ↓ | ↓ |
| 32 | 32 | 42 | 43 | 63 | 50 |
| +24 | +15 | +30 | +14 | +10 | +26 |
| 56 | 47 | 72 | 57 | 73 | 76 |

Read the story.
Write the numbers
  in the beehive.
Write the label words
  on the lines.
Answer the problem.

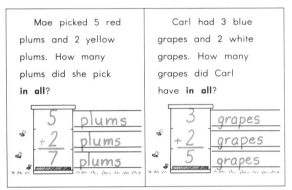

Mae picked 5 red plums and 2 yellow plums. How many plums did she pick **in all**?

5
+2 plums
7 plums
plums

Carl had 3 blue grapes and 2 white grapes. How many grapes did Carl have **in all**?

3 grapes
+2 grapes
5 grapes

41

**Blacklines**

Number Facts (+) #2

Missing Numbers #5

---

*After Class*

| | | |
|---|---|---|
| | 151 | 155 | 105 |
| 220 | 202 | 200 |
| 221 | 212 | 121 |
| 134 | 184 | 143 |
| 148 | 248 | 208 |
| 135 | 153 | 235 |
| 156 | 165 | 136 |

1. **Large pink and white and yellow water lilies bloom on the water. The bee sips sweet nectar from the largest lily. Can you circle the largest number?**

2. Call the children to the Number Line.
   a. **Do you remember the cottontail rabbit who hopped through the cabbage patch in first grade?**
   b. **When he hopped, we counted by 10's.** Point to the purple triangles. **Count by 10's to 200. 10, 20, 30 . . . 200.**

Extra Activity

1
+1
2

1    2
+2  +1
3    3

1    2    3
+3  +2  +1
4    4    4

1    2    3    4
+4  +3  +2  +1
5    5    5    5

1    2    3    4    5
+5  +4  +3  +2  +1
6    6    6    6    6

1    2    3    4    5    6
+6  +5  +4  +3  +2  +1
7    7    7    7    7    7

42

Fill in the whole and parts.
Trace and write the facts.

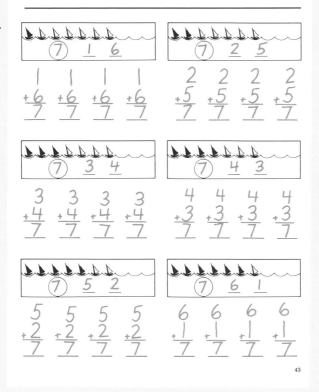

⑦  1  6

| 1 | 1 | 1 | 1 |
| +6 | +6 | +6 | +6 |
| 7 | 7 | 7 | 7 |

⑦  2  5

| 2 | 2 | 2 | 2 |
| +5 | +5 | +5 | +5 |
| 7 | 7 | 7 | 7 |

⑦  3  4

| 3 | 3 | 3 | 3 |
| +4 | +4 | +4 | +4 |
| 7 | 7 | 7 | 7 |

⑦  4  3

| 4 | 4 | 4 | 4 |
| +3 | +3 | +3 | +3 |
| 7 | 7 | 7 | 7 |

⑦  5  2

| 5 | 5 | 5 | 5 |
| +2 | +2 | +2 | +2 |
| 7 | 7 | 7 | 7 |

⑦  6  1

| 6 | 6 | 6 | 6 |
| +1 | +1 | +1 | +1 |
| 7 | 7 | 7 | 7 |

43

## Before Class

### Materials

6, 7 sailboats

Addition 5–7 flash cards

### Chalkboard

| 25 | 43 | 60 | 32 | 14 | 12 | 35 | 54 |
| + 2 | + 4 | + 5 | + 3 | + 3 | +43 | +32 | +13 |

## Class Time

1. Call the children to the teaching corner.

   a. **Pea vines grow in the garden. Long green pea pods hang on the vines.** *Caw, caw!* **A hungry black crow swoops down to a pea pod. He pecks the pod open. How many peas are inside the pod?**

   Draw 10 circles in the pod.

   b. **Count by 10's to 200 as I write by 10's.** Write horizontally.

2. Stand near the boats and waves.

   3 dark boats, 3 light boats

   Circle the boats with your finger.

   **The whole number is __.**

   **Its parts are __ and __.**

   **The addition fact is __.** 3+3=6

3. 3 dark boats, 4 light boats

   Circle the boats . . .

   **The whole number is __.**

   **Its parts are __ and __.**

⬡ 10

Answer these facts.

$$\begin{array}{r}3\\+4\\\hline 7\end{array}\quad\begin{array}{r}2\\+5\\\hline 7\end{array}\quad\begin{array}{r}4\\+2\\\hline 6\end{array}\quad\begin{array}{r}4\\+3\\\hline 7\end{array}\quad\begin{array}{r}2\\+1\\\hline 3\end{array}\quad\begin{array}{r}3\\+4\\\hline 7\end{array}\quad\begin{array}{r}6\\+1\\\hline 7\end{array}$$

$$\begin{array}{r}2\\+5\\\hline 7\end{array}\quad\begin{array}{r}4\\+3\\\hline 7\end{array}\quad\begin{array}{r}4\\+3\\\hline 7\end{array}\quad\begin{array}{r}5\\+1\\\hline 6\end{array}\quad\begin{array}{r}3\\+2\\\hline 5\end{array}\quad\begin{array}{r}3\\+4\\\hline 7\end{array}\quad\begin{array}{r}5\\+2\\\hline 7\end{array}$$

$$\begin{array}{r}5\\+2\\\hline 7\end{array}\quad\begin{array}{r}3\\+3\\\hline 6\end{array}\quad\begin{array}{r}3\\+1\\\hline 4\end{array}\quad\begin{array}{r}2\\+4\\\hline 6\end{array}\quad\begin{array}{r}4\\+3\\\hline 7\end{array}\quad\begin{array}{r}2\\+2\\\hline 4\end{array}\quad\begin{array}{r}2\\+4\\\hline 6\end{array}\quad\begin{array}{r}4\\+3\\\hline 7\end{array}$$

$$\begin{array}{r}1\\+6\\\hline 7\end{array}\quad\begin{array}{r}1\\+5\\\hline 6\end{array}\quad\begin{array}{r}2\\+5\\\hline 7\end{array}\quad\begin{array}{r}4\\+3\\\hline 7\end{array}\quad\begin{array}{r}4\\+2\\\hline 6\end{array}\quad\begin{array}{r}3\\+4\\\hline 7\end{array}\quad\begin{array}{r}2\\+4\\\hline 6\end{array}\quad\begin{array}{r}4\\+3\\\hline 7\end{array}$$

$$\begin{array}{r}3\\+4\\\hline 7\end{array}\quad\begin{array}{r}3\\+4\\\hline 7\end{array}\quad\begin{array}{r}5\\+2\\\hline 7\end{array}\quad\begin{array}{r}2\\+3\\\hline 5\end{array}\quad\begin{array}{r}2\\+5\\\hline 7\end{array}\quad\begin{array}{r}3\\+4\\\hline 7\end{array}\quad\begin{array}{r}2\\+5\\\hline 7\end{array}\quad\begin{array}{r}4\\+2\\\hline 6\end{array}$$

$$\begin{array}{r}2\\+4\\\hline 6\end{array}\quad\begin{array}{r}5\\+2\\\hline 7\end{array}\quad\begin{array}{r}2\\+2\\\hline 4\end{array}\quad\begin{array}{r}4\\+3\\\hline 7\end{array}\quad\begin{array}{r}4\\+1\\\hline 5\end{array}\quad\begin{array}{r}1\\+3\\\hline 4\end{array}\quad\begin{array}{r}5\\+2\\\hline 7\end{array}\quad\begin{array}{r}3\\+4\\\hline 7\end{array}$$

"Peter and Andrew . . . were fishers." Matthew 4:18

44

**The addition fact is __.** 3+4=7

4. ⬚ 4 dark boats, 3 light boats
   Circle the boats . . .
   **The whole number is __.**
   **Its parts are __ and __.**
   **The addition fact is __.** 4+3=7

5. Flash Addition 5-7 cards for one minute.
   **Answer together.**

6. Do the Addition samples.

7. Do the Speed Drill in Lesson 10.

8. Assign Lesson 10.

Answer these problems.

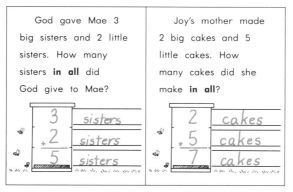

| ↓ | ↓ | ↓ | ↓ | ↓ | ↓ |
|---|---|---|---|---|---|
| 54 | 13 | 32 | 34 | 42 | 24 |
| + 2 | + 2 | + 5 | + 3 | + 3 | + 2 |
| 56 | 15 | 37 | 37 | 45 | 26 |

| ↓ | ↓ | ↓ | ↓ | ↓ | ↓ |
|---|---|---|---|---|---|
| 32 | 12 | 35 | 24 | 40 | 34 |
| +24 | +55 | +22 | +43 | +35 | +42 |
| 56 | 67 | 57 | 67 | 75 | 76 |

Read the story.
Write the numbers
 in the beehive.
Write the label words
 on the lines.
Answer the problem.

God gave Mae 3 big sisters and 2 little sisters. How many sisters **in all** did God give to Mae?

3 sisters
+ 2 sisters
5 sisters

Joy's mother made 2 big cakes and 5 little cakes. How many cakes did she make **in all**?

2 cakes
+ 5 cakes
7 cakes

45

**Blacklines**

2-Place Computation (+) #1
Number Facts (+) #2
Form B

*After Class*

| 2+3 | 3+4 | 3+3 |
|---|---|---|
| 4+3 | 2+4 | 3+4 |
| 2+2 | 2+3 | 4+2 |
| 3+2 | 3+4 | 3+2 |
| 3+3 | 4+2 | 4+3 |

1. Drill individuals at the Addition Grid on the chalkboard. Can each child answer all the facts in 20 seconds?

2. Chalkboard Drill: **Write the number that comes before 156, 103, 141, 198, 130, 214, 202, 223, 231, 250.**

Speed Drill

| 3 | 4 | 5 | 2 | 2 | 4 |
|---|---|---|---|---|---|
| +4 | +2 | +2 | +4 | +3 | +3 |
| 7 | 6 | 7 | 6 | 5 | 7 |

| 2 | 4 | 2 | 5 | 4 | 2 |
|---|---|---|---|---|---|
| +5 | +3 | +3 | +2 | +2 | +5 |
| 7 | 7 | 5 | 7 | 6 | 7 |

| 2 | 5 | 3 | 2 | 3 | 4 | 4 | 2 |
|---|---|---|---|---|---|---|---|
| +5 | +2 | +4 | +3 | +3 | +3 | +2 | +5 |
| 7 | 7 | 7 | 5 | 6 | 7 | 6 | 7 |

| 5 | 3 | 2 | 4 | 3 | 3 | 2 | 4 |
|---|---|---|---|---|---|---|---|
| +2 | +4 | +5 | +2 | +4 | +2 | +5 | +3 |
| 7 | 7 | 7 | 6 | 7 | 5 | 7 | 7 |

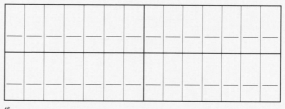

46

⟨ **11** ⟩

Trace the whole and parts.
Trace and write the facts.

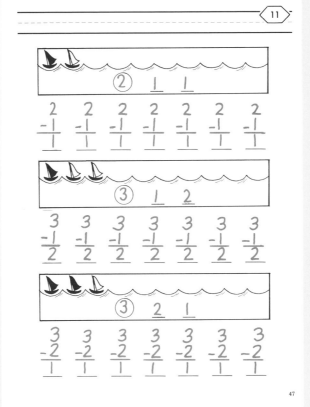

② | |

$$\begin{array}{r} 2 \\ -1 \\ \hline 1 \end{array} \quad \begin{array}{r} 2 \\ -1 \\ \hline 1 \end{array} \quad \begin{array}{r} 2 \\ -1 \\ \hline 1 \end{array} \quad \begin{array}{r} 2 \\ -1 \\ \hline 1 \end{array} \quad \begin{array}{r} 2 \\ -1 \\ \hline 1 \end{array} \quad \begin{array}{r} 2 \\ -1 \\ \hline 1 \end{array} \quad \begin{array}{r} 2 \\ -1 \\ \hline 1 \end{array}$$

③ | 2

$$\begin{array}{r} 3 \\ -1 \\ \hline 2 \end{array} \quad \begin{array}{r} 3 \\ -1 \\ \hline 2 \end{array} \quad \begin{array}{r} 3 \\ -1 \\ \hline 2 \end{array} \quad \begin{array}{r} 3 \\ -1 \\ \hline 2 \end{array} \quad \begin{array}{r} 3 \\ -1 \\ \hline 2 \end{array} \quad \begin{array}{r} 3 \\ -1 \\ \hline 2 \end{array} \quad \begin{array}{r} 3 \\ -1 \\ \hline 2 \end{array}$$

③ 2 |

$$\begin{array}{r} 3 \\ -2 \\ \hline 1 \end{array} \quad \begin{array}{r} 3 \\ -2 \\ \hline 1 \end{array} \quad \begin{array}{r} 3 \\ -2 \\ \hline 1 \end{array} \quad \begin{array}{r} 3 \\ -2 \\ \hline 1 \end{array} \quad \begin{array}{r} 3 \\ -2 \\ \hline 1 \end{array} \quad \begin{array}{r} 3 \\ -2 \\ \hline 1 \end{array} \quad \begin{array}{r} 3 \\ -2 \\ \hline 1 \end{array}$$

47

## Before Class

Tack Subtraction 2 and 3 flash cards above the waves in this order:

### Materials
2, 3 sailboats
Large penny
*Subtraction 2 and 3 flash cards*

$$\begin{array}{r} 2 \\ -1 \\ \hline 1 \end{array} \qquad \begin{array}{r} 3 \\ -1 \\ \hline 2 \end{array} \qquad \begin{array}{r} 3 \\ -2 \\ \hline 1 \end{array}$$

### Chalkboard

| | | |
|---|---|---|
| | | 136 163 183 |
| | | 200 100 101 |
| | | 108 106 180 |
| 120 130 150 | | 217 237 207 |
| 232 132 182 | | 165 105 150 |

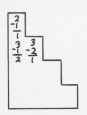

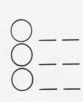

## Class Time

1. **When the black crow pecked a pea pod open, how many peas were inside?** 10
   a. **Girls, count by 10's to 200.**
   b. **Boys, count by 10's to 200.**

2. **The thirsty bee buzzes toward the largest lily for a drink. Can you find the largest number?**

3. Stand near the boats and waves.

   | 1 dark boat, 1 light boat |

   Circle the boats with your finger.
   **2 boats in the sea;**
   **2 is the whole number.**
   **What part of the 2 has dark sails?** 1
   **What part of the 2 has light sails?** 1
   **2 is the whole number.**
   **Its parts are 1 and 1.**
   a. Fill in (2) 1 1 as everyone repeats:
      **2 is the whole number.**
      **Its parts are 1 and 1.**
   b. Point to the flash card: **2−1=1 . . .**

Answer these facts.

11

Extra Activity

"Peter and Andrew . . . were fishers." Matthew 4:18

48

4. | 1 dark boat, 2 light boats |

Circle the boats . . .

**3 boats in the sea;**
**3 is the whole number.**
**What part of the 3 has dark sails? 1**
**What part of the 3 has light sails? 2**
**3 is the whole number.**
**Its parts are 1 and 2.**

a. Fill in (3) 1 2 as everyone repeats:
**3 is the whole number.**
**Its parts are 1 and 2.**

b. Point to the flash card: **3−1=2 . . .**

5. | 2 dark boats, 1 light boat |

Circle the boats . . .

**3 boats in the sea;**
**3 is the whole number.**
**What part of the 3 has dark sails? 2**
**What part of the 3 has light sails? 1**
**3 is the whole number.**
**Its parts are 2 and 1.**

a. Fill in (3) 2 1 as everyone repeats:

**3 is the whole number.**
**Its parts are 2 and 1.**

b. Point to the flash card: **3−2=1 . . .**

6. **Say the facts as I fill the steps. 2−1=1, 3−1=2, 3−2=1.**

7. Hold the large penny. **Penny, 1¢; penny, 1¢; penny, 1¢ . . .**

a. **Answer together.**

| | |
|---|---|
| **10 pennies=** | **21 pennies=** |
| **14 pennies=** | **18 pennies=** |

b. **How many pennies would make 12¢?**
Continue with

| | | |
|---|---|---|
| **20¢** | **27¢** | **25¢** |
| **23¢** | **16¢** | **11¢** |

8. Assign Lesson 11.

60

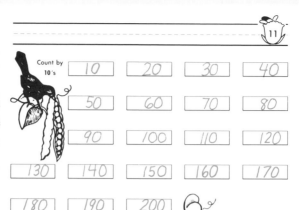

Count by 10's to 200.
The child may refer to his 1,000 book for exercises like this.

| Count by 10's | | | |
|---|---|---|---|
| 10 | 20 | 30 | 40 |
| 50 | 60 | 70 | 80 |
| 90 | 100 | 110 | 120 |
| 130 | 140 | 150 | 160 | 170 |
| 180 | 190 | 200 | | |

Circle the largest number.

| 31 | (78) | 20 |
|---|---|---|

| | | | (203) | 170 | 197 |
|---|---|---|---|---|---|
| | | | 226 | (227) | 225 |
| 115 | 110 | (117) | 201 | 102 | (210) |
| 129 | (132) | 114 | 239 | 139 | (249) |
| (142) | 104 | 124 | 230 | 223 | (235) |

49

## After Class

Extra Activity

116  119  112
43  24  64       205  207  209
31  21  41       144  124  164
89  86  83       107  157  170

1. Drill each child with Subtraction 2 and 3 flash cards.

2. **The bee buzzes back to the waterlilies for another drink of nectar. This time he flies down to the *smallest* lily. Can you find the smallest number?** Circle it.

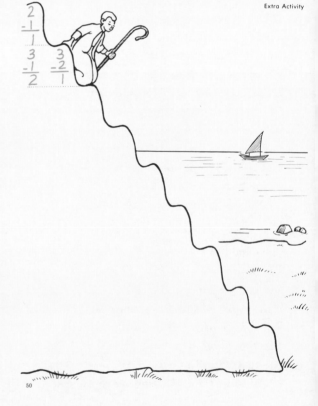

50

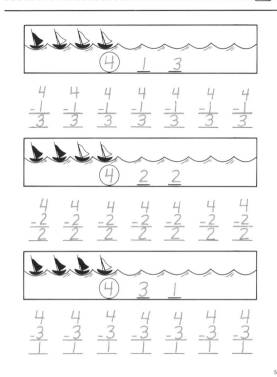

Trace the whole and parts.
Trace and write the facts.

51

## Before Class

Tack Subtraction 4 flash cards above the waves
  in this order:

$$\begin{array}{r} 4 \\ -1 \\ \hline 3 \end{array} \quad \begin{array}{r} 4 \\ -2 \\ \hline 2 \end{array} \quad \begin{array}{r} 4 \\ -3 \\ \hline 1 \end{array}$$

**Materials**
  4 sailboats
  Subtraction 2–4 flash cards
  *Subtraction 2–4 flash cards*

**Chalkboard**

126  226  127
243  248  240

163  136  166
209  210  211
218  118  219
240  214  204

## Class Time

1. Have each child bring *My 1,000 Book* to the
   teaching corner.
   a. **Count by 10's to 200.**
   b. **Count on to 250 by 1's.**

2. **God's eye sees every precious thing. He
   sees the bee sit on the smallest lily for a
   sweet drink of nectar.** Circle the smallest
   number.

3. Stand near the boats and waves.

   | 1 dark boat, 3 light boats |

   Circle the boats with your finger.
   **4 boats in the sea:**
   **4 is the whole number.**
   **What part of the 4 has dark sails?** 1
   **What part of the 4 has light sails?** 3
   **4 is the whole number.**
   **Its parts are 1 and 3.**
   a. Ask a child to fill in the whole and parts as
      everyone repeats: **4 is the . . . Its parts
      are . . .**

**12**

Answer these facts.

Extra Activity

$$\begin{array}{ccccccc}
4 & 4 & 4 & 4 & 3 & 4 & 3 \\
-3 & -1 & -2 & -3 & -2 & -2 & -1 \\
\hline
1 & 3 & 2 & 1 & 1 & 2 & 2
\end{array}$$

$$\begin{array}{ccccccc}
4 & 4 & 3 & 4 & 3 & 4 & 4 \\
-3 & -1 & -1 & -3 & -1 & -3 & -3 \\
\hline
1 & 3 & 2 & 1 & 2 & 1 & 1
\end{array}$$

$$\begin{array}{cccccccc}
2 & 4 & 4 & 4 & 4 & 4 & 3 & 2 \\
-1 & -1 & -2 & -1 & -2 & -3 & -2 & -1 \\
\hline
1 & 3 & 2 & 3 & 2 & 1 & 1 & 1
\end{array}$$

$$\begin{array}{cccccccc}
3 & 4 & 4 & 4 & 4 & 3 & 4 & 3 \\
-2 & -3 & -1 & -2 & -3 & -2 & -2 & -1 \\
\hline
1 & 1 & 3 & 2 & 1 & 1 & 2 & 2
\end{array}$$

$$\begin{array}{cccccccc}
4 & 4 & 4 & 4 & 4 & 4 & 4 & 4 \\
-2 & -3 & -2 & -1 & -3 & -2 & -1 & -3 \\
\hline
2 & 1 & 2 & 3 & 1 & 2 & 3 & 1
\end{array}$$

$$\begin{array}{cccccccc}
3 & 3 & 4 & 4 & 4 & 3 & 2 & 4 \\
-2 & -1 & -1 & -2 & -2 & -2 & -1 & -1 \\
\hline
1 & 2 & 3 & 2 & 2 & 1 & 1 & 3
\end{array}$$

"Peter and Andrew . . . were fishers."  Matthew 4:18

52

---

b. Point to the flash card: **4—1=3** . . .

4. | 2 dark boats, 2 light boats |

Circle the boats . . .

**4 boats in the sea;**
**4 is the whole number.**
**What part of the 4 has dark sails?** 2
**What part of the 4 has light sails?** 2
**4 is the whole number.**
**Its parts are 2 and 2.**

a. Ask a child to fill in the whole and parts as everyone repeats: **4 is the . . . Its parts are . . .**

b. Point to the flash card: **4—2=2** . . .

5. | 3 dark boats, 1 light boat |

Circle the boats . . .

**4 boats in the sea;**
**4 is the whole number.**
**What part of the 4 has dark sails?** 3
**What part of the 4 has light sails?** 1
**4 is the whole number.**
**Its parts are 3 and 1.**

a. Ask a child to fill in the whole and parts as everyone repeats: **4 is the . . . Its parts are . . .**

b. Point to the flash card: **4—3=1** . . .

6. Ask a child to fill the steps on the board as everyone says Subtraction 2–4 facts.

7. Flash Subtraction 2–4 cards. **Answer quickly!**

8. Assign Lesson 12.

_____

_____ 12

Count by 10's to 200.

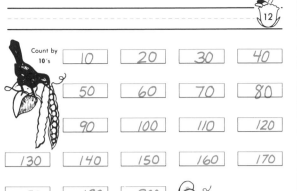

| Count by 10's | 10 | 20 | 30 | 40 |
|---|---|---|---|---|
| | 50 | 60 | 70 | 80 |
| | 90 | 100 | 110 | 120 |
| 130 | 140 | 150 | 160 | 170 |
| 180 | 190 | 200 | | |

**Blackline**

Form A: 150–249

Circle the largest number.

| 31 | (78) | 20 | | 203 | 130 | 202 |
|---|---|---|---|---|---|---|

| | | | | 207 | (227) | 189 |
|---|---|---|---|---|---|---|
| 107 | (127) | 117 | (245) | 238 | 210 |
| 122 | (132) | 103 | 137 | (139) | 138 |
| 142 | 224 | (242) | 234 | 163 | (235) |

53

## *After Class*

|       |     |       |
|-------|-----|-------|
| ___ 207 ___ | ___ 118 ___ |
| ___ 164 ___ | ___ 236 ___ |
| ___ 189 ___ | ___ 200 ___ |
| ___ 220 ___ | ___ 171 ___ |

1. Double Drill: Subtraction 2–4 flash cards.

2. Motion: **Before, after, between** . . . Do the samples.

3. Have individuals count by 10's to 200.

Extra Activity

2 −1 1   3 −1 2   3 −2 1   4 −1 3   4 −2 2   4 −3 1

54

**13**

Trace the whole and parts.
Trace and write the facts.

⛵⛵⛵⛵⛵
(5) 1 4

⛵⛵⛵⛵⛵
(5) 2 3

| 5 | 5 | 5 | 5 |
|---|---|---|---|
| −1 | −1 | −1 | −1 |
| 4 | 4 | 4 | 4 |

| 5 | 5 | 5 | 5 |
|---|---|---|---|
| −2 | −2 | −2 | −2 |
| 3 | 3 | 3 | 3 |

| 5 | 5 | 5 | 5 |
|---|---|---|---|
| −1 | −1 | −1 | −1 |
| 4 | 4 | 4 | 4 |

| 5 | 5 | 5 | 5 |
|---|---|---|---|
| −2 | −2 | −2 | −2 |
| 3 | 3 | 3 | 3 |

⛵⛵⛵⛵⛵
(5) 3 2

⛵⛵⛵⛵⛵
(5) 4 1

| 5 | 5 | 5 | 5 |
|---|---|---|---|
| −3 | −3 | −3 | −3 |
| 2 | 2 | 2 | 2 |

| 5 | 5 | 5 | 5 |
|---|---|---|---|
| −4 | −4 | −4 | −4 |
| 1 | 1 | 1 | 1 |

| 5 | 5 | 5 | 5 |
|---|---|---|---|
| −3 | −3 | −3 | −3 |
| 2 | 2 | 2 | 2 |

| 5 | 5 | 5 | 5 |
|---|---|---|---|
| −4 | −4 | −4 | −4 |
| 1 | 1 | 1 | 1 |

55

## Before Class

Tack Subtraction 5 flash cards above the waves in this order:

| 5 | 5 | 5 | 5 |
|---|---|---|---|
| −1 | −2 | −3 | −4 |
| 4 | 3 | 2 | 1 |

Materials

5 sailboats

*Subtraction 2–5 flash cards*

Chalkboard

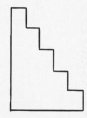

107  174  147
223  228  220
165  156  176

235  233  223
146  164  160
218  214  219
139  193  133

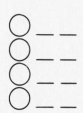

## Class Time

1. Have the children stand in a circle with you.
   **Count 150–250 by 1's.**

2. Have the children circle the smallest number.

3. Motion: **Ones, tens, hundreds . . .**
   **The lamb is in __. ones' place**
   **The pig is in __. tens' place**
   **The pony is in __. hundreds' place**

4. Stand near the boats and waves.

   | 1 dark boat, 4 light boats |

   Circle the boats with your finger.
   **5 boats in the sea;**
   **5 is the whole number.**
   **What part of the 5 has dark sails?** 1
   **What part of the 5 has light sails?** 4
   **5 is the whole number.**
   **Its parts are 1 and 4.**

   a. Ask a child to fill in the whole and parts as everyone repeats: **5 is the . . . Its parts are . . .**

   b. Point to the flash card: **5−1=4 . . .**

Answer these facts.

⬡ 13

( Extra Activity )

| 5 | 5 | 5 | 5 | 5 | 5 | 5 |
|---|---|---|---|---|---|---|
| −4 | −2 | −1 | −3 | −2 | −1 | −2 |
| 1 | 3 | 4 | 2 | 3 | 4 | 3 |

| 5 | 5 | 5 | 5 | 5 | 5 | 5 |
|---|---|---|---|---|---|---|
| −2 | −1 | −2 | −3 | −1 | −2 | −4 |
| 3 | 4 | 3 | 2 | 4 | 3 | 1 |

| 5 | 4 | 5 | 4 | 5 | 5 | 4 | 5 |
|---|---|---|---|---|---|---|---|
| −3 | −1 | −4 | −2 | −3 | −4 | −3 | −3 |
| 2 | 3 | 1 | 2 | 2 | 1 | 1 | 2 |

| 5 | 3 | 5 | 4 | 5 | 4 | 5 | 3 |
|---|---|---|---|---|---|---|---|
| −2 | −1 | −3 | −3 | −4 | −2 | −3 | −2 |
| 3 | 2 | 2 | 1 | 1 | 2 | 2 | 1 |

| 5 | 5 | 5 | 5 | 5 | 5 | 5 | 5 |
|---|---|---|---|---|---|---|---|
| −1 | −3 | −2 | −4 | −3 | −4 | −3 | −4 |
| 4 | 2 | 3 | 1 | 2 | 1 | 2 | 1 |

| 5 | 5 | 5 | 5 | 5 | 5 | 5 | 5 |
|---|---|---|---|---|---|---|---|
| −4 | −3 | −4 | −3 | −4 | −2 | −3 | −1 |
| 1 | 2 | 1 | 2 | 1 | 3 | 2 | 4 |

"He arose . . . and said unto the sea, Peace be still." Mark 4:39

56

5. |2 dark boats, 3 light boats|

Circle the boats . . .

**5 boats in the sea;**
**5 is the whole number.**
**What part of the 5 has dark sails?** 2
**What part of the 5 has light sails?** 3
**5 is the whole number.**
**Its parts are 2 and 3.**

a. Ask a child to fill in the whole and parts as everyone repeats: **5 is the . . . Its parts are . . .**

b. Point to the flash card: **5−2=3** . . .

6. |3 dark boats, 2 light boats|

Circle the boats . . .

**5 boats in the sea;**
**5 is the whole number.**
**What part of the 5 has dark sails?** 3
**What part of the 5 has light sails?** 2
**5 is the whole number.**
**Its parts are 3 and 2.**

a. Ask a child to fill in the whole and parts as everyone repeats: **5 is the . . . Its parts are . . .**

b. Point to the flash card: **5−3=2** . . .

7. |4 dark boats, 1 light boat|

Circle the boats . . .

**5 boats in the sea;**
**5 is the whole number.**
**What part of the 5 has dark sails?** 4
**What part of the 5 has light sails?** 1
**5 is the whole number.**
**Its parts are 4 and 1.**

a. Ask a child to fill in the whole and parts as everyone repeats: **5 is the . . . Its parts are . . .**

b. Point to the flash card: **5−4=1** . . .

8. **Who slept in a little basket boat made of bulrushes?** Moses (Exodus 2)

9. Ask a child to fill in the steps on the board as everyone says Subtraction 2–5 facts.

10. Assign Lesson 13.

**13**

Write the numbers in the correct places.

| | hundreds | tens | ones | | hundreds | tens | ones |
|---|---|---|---|---|---|---|---|
| 247 | 2 | 4 | 7 | 28 | | 2 | 8 |
| 53 | | 5 | 3 | 105 | 1 | 0 | 5 |
| 210 | 2 | 1 | 0 | 234 | 2 | 3 | 4 |
| 168 | 1 | 6 | 8 | 179 | 1 | 7 | 9 |
| 200 | 2 | 0 | 0 | 203 | 2 | 0 | 3 |

Count the pennies.
Write the amount.
Remember the cent sign.

 9¢

**Blacklines**

Skip Counting (10's) #1

Missing Numbers #6

Circle the smallest number.

85 (31) 76

| 60 | 59 | (58) |
|---|---|---|
| 87 | 96 | (86) |

| (18) | 80 | 81 | 16 | (15) | 51 |
|---|---|---|---|---|---|
| 34 | 36 | (33) | 78 | (57) | 75 |

57

*After Class*

| ↓ | ↓ | ↓ | ↓ | ↓ | ↓ |
|---|---|---|---|---|---|
| 53 | 34 | 43 | 25 | 55 | 45 |
| −32 | −12 | −23 | −14 | −43 | −32 |

1. Drill each child with Subtraction 2–5 flash cards.

2. Call the children to the 2-digit samples.

   a. Trace the arrows. **Ones' place first; ones' place first . . .**

   b. Have each child say **ones' place first,** then answer a problem.

3. Chalkboard Drill: **Write the number that comes after 225, 138, 201, 167, 219, 174, 212, 190, 246, 133.**

Extra Activity

58

Fill in the whole and parts.
Trace and write the facts.

| 6 | 6 | 6 | 6 |
|---|---|---|---|
| −1 | −1 | −1 | −1 |
| 5 | 5 | 5 | 5 |

| 6 | 6 | 6 | 6 |
|---|---|---|---|
| −2 | −2 | −2 | −2 |
| 4 | 4 | 4 | 4 |

| 6 | 6 | 6 | 6 |
|---|---|---|---|
| −3 | −3 | −3 | −3 |
| 3 | 3 | 3 | 3 |

| 6 | 6 | 6 | 6 |
|---|---|---|---|
| −4 | −4 | −4 | −4 |
| 2 | 2 | 2 | 2 |

| 6 | 6 | 6 | 6 |
|---|---|---|---|
| −5 | −5 | −5 | −5 |
| 1 | 1 | 1 | 1 |

59

## Before Class

Tack Subtraction 6 flash cards above the waves
in this order:

| 6 | 6 | 6 | 6 | 6 |
|---|---|---|---|---|
| −1 | −2 | −3 | −4 | −5 |
| 5 | 4 | 3 | 2 | 1 |

### Materials

Subtraction 2–5 flash cards
*1 dime for each child*
*Subtraction 3–6 flash cards*

### Chalkboard

| 36 | 25 | 46 | 45 | 23 | 56 |
|---|---|---|---|---|---|
| −24 | −13 | −23 | −34 | −12 | −22 |

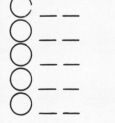

## Class Time

1. Flash Subtraction 2–5 cards for one minute.
   **Answer together.**

2. Stand near the beehive on the board. **5 boys
   played ball. Then 3 of them went home.
   How many boys were left? Tell me what to
   write in the beehive.**

3. Stand near the boats and waves.

   | 1 dark boat, 5 light boats |
   |---|

   Circle the boats with your finger.
   **6 boats in the sea;**
   **6 is the whole number.**
   **What part of the 6 has dark sails?** 1
   **What part of the 6 has light sails?** 5
   **6 is the whole number.**
   **Its parts are 1 and 5.**
   a. Ask a child to fill in the whole and parts as
      everyone repeats: **6 is the . . . Its parts
      are . . .**
   b. Point to the flash card: **6−1=5 . . .**

## 14

Answer these facts.

| 6<br>−5<br>1 | 6<br>−3<br>3 | 6<br>−4<br>2 | 6<br>−2<br>4 | 5<br>−4<br>1 | 6<br>−4<br>2 | 6<br>−1<br>5 |
|---|---|---|---|---|---|---|
| 5<br>−2<br>3 | 5<br>−4<br>1 | 5<br>−1<br>4 | 4<br>−2<br>2 | 5<br>−3<br>2 | 4<br>−3<br>1 | 6<br>−1<br>5 |

| 6<br>−4<br>2 | 6<br>−3<br>3 | 5<br>−4<br>1 | 6<br>−4<br>2 | 6<br>−2<br>4 | 6<br>−1<br>5 | 6<br>−4<br>2 | 6<br>−3<br>3 |
|---|---|---|---|---|---|---|---|
| 5<br>−2<br>3 | 6<br>−5<br>1 | 5<br>−3<br>2 | 6<br>−2<br>4 | 6<br>−5<br>1 | 2<br>−1<br>1 | 6<br>−2<br>4 | 6<br>−5<br>1 |
| 3<br>−2<br>1 | 6<br>−3<br>3 | 6<br>−2<br>4 | 6<br>−4<br>2 | 6<br>−5<br>1 | 5<br>−4<br>1 | 4<br>−3<br>1 | 6<br>−2<br>4 |
| 6<br>−4<br>2 | 6<br>−3<br>3 | 6<br>−5<br>1 | 6<br>−4<br>2 | 6<br>−2<br>4 | 6<br>−1<br>5 | 6<br>−4<br>2 | 6<br>−3<br>3 |

"He arose . . . and said unto the sea, Peace be still." Mark 4:39

4. | 2 dark boats, 4 light boats |

   Circle the boats . . .

   **6 boats in the sea;**

   **6 is the whole number.**

   **What part of the 6 has dark sails?** 2

   **What part of the 6 has light sails?** 4

   **6 is the whole number.**

   **Its parts are 2 and 4.**

   a. Ask a child to fill in the whole and parts as everyone repeats: **6 is the . . . Its parts are . . .**

   b. Point to the flash card: **6−2=4 . . .**

5. | 3 dark boats, 3 light boats |

   Circle the boats . . .

   **6 boats in the sea;**

   **6 is the whole number.**

   **What part of the 6 has dark sails?** 3

   **What part of the 6 has light sails?** 3

   **6 is the whole number.**

   **Its parts are 3 and 3.**

   a. Ask a child to fill in the whole and parts as everyone repeats: **6 is the . . . Its parts are . . .**

   b. Point to the flash card: **6−3=3 . . .**

6. Proceed step by step through

   | 4 dark boats, 2 light boats |

   | 5 dark boats, 1 light boat |

7. Point to the Subtraction 6 flash cards.

   a. **Girls, say each fact once.**

   b. **Boys, say each fact once.**

8. Do the 2-digit samples.

9. Assign Lesson 14.

Write the numbers in the
   correct places.

| | hundreds | tens | ones | | hundreds | tens | ones |
|---|---|---|---|---|---|---|---|
| 236 | 2 | 3 | 6 | 204 | 2 | 0 | 4 |
| 153 | 1 | 5 | 3 | 185 | 1 | 8 | 5 |
| 76 | | 7 | 6 | 203 | 2 | 0 | 3 |
| 149 | 1 | 4 | 9 | 76 | | 7 | 6 |
| 215 | 2 | 1 | 5 | 94 | | 9 | 4 |

Count the pennies.
Write the amount.
Remember the cent sign.

8¢

**Blacklines**

Skip Counting (10's) #1

Missing Numbers #6

Circle the smallest number.

85  (31)  76

| 203 | (170) | 197 |
|---|---|---|
| 226 | 227 | (225) |
| 201 | (102) | 210 |
| 239 | (139) | 249 |

| 115 | (113) | 117 |
|---|---|---|
| 129 | 132 | (114) |

61

### After Class

1. Double Drill: Subtraction 3–6 flash cards.

2. Give each child one dime.

   a. **What coin is this? How much is a dime worth? Whose picture is on the dime?**
   Franklin D. Roosevelt
   **We count dimes by __.** 10's

   b. **Hold up your dime and say "dime, 10¢; dime, 10¢ . . ."**

   c. **Let's count each child's dime to see how many cents we have. 10¢, 20¢, 30¢ . . .**

Extra Activity

62

**15**

Fill in the whole and parts.
Trace and write the facts.

15

| 6 | 1 | 5 |

6   6   6   6
-1  -1  -1  -1
 5   5   5   5

| 6 | 2 | 4 |   | 6 | 3 | 3 |

6   6   6   6     6   6   6   6
-2  -2  -2  -2    -3  -3  -3  -3
 4   4   4   4     3   3   3   3

| 6 | 4 | 2 |   | 6 | 5 | 1 |

6   6   6   6     6   6   6   6
-4  -4  -4  -4    -5  -5  -5  -5
 2   2   2   2     1   1   1   1

63

## Before Class

**Materials**

6 sailboats

*Subtraction 4–6 flash cards*

**Chalkboard**

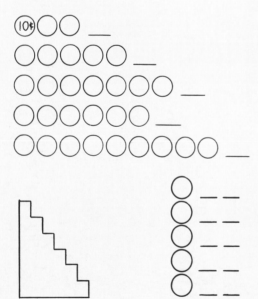

## Class Time

1. **I will count 150–250, but I will stop many times. When I stop, you say the next number.**

2. **Count by 10's to 200.**

3. a. Have the children say **dime, 10¢** as you fill in each dime.

   b. Have individuals count aloud as they do the Money samples.

4. Stand near the boats and waves.

   | 1 dark boat, 5 light boats |

   Circle the boats with your finger.

   **6 boats in the sea;**

   **6 is the whole number.**

   **What part of the 6 has dark sails?** 1

   **What part of the 6 has light sails?** 5

   **6 is the whole number.**

   **Its parts are 1 and 5.**

   a. Ask a child to fill in the whole and parts as everyone repeats: **6 is the . . . Its parts are . . .**

Answer these facts.

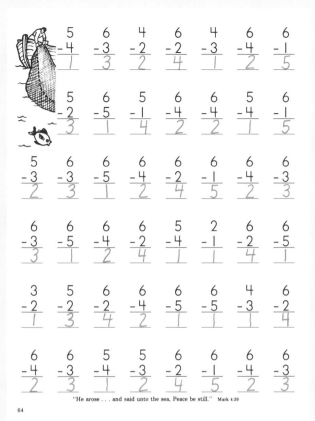

⬡ 15

⬭ Extra Activity

$$\begin{array}{cccccccc} 5 & 6 & 4 & 6 & 4 & 6 & 6 \\ -4 & -3 & -2 & -2 & -3 & -4 & -1 \\ \hline 1 & 3 & 2 & 4 & 1 & 2 & 5 \end{array}$$

$$\begin{array}{ccccccc} 5 & 6 & 5 & 6 & 6 & 5 & 6 \\ -2 & -5 & -1 & -4 & -4 & -4 & -1 \\ \hline 3 & 1 & 4 & 2 & 2 & 1 & 5 \end{array}$$

$$\begin{array}{cccccccc} 5 & 6 & 6 & 6 & 6 & 6 & 6 & 6 \\ -3 & -3 & -5 & -4 & -2 & -1 & -4 & -3 \\ \hline 2 & 3 & 1 & 2 & 4 & 5 & 2 & 3 \end{array}$$

$$\begin{array}{cccccccc} 6 & 6 & 6 & 6 & 5 & 2 & 6 & 6 \\ -3 & -5 & -4 & -2 & -4 & -1 & -2 & -5 \\ \hline 3 & 1 & 2 & 4 & 1 & 1 & 4 & 1 \end{array}$$

$$\begin{array}{cccccccc} 3 & 5 & 6 & 6 & 6 & 6 & 4 & 6 \\ -2 & -2 & -2 & -4 & -5 & -5 & -3 & -2 \\ \hline 1 & 3 & 4 & 2 & 1 & 1 & 1 & 4 \end{array}$$

$$\begin{array}{cccccccc} 6 & 6 & 5 & 5 & 6 & 6 & 6 & 6 \\ -4 & -3 & -4 & -3 & -2 & -1 & -4 & -3 \\ \hline 2 & 3 & 1 & 2 & 4 & 5 & 2 & 3 \end{array}$$

"He arose . . . and said unto the sea, Peace be still." Mark 4:39

64

b. Point to the flash card: **6−1=5** . . .

5. ⬛ 2 dark boats, 4 light boats
   Circle the boats . . .
   **6 boats in the sea;**
   **6 is the whole number.**
   **What part of the 6 has dark sails?** 2
   **What part of the 6 has light sails?** 4
   **6 is the whole number.**
   **Its parts are 2 and 4.**

   a. Ask a child to fill in the whole and parts as everyone repeats: **6 is the . . . Its parts are . . .**

   b. Point to the flash card: **6−2=4** . . .

6. ⬛ 3 dark boats, 3 light boats
   Circle the boats . . .
   **6 boats in the sea;**
   **6 is the whole number.**
   **What part of the 6 has dark sails?** 3
   **What part of the 6 has light sails?** 3
   **6 is the whole number.**
   **Its parts are 3 and 3.**

   a. Ask a child to fill in the whole and parts as everyone repeats: **6 is the . . . Its parts are . . .**

   b. Point to the flash card: **6−3=3** . . .

7. Proceed step by step through

   4 dark boats, 2 light boats

   5 dark boats, 1 light boat

8. **Say the Subtraction 2–6 facts as I fill the steps.**

9. Assign Lesson 15.

15

Answer these problems.

| | | | | | |
|---|---|---|---|---|---|
| ↓ | ↓ | ↓ | ↓ | ↓ | ↓ |
| 64 | 35 | 65 | 65 | 65 | 65 |
| -51 | -11 | -34 | -41 | -10 | -23 |
| 13 | 24 | 31 | 24 | 55 | 42 |

| | | | | | |
|---|---|---|---|---|---|
| ↓ | ↓ | ↓ | ↓ | ↓ | ↓ |
| 66 | 66 | 66 | 54 | 44 | 55 |
| -24 | -11 | -42 | -23 | -20 | -42 |
| 42 | 55 | 24 | 31 | 24 | 13 |

Circle the smallest number.

85 (31) 76

| | | | | | |
|---|---|---|---|---|---|
| | | | (107) | 127 | 117 |
| | | | (142) | 224 | 242 |
| 203 | (189) | 202 | 122 | 132 | (103) |
| (137) | 139 | 138 | 242 | 202 | (189) |
| 234 | (227) | 235 | 163 | 203 | (132) |
| 245 | 238 | (210) | (235) | 238 | 245 |

65

**Blacklines**

Number Facts (−) #3

Missing Numbers #7

## After Class

| | | | | | | |
|---|---|---|---|---|---|---|
| ↓ | ↓ | ↓ | ↓ | ↓ | ↓ | ↓ |
| 66 | 26 | 55 | 16 | 36 | 56 | 45 |
| − 4 | − 3 | − 3 | − 2 | − 6 | − 5 | − 3 |

Use white chalk for 1's place numbers.
Use green chalk for 10's place numbers.

1. Drill each child with Subtraction 4–6 flash cards.

2. Stand near the Subtraction samples.

   a. Trace the arrows. **Ones' place, first; ones' place first . . .**

   b. **6−4=__.** Write 2.

   **6−nothing=__.** Write 6.

   c. Have the children finish the samples.

Extra Activity

66

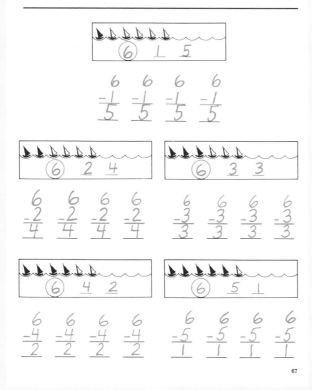

Fill in the whole and parts.
Trace and write the facts.

## Before Class

**Materials**

    5, 6 sailboats

    Large dime

**Chalkboard**

| 46 | 35 | 16 | 56 | 36 | 55 | 26 |
|----|----|----|----|----|----|----|
| − 4 | − 3 | − 5 | − 3 | − 2 | − 2 | − 6 |

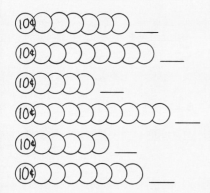

## Class Time

1. Stand near the boats and waves.

    2 dark boats, 3 light boats

    Circle the boats with your finger.

    **The whole number is __.**

    **Its parts are __ and __.**

    **The subtraction fact is __.** $5-2=3$

2. 3 dark boats, 2 light boats

    Circle the boats . . .

    **The whole number is __.**

    **Its parts are __ and __.**

    **The subtraction fact is __.** $5-3=2$

3. 2 dark boats, 4 light boats

    Circle the boats . . .

    **The whole number is __.**

    **Its parts are __ and __.**

    **The subtraction fact is __.** $6-2=4$

⟨ 16 ⟩

Answer these facts.

Speed Drill

$$6 - 1 = 5 \quad 6 - 5 = 1 \quad 5 - 3 = 2 \quad 6 - 4 = 2 \quad 6 - 3 = 3 \quad 4 - 3 = 1 \quad 6 - 2 = 4$$

$$6 - 2 = 4 \quad 6 - 5 = 1 \quad 5 - 2 = 3 \quad 5 - 3 = 2 \quad 6 - 4 = 2 \quad 4 - 3 = 1 \quad 6 - 1 = 5$$

$$6 - 3 = 3 \quad 5 - 2 = 3 \quad 6 - 5 = 1 \quad 3 - 2 = 1 \quad 5 - 4 = 1 \quad 4 - 3 = 1 \quad 6 - 4 = 2 \quad 4 - 2 = 2$$

$$6 - 4 = 2 \quad 6 - 3 = 3 \quad 6 - 5 = 1 \quad 6 - 2 = 4 \quad 5 - 3 = 2 \quad 6 - 5 = 1 \quad 6 - 4 = 2 \quad 6 - 2 = 4$$

$$6 - 2 = 4 \quad 6 - 4 = 2 \quad 2 - 1 = 1 \quad 6 - 4 = 2 \quad 6 - 2 = 4 \quad 5 - 4 = 1 \quad 6 - 3 = 3 \quad 4 - 2 = 2$$

$$6 - 5 = 1 \quad 5 - 4 = 1 \quad 6 - 3 = 3 \quad 4 - 1 = 3 \quad 5 - 2 = 3 \quad 6 - 3 = 3 \quad 6 - 4 = 2 \quad 5 - 3 = 2$$

"He arose . . . and said unto the sea, Peace be still." Mark 4:39

68

4. ⬚ 3 dark boats, 3 light boats

   Circle the boats . . .

   **The whole number is __.**
   **Its parts are __ and __.**
   **The subtraction fact is __.** 6−3=3

5. ⬚ 4 dark boats, 2 light boats

   Circle the boats . . .

   **The whole number is __.**
   **Its parts are __ and __.**
   **The subtraction fact is __.** 6−4=2

6. **Who asked to be thrown out of a boat into the sea?** Jonah (Jonah 1:12)

7. a. **Which place comes first?** ones
   b. Do the subtraction samples.

8. a. Hold the large dime. **Dime, 10¢ . . .**
   b. Have individuals count aloud as they do the Money samples.

9. Do the Speed Drill in Lesson 16.

10. Assign Lesson 16.

16

Answer these problems.

| ↓ | ↓ | ↓ | ↓ | ↓ | ↓ |
|---|---|---|---|---|---|
| 64 | 66 | 66 | 62 | 65 | 65 |
| −21 | −46 | −45 | −20 | −15 | −52 |
| 43 | 20 | 21 | 42 | 50 | 13 |

| ↓ | ↓ | ↓ | ↓ | ↓ | ↓ |
|---|---|---|---|---|---|
| 46 | 63 | 65 | 65 | 54 | 56 |
| −33 | −13 | −23 | −44 | −34 | −13 |
| 13 | 50 | 42 | 21 | 20 | 43 |

**Blacklines**

Number Facts (−) #3

Form B

Count the dimes.
Write the amount.

80 ¢

60 ¢

90 ¢

50 ¢

69

## After Class

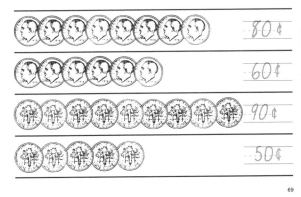

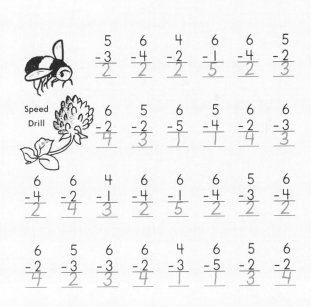

Speed Drill

| 5 | 6 | 4 | 6 | 6 | 5 |
|---|---|---|---|---|---|
| −3 | −4 | −2 | −1 | −4 | −2 |
| 2 | 2 | 2 | 5 | 2 | 3 |

| 6 | 5 | 6 | 5 | 6 | 6 |
|---|---|---|---|---|---|
| −2 | −2 | −5 | −4 | −2 | −3 |
| 4 | 3 | 1 | 1 | 4 | 3 |

| 6 | 6 | 4 | 6 | 6 | 6 | 5 | 6 |
|---|---|---|---|---|---|---|---|
| −4 | −2 | −1 | −4 | −1 | −4 | −3 | −4 |
| 2 | 4 | 3 | 2 | 5 | 2 | 2 | 2 |

| 6 | 5 | 6 | 6 | 4 | 6 | 5 | 6 |
|---|---|---|---|---|---|---|---|
| −2 | −3 | −3 | −2 | −3 | −5 | −2 | −2 |
| 4 | 2 | 3 | 4 | 1 | 1 | 3 | 4 |

1. Call the children to the ship on the board. Point to 5−2=__. **Say this 3 times with your eyes open. Then say it 3 times with your eyes closed.** Drill all the facts.

2. Call the children to the Number Line.
   a. **Begin at 100 and count back to 0.**
   b. **Count by 10's to 200.**

3. **Raise your hand to answer. What number comes before 124, 156, 235, 212, 199, 253, 101, 228?**

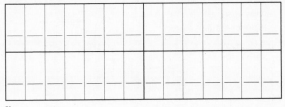

70

**17**

Fill in the whole and parts.
Trace and write the facts.

| 7 | 1 | 6 |

$$\frac{7}{-1}{6} \quad \frac{7}{-1}{6} \quad \frac{7}{-1}{6} \quad \frac{7}{-1}{6}$$

| 7 | 2 | 5 |

$$\frac{7}{-2}{5} \quad \frac{7}{-2}{5} \quad \frac{7}{-2}{5} \quad \frac{7}{-2}{5}$$

| 7 | 3 | 4 |

$$\frac{7}{-3}{4} \quad \frac{7}{-3}{4} \quad \frac{7}{-3}{4} \quad \frac{7}{-3}{4}$$

| 7 | 4 | 3 |

$$\frac{7}{-4}{3} \quad \frac{7}{-4}{3} \quad \frac{7}{-4}{3} \quad \frac{7}{-4}{3}$$

| 7 | 5 | 2 |

$$\frac{7}{-5}{2} \quad \frac{7}{-5}{2} \quad \frac{7}{-5}{2} \quad \frac{7}{-5}{2}$$

| 7 | 6 | 1 |

$$\frac{7}{-6}{1} \quad \frac{7}{-6}{1} \quad \frac{7}{-6}{1} \quad \frac{7}{-6}{1}$$

71

## Before Class

Tack Subtraction flash cards above the waves in this order:

$$\frac{7}{-1}{6} \quad \frac{7}{-2}{5} \quad \frac{7}{-3}{4} \quad \frac{7}{-4}{3} \quad \frac{7}{-5}{2} \quad \frac{7}{-6}{1}$$

**Materials**

7 sailboats

*Subtraction 2-7 flash cards*

*Large penny      Large dime*

**Chalkboard**

| 47 | 25 | 76 | 26 | 37 | 56 | 67 |
|---|---|---|---|---|---|---|
| −24 | −13 | −32 | − 2 | − 3 | − 4 | − 5 |

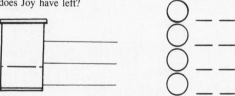

Joy made 6 buns. She gave 4 of them to Grandmother. How many buns does Joy have left?

## Class Time

1. Stand near the boats and waves.

   | 1 dark boat, 6 light boats |

   Circle the boats with your finger.

   **7 boats in the sea;**

   **7 is the whole number.**

   **What part of the 7 has dark sails?** 1

   **What part of the 7 has light sails?** 6

   **7 is the whole number.**

   **Its parts are 1 and 6.**

   a. Ask a child to fill in the whole and parts as everyone repeats: **7 is the . . . Its parts are . . .**

   b. Point to the flash card: **7−1=6 . . .**

2. | 2 dark boats, 5 light boats |

   Circle the boats . . .

   **7 boats in the sea;**

   **7 is the whole number.**

   **What part of the 7 has dark sails?** 2

   **What part of the 7 has light sails?** 5

   **7 is the whole number.**

Answer these facts.

Extra Activity

| | | | | | | |
|---|---|---|---|---|---|---|
| 7 −5 = 2 | 7 −3 = 4 | 7 −2 = 5 | 7 −4 = 3 | 7 −1 = 6 | 7 −6 = 1 | 7 −5 = 2 |
| 7 −5 = 2 | 6 −2 = 4 | 5 −2 = 3 | 7 −5 = 2 | 7 −6 = 1 | 7 −3 = 4 | 7 −4 = 3 |
| 7 −5 = 2 | 7 −1 = 6 | 7 −4 = 3 | 7 −3 = 4 | 5 −4 = 1 | 7 −5 = 2 | 6 −3 = 3 | 7 −3 = 4 |
| 7 −1 = 6 | 4 −2 = 2 | 6 −2 = 4 | 6 −1 = 5 | 7 −4 = 3 | 7 −1 = 6 | 7 −6 = 1 | 7 −5 = 2 |
| 7 −6 = 1 | 6 −3 = 3 | 7 −5 = 2 | 7 −4 = 3 | 4 −3 = 1 | 6 −1 = 5 | 7 −5 = 2 | 7 −4 = 3 |
| 7 −4 = 3 | 6 −5 = 1 | 7 −4 = 3 | 6 −4 = 2 | 7 −2 = 5 | 7 −6 = 1 | 7 −4 = 3 | 7 −5 = 2 |

"He arose . . . and said unto the sea, Peace be still." Mark 4:39

72

**Its parts are 2 and 5.**

a. Ask a child to fill in the whole and parts as everyone repeats: **7 is the . . . Its parts are . . .**

b. Point to the flash card: **7−2=5 . . .**

3. 3 dark boats, 4 light boats

Circle the boats . . .

**7 boats in the sea;**

**7 is the whole number.**

**What part of the 7 has dark sails?** 3

**What part of the 7 has light sails?** 4

**7 is the whole number.**

**Its parts are 3 and 4.**

a. Ask a child to fill in the whole and parts as everyone repeats: **7 is the . . . Its parts are . . .**

b. Point to the flash card: **7−3=4 . . .**

4. Proceed step by step through

4 dark boats, 3 light boats

5 dark boats, 2 light boats

6 dark boats, 1 light boat

5. Do the Subtraction samples.

6. **Read the story problem with me.** Ask a child to fill in the beehive.

7. Assign Lesson 17.

78

Answer these problems.

| ↓ | ↓ | ↓ | ↓ | ↓ | ↓ |
|---|---|---|---|---|---|
| 57 | 57 | 37 | 36 | 47 | 27 |
| − 1 | − 2 | − 5 | − 4 | − 6 | − 4 |
| 56 | 55 | 32 | 32 | 41 | 23 |

| ↓ | ↓ | ↓ | ↓ | ↓ | ↓ |
|---|---|---|---|---|---|
| 73 | 75 | 66 | 75 | 65 | 77 |
| −50 | −34 | −34 | −43 | −10 | −21 |
| 23 | 41 | 32 | 32 | 55 | 56 |

Count the dimes.
Write the amount.

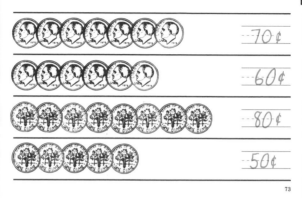

70¢

60¢

80¢

50¢

73

**Blacklines**

Number Facts (−) #3

Missing Numbers #7

Money Identification #1

## After Class

1. Drill each child with Subtraction 2–7 flash cards.

2. Hold the large penny and dime.
   a. **Which coin**
      • **is larger?**
      • **is worth more?**
      • **is smooth on the edge?**
      • **shows Franklin D. Roosevelt?**
      • **shows Abraham Lincoln?**
   b. **We count pennies by __. 1's**
      **We count dimes by __. 10's**

3. Stand near the Number Line. **Watch my pointing stick as we count by 10's and 1's.**
   **10, 20, 21, 22, 23, 24, 25**
   **10, 20, 30, 40, 50, 60, 70, 71, 72**
   **10, 20, 30, 40, 50, 51, 52, 53**

Extra Activity

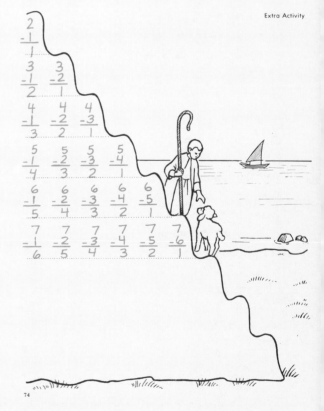

74

Fill in the whole and parts.
Trace and write the facts.

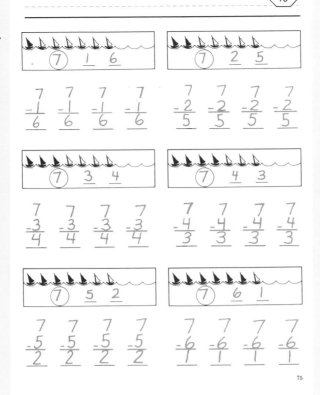

## Before Class

### Materials

Subtraction 2–6 flash cards

7 sailboats

*Subtraction 7 flash cards*

### Chalkboard

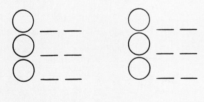

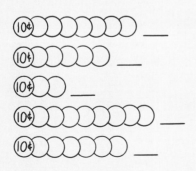

## Class Time

1. Flash Subtraction 2–6 cards for one minute. **Answer together.**

2. Stand near the boats and waves.

   | 1 dark boat, 6 light boats |

   Circle the boats with your finger.

   **7 boats in the sea;**

   **7 is the whole number.**

   **What part of the 7 has dark sails?** 1

   **What part of the 7 has light sails?** 6

   **7 is the whole number.**

   **Its part are 1 and 6.**

   a. Ask a child to fill in the whole and parts as everyone repeats: **7 is the . . . Its parts are . . .**

   b. Point to the flash card: **7−1=6 . . .**

3. | 2 dark boats, 5 light boats |

   Circle the boats . . .

   **7 boats in the sea;**

   **7 is the whole number.**

   **What part of the 7 has dark sails?** 2

# 80

⬡ 18

Answer these facts.

| | | | | | | |
|---|---|---|---|---|---|---|
| 7 −4 = 3 | 7 −6 = 1 | 7 −3 = 4 | 7 −5 = 2 | 7 −2 = 5 | 7 −1 = 6 | 7 −5 = 2 |
| 7 −5 = 2 | 7 −1 = 6 | 7 −2 = 5 | 5 −3 = 2 | 6 −2 = 4 | 2 −1 = 1 | 6 −3 = 3 |
| 7 −3 = 4 | 7 −6 = 1 | 7 −2 = 5 | 6 −3 = 3 | 7 −5 = 2 | 5 −4 = 1 | 7 −5 = 2 | 6 −5 = 1 |
| 6 −5 = 1 | 6 −2 = 4 | 7 −4 = 3 | 7 −2 = 5 | 7 −6 = 1 | 6 −4 = 2 | 7 −6 = 1 | 6 −4 = 2 |
| 7 −4 = 3 | 3 −1 = 2 | 7 −3 = 4 | 7 −5 = 2 | 5 −4 = 1 | 7 −5 = 2 | 7 −2 = 5 | 4 −1 = 3 |
| 7 −4 = 3 | 6 −1 = 5 | 6 −4 = 2 | 7 −6 = 1 | 5 −3 = 2 | 7 −3 = 4 | 7 −5 = 2 | 5 −2 = 3 |

"He arose . . . and said unto the sea, Peace be still." Mark 4:39

76

---

**What part of the 7 has light sails?** 5
**7 is the whole number.**
**Its parts are 2 and 5.**

a. Ask a child to fill in the whole and parts as everyone repeats: **7 is the . . . Its parts are . . .**

b. Point to the flash card: **7−2=5 . . .**

4. ☐ 3 dark boats, 4 light boats
Circle the boats . . .
**7 boats in the sea;**
**7 is the whole number.**
**What part of the 7 has dark sails?** 3
**What part of the 7 has light sails?** 4
**7 is the whole number.**
**Its parts are 3 and 4.**

a. Ask a child to fill in the whole and parts as everyone repeats: **7 is the . . . Its parts are . . .**

b. Point to the flash card: **7−3=4 . . .**

5. Proceed step by step through
☐ 4 dark boats, 3 light boats
☐ 5 dark boats, 2 light boats
☐ 6 dark boats, 1 light boat

6. **Say the Subtraction 7 facts with me. 7−1, 6; 7−2, 5; 7−3, 4 . . .**

7. **Count by 10's and 1's.**
**10, 11, 12, 13, 14**
**10, 20, 30, 40, 50, 60, 61, 62, 63**
**10, 20, 30, 31, 32, 33, 34, 35, 36, 37, 38**

8. Have individuals count aloud as they do the Money samples.

9. Do the Speed Drill in Lesson 18.

10. Assign Lesson 18.

18

Answer these problems.

| ↓ | ↓ | ↓ | ↓ | ↓ | ↓ |
|---|---|---|---|---|---|
| 57 | 27 | 37 | 47 | 17 | 27 |
| − 3 | − 5 | − 4 | − 2 | − 1 | − 6 |
| 54 | 22 | 33 | 45 | 16 | 21 |

| ↓ | ↓ | ↓ | ↓ | ↓ | ↓ |
|---|---|---|---|---|---|
| 74 | 56 | 75 | 65 | 65 | 76 |
| −53 | −40 | −30 | −32 | −43 | −22 |
| 21 | 16 | 45 | 33 | 22 | 54 |

Count the dimes and pennies.
Write the amount.

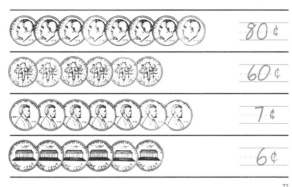

80 ¢

60 ¢

7 ¢

6 ¢

**Blacklines**

Number Facts (−) #4

2-Place Computation (−) #2

Form B

77

---

*After Class*

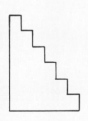

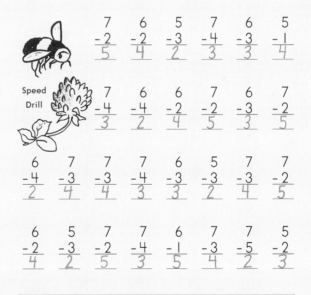

Speed Drill

| 7 | 6 | 5 | 7 | 6 | 5 |
|---|---|---|---|---|---|
| −2 | −2 | −3 | −4 | −3 | −1 |
| 5 | 4 | 2 | 3 | 3 | 4 |

| 7 | 6 | 6 | 7 | 6 | 7 |
|---|---|---|---|---|---|
| −4 | −4 | −2 | −2 | −3 | −2 |
| 3 | 2 | 4 | 5 | 3 | 5 |

| 6 | 7 | 7 | 7 | 6 | 5 | 7 | 7 |
|---|---|---|---|---|---|---|---|
| −4 | −3 | −3 | −4 | −3 | −3 | −3 | −2 |
| 2 | 4 | 4 | 3 | 3 | 2 | 4 | 5 |

| 6 | 5 | 7 | 7 | 6 | 7 | 7 | 5 |
|---|---|---|---|---|---|---|---|
| −2 | −3 | −2 | −4 | −1 | −3 | −5 | −2 |
| 4 | 2 | 5 | 3 | 5 | 4 | 2 | 3 |

1. **Say Subtraction 2–7 facts as I fill the steps.**

2. Drill each child with Subtraction 7 flash cards.

3. Chalkboard Drill
   **Write the three numbers I say.**
   205     250     215
   **Circle the largest number.**
   173     137     147
   **Circle the smallest number.**
   220     240     230
   **Circle the largest number.**

78

19

Fill in the whole and parts.
Trace and write the facts.

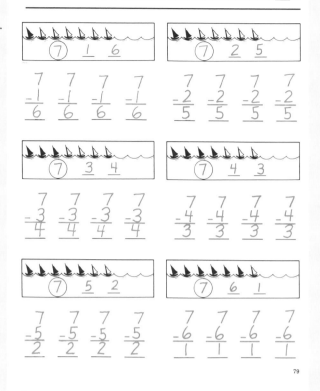

| | | | |
|---|---|---|---|
| 7 | 7 | 7 | 7 |
| -1 | -1 | -1 | -1 |
| 6 | 6 | 6 | 6 |

| | | | |
|---|---|---|---|
| 7 | 7 | 7 | 7 |
| -2 | -2 | -2 | -2 |
| 5 | 5 | 5 | 5 |

| | | | |
|---|---|---|---|
| 7 | 7 | 7 | 7 |
| -3 | -3 | -3 | -3 |
| 4 | 4 | 4 | 4 |

| | | | |
|---|---|---|---|
| 7 | 7 | 7 | 7 |
| -4 | -4 | -4 | -4 |
| 3 | 3 | 3 | 3 |

| | | | |
|---|---|---|---|
| 7 | 7 | 7 | 7 |
| -5 | -5 | -5 | -5 |
| 2 | 2 | 2 | 2 |

| | | | |
|---|---|---|---|
| 7 | 7 | 7 | 7 |
| -6 | -6 | -6 | -6 |
| 1 | 1 | 1 | 1 |

79

## Before Class

### Materials

Subtraction 2–7 flash cards

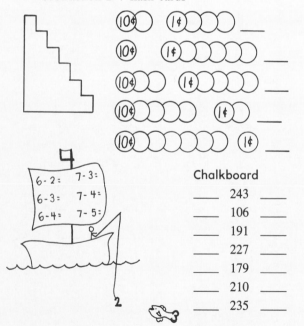

6-2:   7-3:
6-3:   7-4:
6-4:   7-5:

2

Chalkboard

___ 243 ___
___ 106 ___
___ 191 ___
___ 227 ___
___ 179 ___
___ 210 ___
___ 235 ___

*Note:* Be sure to form the numbers hidden in the picture: flag—4; hook—2; fish tail—3.

## Class Time

1. **Say the subtraction facts as I fill the steps.**

2. Stand near the ship on the board.
   a. **Say each fact 3 times.**
   b. **Did you spy the answers in the picture?**

3. Double Drill: Subtraction 2–7 flash cards.

4. **Close your eyes.**
   a. **John had 7 mints. He gave 4 of them to his little brother. How many mints does John have left? Open your eyes. Who can give us the whole problem?**
      7 mints − 4 mints = 3 mints.
   b. **7 black birds ate corn. Then 5 of them flew away. How many birds are left? Who can . . . ?**
      7 birds − 5 birds = 2 birds.

5. Stand near the Number Line.
   a. **Count by 10's to 200.**

Answer these facts.

Extra Activity

$$\begin{array}{ccccccc}
4 & 7 & 6 & 7 & 7 & 7 & 7 \\
-2 & -3 & -1 & -4 & -1 & -6 & -5 \\
\hline
2 & 4 & 5 & 3 & 6 & 1 & 2
\end{array}$$

$$\begin{array}{ccccccc}
7 & 6 & 5 & 7 & 7 & 7 & 7 \\
-4 & -2 & -2 & -5 & -6 & -3 & -4 \\
\hline
3 & 4 & 3 & 2 & 1 & 4 & 3
\end{array}$$

$$\begin{array}{cccccccc}
7 & 7 & 7 & 7 & 5 & 7 & 6 & 7 \\
-5 & -1 & -5 & -3 & -4 & -5 & -3 & -3 \\
\hline
2 & 6 & 2 & 4 & 1 & 2 & 3 & 4
\end{array}$$

$$\begin{array}{cccccccc}
7 & 7 & 6 & 7 & 7 & 7 & 7 & 7 \\
-1 & -5 & -2 & -2 & -4 & -1 & -6 & -5 \\
\hline
6 & 2 & 4 & 5 & 3 & 6 & 1 & 2
\end{array}$$

$$\begin{array}{cccccccc}
6 & 6 & 7 & 7 & 4 & 6 & 7 & 7 \\
-5 & -3 & -5 & -4 & -3 & -1 & -5 & -4 \\
\hline
1 & 3 & 2 & 3 & 1 & 5 & 2 & 3
\end{array}$$

$$\begin{array}{cccccccc}
7 & 7 & 7 & 6 & 7 & 7 & 7 & 7 \\
-4 & -6 & -4 & -4 & -2 & -6 & -4 & -5 \\
\hline
3 & 1 & 3 & 2 & 5 & 1 & 3 & 2
\end{array}$$

"He arose . . . and said unto the sea, Peace be still."  Mark 4:39

80

b. **Count by 10's to 1's.**
   **10, 20, 30, 40, 41, 42, 43, 44, 45**
   **10, 11, 12, 13, 14, 15, 16, 17**
   **10, 20, 30, 40, 50, 60, 61, 62, 63**

6. **Count the Money samples with me.** Write each amount.

7. Motion: **Before, after, between** . . . Fill in the Before and After samples.

8. Assign Lesson 19.

84

Count the dimes and pennies.
Write the amount.

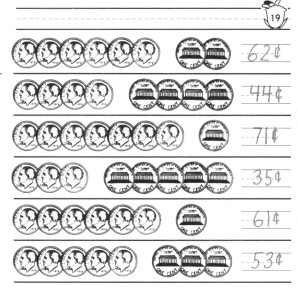

62¢

44¢

71¢

35¢

61¢

53¢

**Blacklines**

Number Facts (−) #4

2-Place Computation (−) #2

Money Identification #1

Read the story.
Write the numbers
  in the beehive.
Write the label words
  on the lines.
Answer the problem.

7 eggs were in a dish.
Then Father ate 3 of the
eggs. How many eggs were
**left** in the dish?

```
  7   eggs
- 3   eggs
  4   eggs
```

81

## After Class

| | | |
|---|---|---|
| ___ 70 ___ | ___ 130 ___ |
| ___ 20 ___ | ___ 180 ___ |
| ___ 90 ___ | ___ 160 ___ |
| ___ 40 ___ | ___ 110 ___ |

1. Fill in the Before and After numbers counting by 10's.

2. Chalkboard Drill: **If you saved 4 dimes, how many cents would you have?** Continue with

    8 dimes          27 pennies

    6 dimes          31 pennies

    10 dimes        14 pennies

    1 dime and 2 pennies

    2 dimes and 3 pennies

Extra Activity

$$\begin{array}{c} 2 \\ -1 \\ \hline 1 \end{array}$$

$$\begin{array}{ccc} 3 & 3 \\ -1 & -2 \\ \hline 2 & 1 \end{array}$$

$$\begin{array}{ccc} 4 & 4 & 4 \\ -1 & -2 & -3 \\ \hline 3 & 2 & 1 \end{array}$$

$$\begin{array}{cccc} 5 & 5 & 5 & 5 \\ -1 & -2 & -3 & -4 \\ \hline 4 & 3 & 2 & 1 \end{array}$$

$$\begin{array}{ccccc} 6 & 6 & 6 & 6 & 6 \\ -1 & -2 & -3 & -4 & -5 \\ \hline 5 & 4 & 3 & 2 & 1 \end{array}$$

$$\begin{array}{cccccc} 7 & 7 & 7 & 7 & 7 & 7 \\ -1 & -2 & -3 & -4 & -5 & -6 \\ \hline 6 & 5 & 4 & 3 & 2 & 1 \end{array}$$

82

Fill in the whole and parts.
Trace and write the facts.

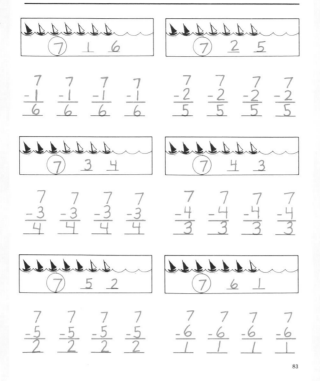

$$\begin{array}{c}7\\-1\\\hline6\end{array}\quad\begin{array}{c}7\\-1\\\hline6\end{array}\quad\begin{array}{c}7\\-1\\\hline6\end{array}\quad\begin{array}{c}7\\-1\\\hline6\end{array}\qquad\begin{array}{c}7\\-2\\\hline5\end{array}\quad\begin{array}{c}7\\-2\\\hline5\end{array}\quad\begin{array}{c}7\\-2\\\hline5\end{array}\quad\begin{array}{c}7\\-2\\\hline5\end{array}$$

$$\begin{array}{c}7\\-3\\\hline4\end{array}\quad\begin{array}{c}7\\-3\\\hline4\end{array}\quad\begin{array}{c}7\\-3\\\hline4\end{array}\quad\begin{array}{c}7\\-3\\\hline4\end{array}\qquad\begin{array}{c}7\\-4\\\hline3\end{array}\quad\begin{array}{c}7\\-4\\\hline3\end{array}\quad\begin{array}{c}7\\-4\\\hline3\end{array}\quad\begin{array}{c}7\\-4\\\hline3\end{array}$$

$$\begin{array}{c}7\\-5\\\hline2\end{array}\quad\begin{array}{c}7\\-5\\\hline2\end{array}\quad\begin{array}{c}7\\-5\\\hline2\end{array}\quad\begin{array}{c}7\\-5\\\hline2\end{array}\qquad\begin{array}{c}7\\-6\\\hline1\end{array}\quad\begin{array}{c}7\\-6\\\hline1\end{array}\quad\begin{array}{c}7\\-6\\\hline1\end{array}\quad\begin{array}{c}7\\-6\\\hline1\end{array}$$

83

## Before Class

### Materials
6, 7 sailboats
*Subtraction 2–7 flash cards*

### Chalkboard

| 26 | 57 | 67 | 46 | 77 | 47 |
|----|----|----|----|----|----|
| − 4 | − 3 | − 5 | − 2 | − 4 | − 2 |

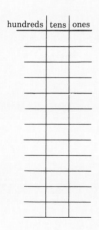

## Class Time

1. Stand near the grid on the board.
   a. Motion: **Ones, tens, hundreds . . .**
   b. **When I call your name, come and write the number I say in the grid.** Use these numbers: **136, 7, 103, 78, 219, 245, 9, 206, 41, 182, 220, 69.**

2. Stand near the boats and waves.

   2 dark boats, 4 light boats

   Circle the boats with your finger.
   **The whole number is __.**
   **Its parts are __ and __.**
   **The subtraction fact is __.** 6−2=4

3. 4 dark boats, 2 light boats

   Circle the boats . . .
   **The whole number is __.**
   **Its parts are __ and __.**
   **The subtraction fact is __.** 6−4=2

## 20

Answer these facts.

$$7 - 1 = 6 \quad 2 - 1 = 1 \quad 6 - 2 = 4 \quad 7 - 5 = 2 \quad 7 - 2 = 5 \quad 7 - 1 = 6 \quad 7 - 4 = 3$$

$$4 - 1 = 3 \quad 7 - 4 = 3 \quad 7 - 2 = 5 \quad 5 - 3 = 2 \quad 7 - 3 = 4 \quad 7 - 6 = 1 \quad 6 - 3 = 3$$

$$6 - 2 = 4 \quad 7 - 6 = 1 \quad 7 - 2 = 5 \quad 6 - 3 = 3 \quad 7 - 5 = 2 \quad 7 - 6 = 1 \quad 7 - 5 = 2 \quad 6 - 5 = 1$$

$$6 - 5 = 1 \quad 7 - 3 = 4 \quad 7 - 4 = 3 \quad 7 - 2 = 5 \quad 5 - 4 = 1 \quad 6 - 4 = 2 \quad 7 - 6 = 1 \quad 6 - 4 = 2$$

$$5 - 2 = 3 \quad 3 - 1 = 2 \quad 7 - 3 = 4 \quad 7 - 5 = 2 \quad 5 - 4 = 1 \quad 7 - 5 = 2 \quad 7 - 2 = 5 \quad 7 - 5 = 2$$

$$7 - 5 = 2 \quad 6 - 1 = 5 \quad 6 - 4 = 2 \quad 7 - 6 = 1 \quad 5 - 3 = 2 \quad 7 - 3 = 4 \quad 7 - 5 = 2 \quad 7 - 4 = 3$$

"He arose . . . and said unto the sea, Peace be still." Mark 4:39

84

**Speed Drill**

4. | 3 dark boats, 4 light boats |

   Circle the boats . . .

   **The whole number is __.**

   **Its parts are __ and __.**

   **The subtraction fact is __.** 7−3=4

5. | 4 dark boats, 3 light boats |

   Circle the boats . . .

   **The whole number is __.**

   **Its parts are __ and __.**

   **The subtraction fact is __.** 7−4=3

6. Do the Subtraction samples.

7. Do the Speed Drill in Lesson 20.

8. Assign Lesson 20.

Count the dimes and pennies.
Write the amount.

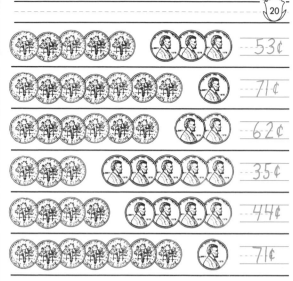

53¢

71¢

62¢

35¢

44¢

71¢

**Blacklines**

Number Facts (−) #4

2-Place Computation (−) #2

Form B

Read the story.
Write the numbers
in the beehive.
Write the label words
on the lines.
Answer the problem.

7 nuts hung on a tree.
God sent a wind. Then 5
of the nuts fell down.
How many nuts were **left**
on the tree?

| | |
|---|---|
| 7 | nuts |
| − 5 | nuts |
| 2 | nuts |

85

## *After Class*

|  |  |  |
|---|---|---|
| 153 | 135 | 150 |
| 106 | 160 | 166 |
| 189 | 198 | 188 |

|  |  |  |
|---|---|---|
| 210 | 202 | 201 |
| 204 | 240 | 214 |
| 146 | 246 | 126 |
| 223 | 123 | 132 |

Speed
Drill

| 7 | 7 | 6 | 7 | 6 | 7 |
|---|---|---|---|---|---|
| −5 | −4 | −4 | −2 | −4 | −4 |
| 2 | 3 | 2 | 5 | 2 | 3 |

| 6 | 6 | 6 | 7 | 7 | 7 |
|---|---|---|---|---|---|
| −1 | −4 | −3 | −3 | −5 | −4 |
| 5 | 2 | 3 | 4 | 2 | 3 |

| 7 | 7 | 6 | 6 | 7 | 6 | 7 | 7 |
|---|---|---|---|---|---|---|---|
| −3 | −5 | −3 | −4 | −2 | −4 | −4 | −5 |
| 4 | 2 | 3 | 2 | 5 | 2 | 3 | 2 |

1. Drill each child with Subtraction 2–7 flash cards.

2. **The bee buzzes to the water lilies. He sits on the smallest lily and sips sweet nectar juice.** Circle the smallest number.

3. Have individuals count by 10's to 200.

| 7 | 6 | 7 | 6 | 7 | 6 | 7 | 7 |
|---|---|---|---|---|---|---|---|
| −5 | −2 | −4 | −4 | −3 | −3 | −5 | −2 |
| 2 | 4 | 3 | 2 | 4 | 3 | 2 | 5 |

86

Fill in the whole and parts.
Trace and write the facts.
Make the twins take turns.

| 🚤🚤🚤🚤🚤🚤🚤🚤 | 🚤🚤🚤🚤🚤🚤🚤🚤 |
|---|---|
| ⑧ 1 7 | ⑧ 2 6 |

$$\begin{array}{cccc} 1 & 7 & 1 & 7 \\ +7 & +1 & +7 & +1 \\ \hline 8 & 8 & 8 & 8 \end{array} \qquad \begin{array}{cccc} 2 & 6 & 2 & 6 \\ +6 & +2 & +6 & +2 \\ \hline 8 & 8 & 8 & 8 \end{array}$$

$$\begin{array}{cccc} 1 & 7 & 1 & 7 \\ +7 & +1 & +7 & +1 \\ \hline 8 & 8 & 8 & 8 \end{array} \qquad \begin{array}{cccc} 2 & 6 & 2 & 6 \\ +6 & +2 & +6 & +2 \\ \hline 8 & 8 & 8 & 8 \end{array}$$

| 🚤🚤🚤🚤🚤🚤🚤🚤 | 🚤🚤🚤🚤🚤🚤🚤🚤 |
|---|---|
| ⑧ 3 5 | ⑧ 4 4 |

$$\begin{array}{cccc} 3 & 5 & 3 & 5 \\ +5 & +3 & +5 & +3 \\ \hline 8 & 8 & 8 & 8 \end{array} \qquad \begin{array}{cccc} 4 & 4 & 4 & 4 \\ +4 & +4 & +4 & +4 \\ \hline 8 & 8 & 8 & 8 \end{array}$$

$$\begin{array}{cccc} 3 & 5 & 3 & 5 \\ +5 & +3 & +5 & +3 \\ \hline 8 & 8 & 8 & 8 \end{array} \qquad \begin{array}{cccc} 4 & 4 & 4 & 4 \\ +4 & +4 & +4 & +4 \\ \hline 8 & 8 & 8 & 8 \end{array}$$

87

## Before Class

Mark the 5's on the Number Line. See
   Patterns, page 213.
Tack Addition 8 flash cards above the waves in
   this order:

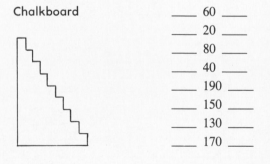

| $\begin{array}{c}1\\+7\\\hline 8\end{array}$ | $\begin{array}{c}7\\+1\\\hline 8\end{array}$ | $\begin{array}{c}2\\+6\\\hline 8\end{array}$ | $\begin{array}{c}6\\+2\\\hline 8\end{array}$ | $\begin{array}{c}3\\+5\\\hline 8\end{array}$ | $\begin{array}{c}5\\+3\\\hline 8\end{array}$ | $\begin{array}{c}4\\+4\\\hline 8\end{array}$ |
|---|---|---|---|---|---|---|

### Materials

8 sailboats
Addition 2–8 flash cards
*Addition 2–8 flash cards*

### Chalkboard

| | |
|---|---|
| ___ 60 ___ |
| ___ 20 ___ |
| ___ 80 ___ |
| ___ 40 ___ |
| ___ 190 ___ |
| ___ 150 ___ |
| ___ 130 ___ |
| ___ 170 ___ |

## Class Time

1. Have each child bring *My 1,000 Book* to the
   teaching corner. **The black crow found 10
   peas in the pod. Count 10 numbers at a
   time to 500.**

2. Fill in the Before and After samples by 10's.

3. Stand near the boats and waves.

   | 1 dark boat, 7 light boats |
   |---|

   Circle the boats with your finger.
   **8 boats in the sea;**
   **8 is the whole number.**
   **What part of the 8 has dark sails?** 1
   **What part of the 8 has light sails?** 7
   **8 is the whole number.**
   **Its parts are 1 and 7 or 7 and 1.**
   a. Point to the flash cards. **These are twin
      facts: 1+7=8 and 7+1=8.**
   b. Pick up a piece of chalk. **Make the twins
      take turns as I write them and you say
      them.** (Write vertically.) **1+7=8,
      7+1=8,  1+7=8,  7+1=8.**

Answer these facts.

Extra Activity

```
  5     2     3     6     1     2     3
 +3    +6    +2    +2    +3    +1    +5
  8     8     5     8     4     3     8

  4     1     2     2     6     2     3
 +4    +7    +5    +4    +1    +6    +3
  8     8     7     6     7     8     6

  2     5     3     6     5     4     1     3
 +6    +3    +4    +2    +2    +2    +5    +5
  8     8     7     8     7     6     6     8

  1     4     3     2     7     2     1     2
 +7    +4    +5    +3    +1    +2    +2    +6
  8     8     8     5     8     4     3     8

  4     4     5     2     3     5     5     5
 +3    +4    +3    +5    +5    +2    +1    +3
  7     8     8     7     8     7     6     8

  7     1     4     1     3     6     5     2
 +1    +6    +3    +7    +4    +2    +3    +4
  8     7     7     8     7     8     8     6
```

"He arose . . . and said unto the sea, Peace be still." Mark 4:39

88

4. | 2 dark boats, 6 light boats |

Circle the boats . . .

**8 boats in the sea;**

**8 is the whole number.**

**What part of the 8 has dark sails?** 2

**What part of the 8 has light sails?** 6

**8 is the whole number.**

**Its parts are 2 and 6 or 6 and 2.**

a. Point to the flash cards: **These are twin facts: 2+6=8 and 6+2=8.**

b. **Make the twins take turns as I write them and you say them. 2+6=8, 6+2=8, 2+6=8, 6+2=8.**

5. | 3 dark boats, 5 light boats |

Circle the boats . . .

**8 boats in the sea;**

**8 is the whole number.**

**What part of the 8 has dark sails?** 3

**What part of the 8 has light sails?** 5

**8 is the whole number.**

**Its parts are 3 and 5 or 5 and 3.**

a. Point to the flash cards: **These are twin**

**facts: 3+5=8 and 5+3=8.**

b. **Make the twins take turns.** Write **3+5=8, 5+3=8, 3+5=8, 5+3=8.**

6. | 4 dark boats, 4 light boats |

Circle the boats . . .

**8 boats in the sea;**

**8 is the whole number.**

**What part of the 8 has dark sails?** 4

**What part of the 8 has light sails?** 4

**8 is the whole number.**

**Its parts are 4 and 4.**

a. Point to the flash card. **This fact has no twin. 4+4=8 . . .**

b. **Say the fact.** Write 4+4=8 . . .

7. **Say Addition 2-8 facts as I fill the steps.**

8. Flash Addition 2-8 cards.

9. Assign Lesson 21.

90

Write the numbers in the correct places.

| | hundreds | tens | ones | | hundreds | tens | ones |
|---|---|---|---|---|---|---|---|
| 37 | | 3 | 7 | 153 | 1 | 5 | 3 |
| 134 | 1 | 3 | 4 | 82 | | 8 | 2 |
| 9 | | | 9 | 208 | 2 | 0 | 8 |
| 76 | | 7 | 6 | 149 | 1 | 4 | 9 |
| 215 | 2 | 1 | 5 | 34 | | 3 | 4 |

Write the numbers that come before and after when you count by 10's.

Count by 10's

| | | | | | |
|---|---|---|---|---|---|
| 70 | 80 | | 150 | 160 | 170 |
| 150 | 160 | | 110 | 120 | 130 |
| 20 | 30 | 40 | 80 | 90 | 100 |
| 170 | 180 | 190 | 130 | 140 | 150 |
| 10 | 20 | 30 | 180 | 190 | 200 |

**Blacklines**

2-Place Computation (+) #1

Money Identification #2

89

*After Class*

1. Double Drill: Addition 2–8 flash cards.

2. Have individuals count by 10's to 500.

3. Call the children to the Number Line.

   a. **Do you remember the bullfrog that leaped from lily pad to lily pad in first grade? When he leaped, we counted by ___. 5's**

   b. Point to the first pink triangle. **Count by 5's to 100.**

Extra Activity

90

Fill in the whole and parts.
Trace and write the facts.
Make the twins take turns.

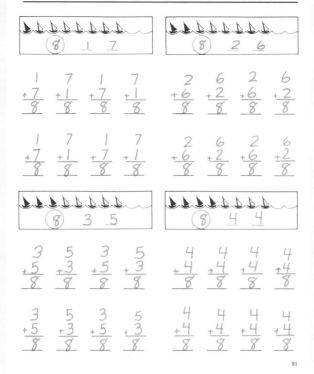

|  |  |  |  |
|---|---|---|---|
| 1<br>+7<br>8 | 7<br>+1<br>8 | 1<br>+7<br>8 | 7<br>+1<br>8 |
| 1<br>+7<br>8 | 7<br>+1<br>8 | 1<br>+7<br>8 | 7<br>+1<br>8 |

|  |  |  |  |
|---|---|---|---|
| 2<br>+6<br>8 | 6<br>+2<br>8 | 2<br>+6<br>8 | 6<br>+2<br>8 |
| 2<br>+6<br>8 | 6<br>+2<br>8 | 2<br>+6<br>8 | 6<br>+2<br>8 |

|  |  |  |  |
|---|---|---|---|
| 3<br>+5<br>8 | 5<br>+3<br>8 | 3<br>+5<br>8 | 5<br>+3<br>8 |
| 3<br>+5<br>8 | 5<br>+3<br>8 | 3<br>+5<br>8 | 5<br>+3<br>8 |

|  |  |  |  |
|---|---|---|---|
| 4<br>+4<br>8 | 4<br>+4<br>8 | 4<br>+4<br>8 | 4<br>+4<br>8 |
| 4<br>+4<br>8 | 4<br>+4<br>8 | 4<br>+4<br>8 | 4<br>+4<br>8 |

## Before Class

### Materials

8 sailboats

*1 nickel for each child*

### Chalkboard

| 54 | 23 | 65 | 24 | 73 | 35 | 46 |
|---|---|---|---|---|---|---|
| +33 | +52 | +23 | +43 | +13 | +52 | +21 |

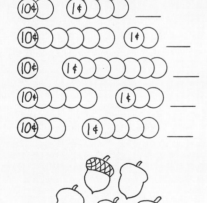

## Class Time

1. Complete the acorns as you explain: **Small round acorns with bumpy caps grow on a large oak tree. One by one the acorns drop to the ground. A bushy-tailed squirrel scurries to collect the acorns. How many did he collect?** 5

   a. **Count by 5's to 100.**

   b. **Start again. Count to 125.**

2. Stand near the boats and waves.

   | 1 dark boat, 7 light boats |
   |---|

   Circle the boats with your finger.

   **8 boats in the sea;**

   **8 is the whole number.**

   **What part of the 8 has dark sails?** 1

   **What part of the 8 has light sails?** 7

   **8 is the whole number.**

   **Its parts are 1 and 7 or 7 and 1.**

   a. Point to the flash cards. **These are twin facts: 1+7=8 and 7+1=8.**

   b. Pick up a piece of chalk. **Make the twins take turns as I write them and you say them. 1+7=8, 7+1=8, 1+7=8 . . .**

**22**

Answer these facts.

| | | | | | | |
|---|---|---|---|---|---|---|
| 6 | 4 | 4 | 3 | 3 | 1 | 3 |
| +2 | +4 | +3 | +3 | +2 | +6 | +5 |
| 8 | 8 | 7 | 6 | 5 | 7 | 8 |

| | | | | | | |
|---|---|---|---|---|---|---|
| 1 | 2 | 2 | 2 | 5 | 2 | 5 |
| +7 | +5 | +3 | +4 | +2 | +6 | +3 |
| 8 | 7 | 5 | 6 | 7 | 8 | 8 |

| | | | | | | |
|---|---|---|---|---|---|---|
| 3 | 6 | 3 | 6 | 7 | 5 | 4 | 2 |
| +4 | +1 | +5 | +2 | +1 | +3 | +2 | +4 |
| 7 | 7 | 8 | 8 | 8 | 8 | 6 | 6 |

| | | | | | | |
|---|---|---|---|---|---|---|
| 4 | 6 | 1 | 4 | 5 | 2 | 3 | 4 |
| +4 | +2 | +6 | +3 | +1 | +3 | +5 | +4 |
| 8 | 8 | 7 | 7 | 6 | 5 | 8 | 8 |

| | | | | | | |
|---|---|---|---|---|---|---|
| 5 | 2 | 2 | 1 | 3 | 5 | 1 | 2 |
| +3 | +6 | +3 | +5 | +4 | +2 | +7 | +6 |
| 8 | 8 | 5 | 6 | 7 | 7 | 8 | 8 |

| | | | | | | |
|---|---|---|---|---|---|---|
| 5 | 2 | 3 | 5 | 4 | 2 | 3 | 6 |
| +3 | +6 | +4 | +2 | +3 | +5 | +5 | +2 |
| 8 | 8 | 7 | 7 | 7 | 7 | 8 | 8 |

"He arose . . . and said unto the sea, Peace be still." Mark 4:39

92

3. 2 dark boats, 6 light boats

Circle the boats . . .

**8 boats in the sea;**

**8 is the whole number.**

**What part of the 8 has dark sails?** 2

**What part of the 8 has light sails?** 6

**8 is the whole number.**

**Its parts are 2 and 6 or 6 and 2.**

a. Point to the flash cards. **These are twin facts: 2+6=8 and 6+2=8.**

b. **Make the twins take turns.** Write 2+6=8, 6+2=8, 2+6=8 . . .

4. 3 dark boats, 5 light boats

Circle the boats . . .

**8 boats in the sea;**

**8 is the whole number.**

**What part of the 8 has dark sails?** 3

**What part of the 8 has light sails?** 5

**8 is the whole number.**

**Its parts are 3 and 5 or 5 and 3.**

a. Point to the flash cards. **These are twin facts: 3+5=8 and 5+3=8.**

b. **Make the twins take turns.** Write. 3+5=8, 5+3=8, 3+5=8 . . .

5. 4 dark boats, 4 light boats

Circle the boats . . .

**8 boats in the sea;**

**8 is the whole number.**

**What part of the 8 has dark sails?** 4

**What part of the 8 has light sails?** 4

**8 is the whole number.**

**Its parts are 4 and 4.**

a. Point to the flash card: **4+4=8.**

b. **Say the fact as I write it. 4+4=8, 4+4=8.**

6. Do the 2-digit samples.

7. Have individuals count aloud as they do the Money samples.

8. Do the Speed Drill in Lesson 22.

9. Assign Lesson 22.

22

Write the numbers in the correct places.

| | hundreds | tens | ones |
|---|---|---|---|
| 214 | 2 | 1 | 4 |
| 106 | 1 | 0 | 6 |
| 40 | | 4 | 0 |
| 57 | | 5 | 7 |
| 235 | 2 | 3 | 5 |

| | hundreds | tens | ones |
|---|---|---|---|
| 159 | 1 | 5 | 9 |
| 63 | | 6 | 3 |
| 248 | 2 | 4 | 8 |
| 120 | 1 | 2 | 0 |
| 84 | | 8 | 4 |

Write the numbers that come before and after when you count by 10's.

Count by 10's

| | | | | | |
|---|---|---|---|---|---|
| 130 | 140 | | 100 | 110 | 120 |
| | 80 | 90 | 30 | 40 | 50 |
| 160 | 170 | 180 | 180 | 190 | 200 |
| 80 | 90 | 100 | 150 | 160 | 170 |
| 90 | 100 | 110 | 40 | 50 | 60 |

**Blacklines**

Number Facts (+) #5

Reading Problems #1

Form B

93

---

## After Class

1. **Say the Addition 2–8 facts as I fill the steps.**

2. **Give each child one nickel.**

   a. **Do you recognize this coin? Whose picture is on the nickel?**
   Thomas Jefferson
   **How much is a nickel worth?** 5¢
   **We count nickels by __.** 5's

   b. **Hold up your nickel and say "nickel, 5¢, nickel, 5¢ . . ."**

   c. **Let's count each child's nickel to see how many cents we have. 5¢, 10¢, 15¢ . . .**

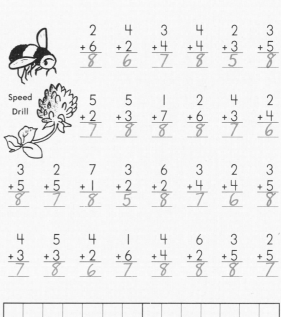

Speed Drill

| | | | | | |
|---|---|---|---|---|---|
| 2 +6 = 8 | 4 +2 = 6 | 3 +4 = 7 | 4 +4 = 8 | 2 +3 = 5 | 3 +5 = 8 |
| 5 +2 = 7 | 5 +3 = 8 | 1 +7 = 8 | 2 +6 = 8 | 4 +3 = 7 | 2 +4 = 6 |

| | | | | | | | |
|---|---|---|---|---|---|---|---|
| 3 +5 = 8 | 2 +5 = 7 | 7 +1 = 8 | 3 +2 = 5 | 6 +2 = 8 | 3 +4 = 7 | 2 +4 = 6 | 3 +5 = 8 |
| 4 +3 = 7 | 5 +3 = 8 | 4 +2 = 6 | 1 +6 = 7 | 4 +4 = 8 | 6 +2 = 8 | 3 +5 = 8 | 2 +5 = 7 |

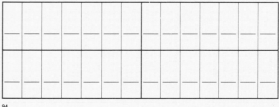

**23**

Fill in the whole and parts.
Trace and write the facts.
Make the twins take turns.

$$\begin{array}{cccc} 1 & 7 & 1 & 7 \\ +7 & +1 & +7 & +1 \\ \hline 8 & 8 & 8 & 8 \end{array}$$

$$\begin{array}{cccc} 1 & 7 & 1 & 7 \\ +7 & +1 & +7 & +1 \\ \hline 8 & 8 & 8 & 8 \end{array}$$

8   1   7

$$\begin{array}{cccc} 2 & 6 & 2 & 6 \\ +6 & +2 & +6 & +2 \\ \hline 8 & 8 & 8 & 8 \end{array}$$

$$\begin{array}{cccc} 2 & 6 & 2 & 6 \\ +6 & +2 & +6 & +2 \\ \hline 8 & 8 & 8 & 8 \end{array}$$

8   2   6

8   3   5

$$\begin{array}{cccc} 3 & 5 & 3 & 5 \\ +5 & +3 & +5 & +3 \\ \hline 8 & 8 & 8 & 8 \end{array}$$

$$\begin{array}{cccc} 3 & 5 & 3 & 5 \\ +5 & +3 & +5 & +3 \\ \hline 8 & 8 & 8 & 8 \end{array}$$

8   4   4

$$\begin{array}{cccc} 4 & 4 & 4 & 4 \\ +4 & +4 & +4 & +4 \\ \hline 8 & 8 & 8 & 8 \end{array}$$

$$\begin{array}{cccc} 4 & 4 & 4 & 4 \\ +4 & +4 & +4 & +4 \\ \hline 8 & 8 & 8 & 8 \end{array}$$

## Before Class

**Materials**

Addition 6–8 flash cards

*Addition 6–8 flash cards*

**Chalkboard**

| 43 | 35 | 24 | 82 | 23 | 51 | 72 | 63 |
|---|---|---|---|---|---|---|---|
| + 5 | + 2 | + 3 | + 6 | + 4 | + 7 | + 4 | + 5 |

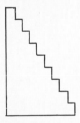

## Class Time

1. Flash Addition 6–8 cards for one minute.

2. Do the Addition samples.

3. Stand near the boats and waves.

   1 dark boat, 7 light boats

   Circle the boats with your finger.
   **The whole number is __.**
   **Its parts are __ and __ or __ and __.**
   **The facts are __.** 1+7=8 and 7+1=8

4. 2 dark boats, 6 light boats

   Circle the boats . . .
   **The whole number is __.**
   **Its parts are __ and __ or __ and __.**
   **The facts are __.** 2+6=8 and 6+2=8

5. 3 dark boats, 5 light boats

   Circle the boats . . .
   **The whole number is __.**
   **Its parts are __ and __ or __ and __.**
   **The facts are __.** 3+5=8 and 5+3=8

Answer these facts.

⟨ 23 ⟩

| 1 | 2 | 5 | 6 | 1 | 4 | 2 |
|---|---|---|---|---|---|---|
| +7 | +6 | +1 | +2 | +7 | +3 | +6 |
| 8 | 8 | 6 | 8 | 8 | 7 | 8 |

| 2 | 5 | 2 | 7 | 6 | 2 | 5 |
|---|---|---|---|---|---|---|
| +6 | +3 | +5 | +1 | +1 | +6 | +3 |
| 8 | 8 | 7 | 8 | 7 | 8 | 8 |

( Extra Activity )

| 4 | 5 | 3 | 4 | 5 | 6 | 5 | 3 |
|---|---|---|---|---|---|---|---|
| +4 | +3 | +4 | +4 | +2 | +2 | +3 | +5 |
| 8 | 8 | 7 | 8 | 7 | 8 | 8 | 8 |

| 5 | 4 | 3 | 2 | 7 | 3 | 3 | 2 |
|---|---|---|---|---|---|---|---|
| +3 | +4 | +5 | +4 | +1 | +5 | +4 | +6 |
| 8 | 8 | 8 | 6 | 8 | 8 | 7 | 8 |

| 2 | 4 | 5 | 2 | 3 | 5 | 5 | 3 |
|---|---|---|---|---|---|---|---|
| +5 | +2 | +3 | +5 | +5 | +2 | +3 | +3 |
| 7 | 6 | 8 | 7 | 8 | 7 | 8 | 6 |

| 2 | 1 | 4 | 1 | 3 | 6 | 1 | 3 |
|---|---|---|---|---|---|---|---|
| +4 | +6 | +3 | +7 | +4 | +2 | +5 | +5 |
| 6 | 7 | 7 | 8 | 7 | 8 | 6 | 8 |

"He arose . . . and said unto the sea, Peace be still."  Mark 4:39

96

---

6. [ 4 dark boats, 4 light boats ]

   Circle the boats . . .

   **The whole number is __.**

   **Its parts are __ and __.**

   **The fact is __.** 4+4=8.

7. Ask a child to fill in the steps as everyone repeats Addition 2–8 facts.

8. Have each child get his 1,000 book.

   a. **How many acorns did the squirrel collect?** 5

   b. **Count by 5's to 155.**

9. Assign Lesson 23.

**Reminder . . .**

   As you teach Addition Families 8–10 in the next number of lessons, review the corresponding subtraction facts. Post subtraction flash cards with the answers showing and daily recite them with the class as you point to them.

8
-6
2

8
-4
4

8
-5
3

**23**

Count by 5's to 155.
The child may use his 1,000 book.

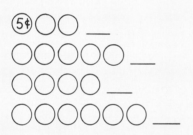

| Count by 5's | 5 | 10 | 15 |
|---|---|---|---|
| 20 | 25 | 30 | 35 | 40 |
| 45 | 50 | 55 | 60 | 65 |
| 70 | 75 | 80 | 85 | 90 |
| 95 | 100 | 105 | 110 | 115 |
| 120 | 125 | 130 | 135 | 140 |
| 145 | 150 | 155 | | |

**Blacklines**

Number Facts (+) #5

2-Place Computation (+) #1

Answer these problems.

```
 73    83    66    75    65    82
+ 5   + 4   + 2   + 2   + 3   + 4
 78    87    68    77    68    86

 24    34    24    13    54    31
+62   +34   +53   +55   +33   +47
 86    68    77    68    87    78
```

97

*After Class*

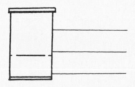

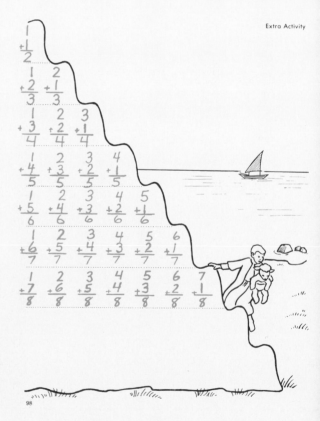

Extra Activity

Five boys waded in the
stream. Three boys sat on
the bank. How many boys
is that altogether?

1. Drill each child with Addition 6–8 flash cards.

2. Stand near the Nickel samples.

   a. **Say "nickel, 5¢" as I fill in each circle.**

   b. **Count the nickels with me.** Write each
     amount.

3. **Read the story problem to me.** Ask a child
   to fill the beehive.

Fill in the whole and parts.
Trace and write the facts.
Make the twins take turns.

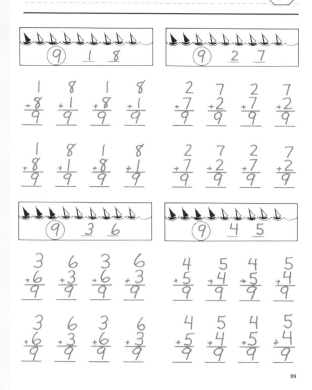

$$\begin{array}{c}1\\+8\\\hline 9\end{array}\quad\begin{array}{c}8\\+1\\\hline 9\end{array}\quad\begin{array}{c}1\\+8\\\hline 9\end{array}\quad\begin{array}{c}8\\+1\\\hline 9\end{array}\qquad\begin{array}{c}2\\+7\\\hline 9\end{array}\quad\begin{array}{c}7\\+2\\\hline 9\end{array}\quad\begin{array}{c}2\\+7\\\hline 9\end{array}\quad\begin{array}{c}7\\+2\\\hline 9\end{array}$$

$$\begin{array}{c}1\\+8\\\hline 9\end{array}\quad\begin{array}{c}8\\+1\\\hline 9\end{array}\quad\begin{array}{c}1\\+8\\\hline 9\end{array}\quad\begin{array}{c}8\\+1\\\hline 9\end{array}\qquad\begin{array}{c}2\\+7\\\hline 9\end{array}\quad\begin{array}{c}7\\+2\\\hline 9\end{array}\quad\begin{array}{c}2\\+7\\\hline 9\end{array}\quad\begin{array}{c}7\\+2\\\hline 9\end{array}$$

$$\begin{array}{c}3\\+6\\\hline 9\end{array}\quad\begin{array}{c}6\\+3\\\hline 9\end{array}\quad\begin{array}{c}3\\+6\\\hline 9\end{array}\quad\begin{array}{c}6\\+3\\\hline 9\end{array}\qquad\begin{array}{c}4\\+5\\\hline 9\end{array}\quad\begin{array}{c}5\\+4\\\hline 9\end{array}\quad\begin{array}{c}4\\+5\\\hline 9\end{array}\quad\begin{array}{c}5\\+4\\\hline 9\end{array}$$

$$\begin{array}{c}3\\+6\\\hline 9\end{array}\quad\begin{array}{c}6\\+3\\\hline 9\end{array}\quad\begin{array}{c}3\\+6\\\hline 9\end{array}\quad\begin{array}{c}6\\+3\\\hline 9\end{array}\qquad\begin{array}{c}4\\+5\\\hline 9\end{array}\quad\begin{array}{c}5\\+4\\\hline 9\end{array}\quad\begin{array}{c}4\\+5\\\hline 9\end{array}\quad\begin{array}{c}5\\+4\\\hline 9\end{array}$$

99

## Before Class

Tack Addition 9 flash cards above the waves in this order:

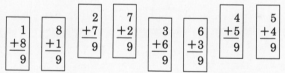

$$\begin{array}{c}1\\+8\\\hline 9\end{array}\quad\begin{array}{c}8\\+1\\\hline 9\end{array}\quad\begin{array}{c}2\\+7\\\hline 9\end{array}\quad\begin{array}{c}7\\+2\\\hline 9\end{array}\quad\begin{array}{c}3\\+6\\\hline 9\end{array}\quad\begin{array}{c}6\\+3\\\hline 9\end{array}\quad\begin{array}{c}4\\+5\\\hline 9\end{array}\quad\begin{array}{c}5\\+4\\\hline 9\end{array}$$

### Materials

9 sailboats

### Chalkboard

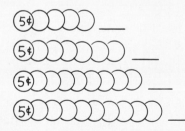

| | | |
|---|---|---|
| | 108 | 208 | 118 |
| | 243 | 234 | 134 |
| | 105 | 150 | 151 |
| 165 185 175 | 239 | 229 | 219 |
| 210 211 201 | 230 | 203 | 223 |

## Class Time

1. Have each child bring *My 1,000 Book* to the teaching corner.
   a. **Boys, count by 5's to 155.**
   b. **Girls, count by 5's to 155.**
   c. **Everyone begin at 100. 100, 105 . . . 155.**

2. Have individuals count aloud as they do the Money samples.

3. **God put nectar into the smallest water lily. The honey bee darts down to suck up the nectar.** Circle the smallest number.

4. Stand near the boats and waves.

   | 1 dark boat, 8 light boats |
   |---|

   Circle the boats with your finger.
   **9 boats in the sea;**
   **9 is the whole number.**
   **What part of the 9 has dark sails?** 1
   **What part of the 9 has light sails?** 8
   **9 is the whole number.**
   **Its parts are 1 and 8 or 8 and 1.**

98

< 24 >

Answer these facts.

Speed Drill

| | | | | | | |
|---|---|---|---|---|---|---|
| 3 | 4 | 2 | 4 | 3 | 2 | 2 |
| +6 | +5 | +3 | +3 | +5 | +4 | +7 |
| 9 | 9 | 5 | 7 | 8 | 6 | 9 |

| 8 | 4 | 5 | 5 | 3 | 6 | 5 |
|---|---|---|---|---|---|---|
| +1 | +2 | +3 | +2 | +2 | +3 | +4 |
| 9 | 6 | 8 | 7 | 5 | 9 | 9 |

| 7 | 2 | 1 | 4 | 3 | 2 | 3 | 6 |
|---|---|---|---|---|---|---|---|
| +2 | +6 | +7 | +5 | +6 | +5 | +4 | +3 |
| 9 | 8 | 8 | 9 | 9 | 7 | 7 | 9 |

| 4 | 4 | 3 | 5 | 6 | 6 | 4 | 1 |
|---|---|---|---|---|---|---|---|
| +5 | +3 | +4 | +4 | +3 | +2 | +4 | +8 |
| 9 | 7 | 7 | 9 | 9 | 8 | 8 | 9 |

| 2 | 3 | 3 | 6 | 7 | 6 | 8 | 7 |
|---|---|---|---|---|---|---|---|
| +7 | +6 | +5 | +3 | +2 | +2 | +1 | +1 |
| 9 | 9 | 8 | 9 | 9 | 8 | 9 | 8 |

| 3 | 1 | 2 | 4 | 2 | 5 | 5 | 7 |
|---|---|---|---|---|---|---|---|
| +5 | +8 | +6 | +5 | +7 | +3 | +4 | +2 |
| 8 | 9 | 8 | 9 | 9 | 8 | 9 | 9 |

"He arose . . . and said unto the sea, Peace be still." Mark 4:39

100

a. Point to the flash cards. **These are twin facts: 1+8=9 and 8+1=9.**

b. **Say the twins with me. 1+8, 9; 8+1, 9; 1+8, 9 . . .**

5. | 2 dark boats, 7 light boats |

Circle the boats . . .

**9 boats in the sea;**

**9 is the whole number.**

**What part of the 9 has dark sails?** 2

**What part of the 9 has light sails?** 7

**9 is the whole number.**

**Its parts are 2 and 7 or 7 and 2.**

a. Point to the flash cards. **These are twin facts: 2+7=9 and 7+2=9.**

b. **Say the twins with me. 2+7, 9; 7+2, 9; 2+7, 9 . . .**

6. | 3 dark boats, 6 light boats |

Circle the boats . . .

**9 boats in the sea;**

**9 is the whole number.**

**What part of the 9 has dark sails?** 3

**What part of the 9 has light sails?** 6

**9 is the whole number.**

**Its parts are 3 and 6 or 6 and 3.**

a. Point to the flash cards. **These are twin facts: 3+6=9 and 6+3=9.**

b. **Say the twins with me. 3+6, 9; 6+3, 9; 3+6, 9 . . .**

7. | 4 dark boats, 5 light boats |

Circle the boats . . .

**9 boats in the sea;**

**9 is the whole number.**

**What part of the 9 has dark sails?** 4

**What part of the 9 has light sails?** 5

**9 is the whole number.**

**Its parts are 4 and 5 or 5 and 4.**

a. Point to the flash cards. **These are twin facts: 4+5=9 and 5+4=9.**

b. **Say the twins with me. 4+5, 9; 5+4, 9; 4+5, 9 . . .**

8. Do the Speed Drill in Lesson 24.

9. Assign Lesson 24.

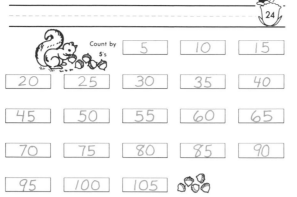

Count by 5's to 105.

Count by 5's

| 5 | 10 | 15 |
|---|----|----|

| 20 | 25 | 30 | 35 | 40 |
|----|----|----|----|----|

| 45 | 50 | 55 | 60 | 65 |
|----|----|----|----|----|

| 70 | 75 | 80 | 85 | 90 |
|----|----|----|----|----|

| 95 | 100 | 105 |
|----|-----|-----|

**Blacklines**

Number Facts (+) #5

Skip Counting (5's) #2

Form B

Count the nickels.
Write the amount.

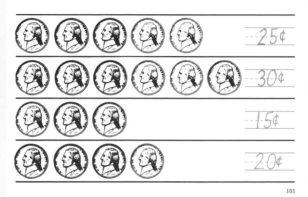

25¢

30¢

15¢

20¢

101

---

*After Class*

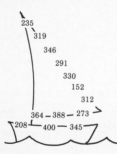

235
319
346
291
330
152
312
364 — 388 — 273
208 — 400 — 345

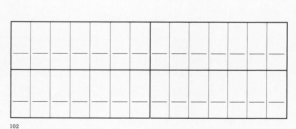

Speed
Drill

| 3 | 5 | 4 | 2 | 6 | 2 |
|---|---|---|---|---|---|
| +4 | +3 | +4 | +4 | +2 | +5 |
| 7 | 8 | 8 | 6 | 8 | 7 |

| 3 | 2 | 6 | 4 | 3 | 2 |
|---|---|---|---|---|---|
| +5 | +4 | +2 | +3 | +4 | +6 |
| 8 | 6 | 8 | 7 | 7 | 8 |

| 2 | 3 | 3 | 3 | 4 | 3 | 5 | 3 |
|---|---|---|---|---|---|---|---|
| +5 | +5 | +4 | +5 | +2 | +5 | +3 | +4 |
| 7 | 8 | 7 | 8 | 6 | 8 | 8 | 7 |

| 4 | 3 | 6 | 1 | 4 | 6 | 3 | 5 |
|---|---|---|---|---|---|---|---|
| +4 | +4 | +2 | +6 | +3 | +2 | +3 | +3 |
| 8 | 7 | 8 | 7 | 7 | 8 | 6 | 8 |

1. **Say the Addition 2-9 facts as I fill the steps.**

2. Stand near the sailboat on the board. **See how quickly you can sail through these numbers.**
   a. Drill the group.
   b. Drill individuals.

3. Have individuals count by 5's to 200.

102

**25**

Fill in the whole and parts.
Trace and write the facts.
Make the twins take turns.

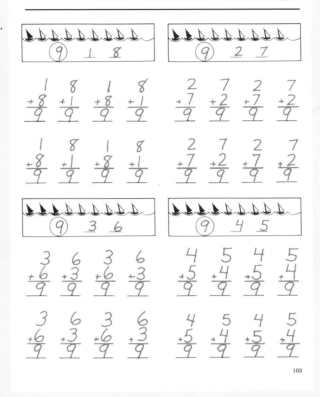

## Before Class

### Materials

9 sailboats
Addition 6–9 flash cards
Large penny, nickel, and dime
*Addition 6–9 flash cards*

### Chalkboard

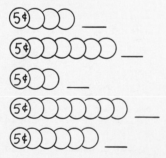

## Class Time

1. Stand near the boats and waves.
   **Who stood up in a boat and stopped the wind?** Jesus (Luke 8:24)

2. 1 dark boat, 8 light boats
   Circle the boats with your finger.
   **9 boats in the sea;**
   **9 is the whole number.**
   **What part of the 9 has dark sails?** 1
   **What part of the 9 has light sails?** 8
   **9 is the whole number.**
   **Its parts are 1 and 8 or 8 and 1.**
   a. Point to the flash cards. **These are twin facts: 1+8=9 and 8+1=9.**
   b. **Say the twins with me. 1+8, 9; 8+1, 9; 1+8, 9 . . .**

3. 2 dark boats, 7 light boats
   Circle the boats . . .
   **9 boats in the sea;**
   **9 is the whole number.**
   **What part of the 9 has dark sails?** 2
   **What part of the 9 has light sails?** 7

$$\begin{array}{cccccccc}
7 & 2 & 3 & 4 & 3 & 2 & 4 \\
+2 & +7 & +6 & +3 & +5 & +4 & +5 \\
\hline
9 & 9 & 9 & 7 & 8 & 6 & 9
\end{array}$$

$$\begin{array}{ccccccc}
4 & 4 & 5 & 5 & 4 & 6 & 5 \\
+5 & +2 & +3 & +2 & +5 & +3 & +4 \\
\hline
9 & 6 & 8 & 7 & 9 & 9 & 9
\end{array}$$

$$\begin{array}{cccccccc}
3 & 2 & 1 & 4 & 3 & 2 & 3 & 2 \\
+6 & +6 & +7 & +5 & +6 & +5 & +4 & +7 \\
\hline
9 & 8 & 8 & 9 & 9 & 7 & 7 & 9
\end{array}$$

$$\begin{array}{cccccccc}
8 & 4 & 3 & 5 & 6 & 6 & 4 & 1 \\
+1 & +3 & +4 & +4 & +3 & +2 & +4 & +8 \\
\hline
9 & 7 & 7 & 9 & 9 & 8 & 8 & 9
\end{array}$$

$$\begin{array}{cccccccc}
7 & 3 & 3 & 6 & 7 & 6 & 8 & 6 \\
+1 & +6 & +5 & +3 & +2 & +2 & +1 & +3 \\
\hline
8 & 9 & 8 & 9 & 9 & 8 & 9 & 9
\end{array}$$

$$\begin{array}{cccccccc}
7 & 1 & 2 & 4 & 2 & 5 & 5 & 3 \\
+2 & +8 & +6 & +5 & +7 & +3 & +4 & +5 \\
\hline
9 & 9 & 8 & 9 & 9 & 8 & 9 & 8
\end{array}$$

"He arose . . . and said unto the sea, Peace be still." Mark 4:39

104

9 is the whole number.
Its parts are 2 and 7 or 7 and 2.
a. **These are twin facts: 2+7=9 and 7+2=9.**
b. **Say the twins. 2+7, 9;  7+2, 9; 2+7, 9 . . .**

4. 3 dark boats, 6 light boats
**Circle the boats . . .**
**9 boats in the sea;**
**9 is the whole number.**
**What part of the 9 has dark sails?** 3
**What part of the 9 has light sails?** 6
**9 is the whole number.**
**Its parts are 3 and 6 or 6 and 3.**
a. **These are twin facts: 3+6=9 and 6+3=9.**
b. **Say the twins. 3+6, 9;  6+3, 9; 3+6, 9 . . .**

5. 4 dark boats, 5 light boats
**Circle the boats . . .**
**9 boats in the sea;**
**9 is the whole number.**
**What part of the 9 has dark sails?** 4

**What part of the 9 has light sails?** 5
**9 is the whole number.**
**Its parts are 4 and 5 or 5 and 4.**
a. **These are twin facts: 4+5=9 and 5+4=9.**
b. **Say the twins. 4+5, 9;  5+4, 9;  4+5, 9.**

6. Point to the 1+8=9 flash card. **Say this 3 times with your eyes open; then close your eyes and say it 3 more times. 1+8, 9; 1+8, 9 . . .** Drill all the facts.

7. Flash Addition 6–9 cards for one minute.

8. Hold the large coins. Repeat together.
a. **Penny, 1¢; nickel, 5¢; dime, 10¢ . . .**
b. **We count pennies by __.**
**We count nickels by __.**
**We count dimes by __.**
c. Do the nickel samples.

9. Assign Lesson 25.

**25**

Count the nickels.
Write the amount.

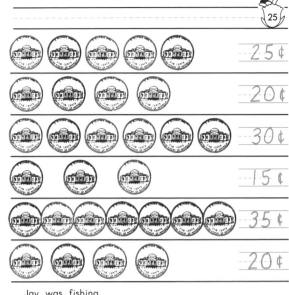

25¢

20¢

30¢

15¢

35¢

20¢

**Blacklines**

Number Facts (+) #6

Skip Counting (5's) #2

Read the story.
Write the numbers
in the beehive.
Write the label words
on the lines.
Answer the problem.

Jay was fishing.
3 big fish bit at his
hook. Then 5 little
fish bit at his hook.
How many fish **in all**
bit at Jay's hook?

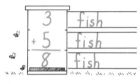

```
  3    fish
+ 5    fish
  8    fish
```

105

*After Class*

| ↓↓ | ↓↓ | ↓↓ | ↓↓ | ↓↓ | ↓↓ |
| --- | --- | --- | --- | --- | --- |
| 324 | 243 | 452 | 517 | 334 | 264 |
| +134 | +514 | +226 | +342 | +634 | +325 |

Use white chalk for ones' place digits.
Use green chalk for tens' place digits.
Use orange chalk for hundreds' place digits.

1. Drill individuals with Addition 6–9 flash cards.

2. Motion: **Ones, tens, hundreds** . . .
   a. Trace the arrows. **Ones' place** *first;* **tens'**
      **place** *second* . . .
   b. 4+4=__. Write 8.
      2+3=__. Write 5.
      3+1=__. Write 4.
   c. Have each child say **ones' place first; tens'**
      **place second** and then answer a problem.

Extra Activity

106

Fill in the whole and parts.
Trace and write the facts.
Make the twins take turns.

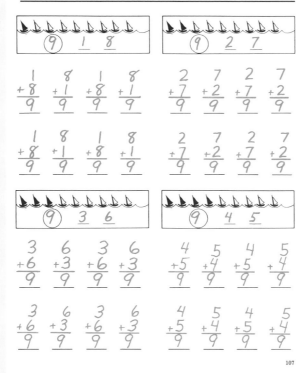

107

## Before Class

### Materials

Addition 2–9 flash cards

Form C

### Chalkboard

| 523 | 617 | 345 | 244 | 263 | 253 | 452 |
|---|---|---|---|---|---|---|
| +234 | +252 | +624 | +554 | +424 | +325 | +237 |

## Class Time

1. Stand near the boats and waves.

   | 2 dark boats, 7 light boats |

   Circle the boats with your finger.

   **The whole number is __.**

   **Its parts are __ and __ or __ and __.** 2 and 7 or 7 and 2.

   **The facts are __.** 2+7=9 and 7+2=9

2. | 3 dark boats, 6 light boats |

   Circle the boats . . .

   **The whole number is __.**

   **Its parts are __ and __ or __ and __.**

   **The facts are __.** 3+6=9 and 6+3=9

3. | 4 dark boats, 5 light boats |

   Circle the boats . . .

   **The whole number is __.**

   **Its parts are __ and __ or __ and __.**

   **The facts are __.** 4+5=9 and 5+4=9

4. **Say the Addition 9 Family in order. 1+8, 9;  2+7, 9;  3+6, 9 . . .**

## 26

Answer these facts.

| | | | | | | |
|---|---|---|---|---|---|---|
| 1 | 7 | 6 | 4 | 3 | 4 | 2 |
| +8 | +1 | +3 | +3 | +5 | +5 | +7 |
| 9 | 8 | 9 | 7 | 8 | 9 | 9 |

| | | | | | | |
|---|---|---|---|---|---|---|
| 8 | 3 | 5 | 5 | 3 | 3 | 5 |
| +1 | +6 | +3 | +2 | +6 | +5 | +4 |
| 9 | 9 | 8 | 7 | 9 | 8 | 9 |

| | | | | | | | |
|---|---|---|---|---|---|---|---|
| 2 | 7 | 1 | 4 | 3 | 2 | 6 | 3 |
| +6 | +2 | +7 | +5 | +6 | +5 | +3 | +4 |
| 8 | 9 | 8 | 9 | 9 | 7 | 9 | 7 |

| | | | | | | | |
|---|---|---|---|---|---|---|---|
| 4 | 4 | 3 | 2 | 6 | 6 | 1 | 4 |
| +3 | +5 | +4 | +7 | +3 | +2 | +8 | +4 |
| 7 | 9 | 7 | 9 | 9 | 8 | 9 | 8 |

| | | | | | | | |
|---|---|---|---|---|---|---|---|
| 2 | 3 | 3 | 6 | 7 | 6 | 4 | 8 |
| +7 | +6 | +5 | +3 | +2 | +2 | +5 | +1 |
| 9 | 9 | 8 | 9 | 9 | 8 | 9 | 9 |

| | | | | | | | |
|---|---|---|---|---|---|---|---|
| 5 | 3 | 2 | 4 | 5 | 5 | 5 | 7 |
| +4 | +6 | +6 | +5 | +4 | +3 | +4 | +2 |
| 9 | 9 | 8 | 9 | 9 | 8 | 9 | 9 |

"He arose . . . and said unto the sea, Peace be still."  Mark 4:39

108

5. Flash Addition 2–9 cards. **Answer quickly!**

6. Flash Card Drill   Addition 2–9 flash cards. Use Form C. **Write the answer to the facts I show. Flower Row: Box 1** (flash a card) **Box 2** (flash a card) **Box 3—Box 4—Box 5—Box 6.** (Stop. Check. Is each child writing only the answer?)

7. Do the 3-digit samples.

8. Do the Speed Drill in Lesson 26.

9. Assign Lesson 26.

Answer these problems.

| | | | | | |
|---|---|---|---|---|---|
| 74<br>+ 5<br>79 | 93<br>+ 4<br>97 | 86<br>+ 2<br>88 | 73<br>+ 5<br>78 | 76<br>+ 3<br>79 | 82<br>+ 7<br>89 |
| 33<br>+46<br>79 | 54<br>+44<br>98 | 21<br>+58<br>79 | 46<br>+33<br>79 | 58<br>+40<br>98 | 36<br>+43<br>79 |
| 23<br>+66<br>89 | 55<br>+24<br>79 | 25<br>+53<br>78 | 23<br>+65<br>88 | 44<br>+53<br>97 | 37<br>+42<br>79 |

Circle the smallest number.
85 (31) 76

| | | | | | |
|---|---|---|---|---|---|
| (230) | 250 | 240 | | | |
| | | | 161 | (151) | 171 |
| 154 | (153) | 158 | 255 | 245 | (235) |
| 259 | (239) | 249 | 167 | (162) | 165 |
| 169 | 268 | (168) | (137) | 237 | 231 |
| 182 | 183 | (180) | (107) | 170 | 207 |

109

**Blacklines**

Form C (Class Time)

Number Facts (+) #6

Form B

## After Class

| | | | | |
|---|---|---|---|---|
| 7<br>+2 | 2<br>+5 | 5<br>+3 | 2<br>+6 | 4<br>+5 |
| 3<br>+5 | 6<br>+3 | 3<br>+4 | 4<br>+2 | 3<br>+5 |
| 4<br>+3 | 2<br>+4 | 2<br>+7 | 5<br>+4 | 6<br>+2 |
| 3<br>+6 | 4<br>+4 | 5<br>+2 | 6<br>+3 | 2<br>+7 |

1. Call the children to the grid on the chalkboard. Drill the facts up and down, left and right. Keep the grid on the board for Lesson 27.

2. Stand near the Number Line. **How many acorns did the squirrel collect? Count by 5's to 200.**

3. **Watch my pointing stick as we count by 5's and then by 1's.**
   5, 10, 11, 12, 13, 14, 15
   5, 10, 15, 16, 17, 18
   5, 10, 15, 20, 25, 30, 31, 32, 33, 34
   5, 6, 7, 8, 9

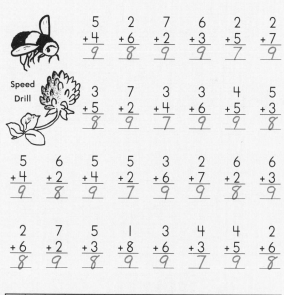

Speed Drill

| | | | | | |
|---|---|---|---|---|---|
| 5<br>+4<br>9 | 2<br>+6<br>8 | 7<br>+2<br>9 | 6<br>+3<br>9 | 2<br>+5<br>7 | 2<br>+7<br>9 |
| 3<br>+5<br>8 | 7<br>+2<br>9 | 3<br>+4<br>7 | 3<br>+6<br>9 | 4<br>+5<br>9 | 5<br>+3<br>8 |

| | | | | | | | |
|---|---|---|---|---|---|---|---|
| 5<br>+4<br>9 | 6<br>+2<br>8 | 5<br>+4<br>9 | 5<br>+2<br>7 | 3<br>+6<br>9 | 2<br>+7<br>9 | 6<br>+2<br>8 | 6<br>+3<br>9 |
| 2<br>+6<br>8 | 7<br>+2<br>9 | 5<br>+3<br>8 | 1<br>+8<br>9 | 3<br>+6<br>9 | 4<br>+3<br>7 | 4<br>+5<br>9 | 2<br>+6<br>8 |

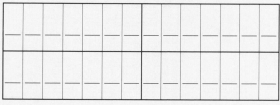

110

**27**

Fill in the whole and parts.
Trace and write the facts.
Make the twins take turns.

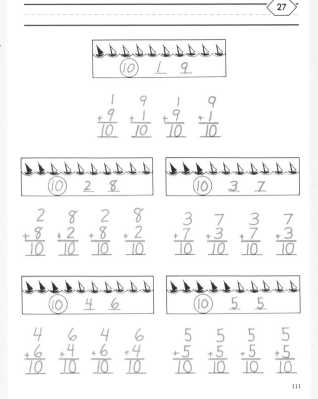

111

## Before Class

Tack Addition 10 flash cards above the waves
in this order:

| | | 2<br>+8<br>10 | 8<br>+2<br>10 | | | 4<br>+6<br>10 | 6<br>+4<br>10 | |
|---|---|---|---|---|---|---|---|---|
| 1<br>+9<br>10 | 9<br>+1<br>10 | | | 3<br>+7<br>10 | 7<br>+3<br>10 | | | 5<br>+5<br>10 |

### Materials

10 sailboats

### Chalkboard

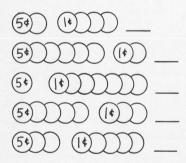

## Class Time

1. Have each child bring *My 1,000 Book* to the
teaching corner. Use responsive counting. **I will
say the first number; you say the next
number.**
   a. **Count by 10's to 500.**
   b. **Count by 5's to 200.**

2. Point to the Number Line.
**Count by 5's and 1's.**
**5, 10, 15, 16, 17**
**5, 10, 15, 20, 25, 26, 27, 28**
**5, 10, 15, 20, 21, 22, 23, 24**
**5, 6, 7, 8, 9**

3. Have individuals count aloud as they do the
Money samples.

4. Stand near the boats and waves.

   | 1 dark boat, 9 light boats |
   |---|

   Circle the boats with your finger.
   **10 boats in the sea;**
   **10 is the whole number.**
   **What part of the 10 has dark sails?** 1

Answer these facts.

Extra Activity

| 7 | 6 | 2 | 3 | 2 | 3 | 7 |
|---|---|---|---|---|---|---|
| +3 | +4 | +8 | +2 | +5 | +3 | +3 |
| 10 | 10 | 10 | 5 | 7 | 6 | 10 |

| 9 | 4 | 4 | 2 | 5 | 8 | 4 |
|---|---|---|---|---|---|---|
| +1 | +2 | +3 | +3 | +5 | +2 | +6 |
| 10 | 6 | 7 | 5 | 10 | 10 | 10 |

| 3 | 1 | 5 | 6 | 4 | 3 | 5 | 7 |
|---|---|---|---|---|---|---|---|
| +6 | +9 | +3 | +4 | +5 | +5 | +2 | +3 |
| 9 | 10 | 8 | 10 | 9 | 8 | 7 | 10 |

| 4 | 5 | 3 | 2 | 6 | 6 | 8 | 3 |
|---|---|---|---|---|---|---|---|
| +6 | +4 | +7 | +6 | +2 | +3 | +2 | +4 |
| 10 | 9 | 10 | 8 | 8 | 9 | 10 | 7 |

| 2 | 3 | 2 | 6 | 8 | 4 | 1 | 7 |
|---|---|---|---|---|---|---|---|
| +8 | +7 | +7 | +3 | +2 | +4 | +9 | +2 |
| 10 | 10 | 9 | 9 | 10 | 8 | 10 | 9 |

| 1 | 2 | 3 | 6 | 5 | 3 | 7 | 4 |
|---|---|---|---|---|---|---|---|
| +8 | +8 | +5 | +4 | +4 | +6 | +3 | +6 |
| 9 | 10 | 8 | 10 | 9 | 9 | 10 | 10 |

"He arose . . . and said unto the sea, Peace be still." Mark 4:39

112

**What part of the 10 has light sails?** 9
**The whole number is 10.**
**Its parts are 1 and 9 or 9 and 1.**

a. Point to the flash cards. **These are twin facts: 1+9=10 and 9+1=10.**

b. **Say the twins with me. 1+9=10, 9+1=10, 1+9=10 . . .**

5. | 2 dark boats, 8 light boats |

Circle the boats . . .

**10 boats in the sea;**
**10 is the whole number.**
**What part of the 10 has dark sails?** 2
**What part of the 10 has light sails?** 8
**10 is the whole number.**
**Its parts are 2 and 8 or 8 and 2.**

a. Point to the flash cards: **These are twin facts: 2+8=10 and 8+2=10.**

b. **Say the twins with me. 2+8=10, 8+2=10, 2+8=10 . . .**

6. Proceed step by step through

| 3 dark boats, 7 light boats |

| 4 dark boats, 6 light boats |

| 5 dark boats, 5 light boats |

7. **Say the Addition 10 Family in order. 1+9, 10;  2+8, 10 . . .**

8. Assign Lesson 27.

**Reminder . . .**
    Continue to review Subtraction Families 8–10 in Lessons 27–30. Recite the facts from flash cards posted with the answers showing. Occasionally review Subtraction Families 2–7 as well.

| 10 |
|---|
| -4 |
| 6 |

| 10 |
|---|
| -3 |
| 7 |

108

Answer these problems.

```
 424     334     279     125     453
+455    +462    +620    +844    +503
 879     796     899     969     956

 824     613     646     592     323
+132    +355    +253    +204    +556
 956     968     899     796     879
```

Read the story.
Write the numbers
  in the beehive.
Write the label words
  on the lines.
Answer the problem.

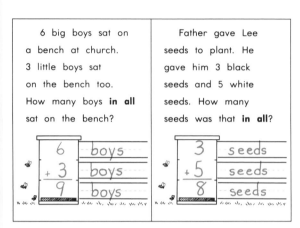

6 big boys sat on
a bench at church.
3 little boys sat
on the bench too.
How many boys **in all**
sat on the bench?

```
  6   boys
+ 3   boys
  9   boys
```

Father gave Lee
seeds to plant. He
gave him 3 black
seeds and 5 white
seeds. How many
seeds was that **in all**?

```
  3   seeds
+ 5   seeds
  8   seeds
```

113

**Blacklines**

Number Facts (+) #6
Money Identification #3

### After Class

1. Drill individuals at the Addition Grid on the
   chalkboard. Can each child answer all the facts
   in 30 seconds?

2. Chalkboard Drill: **Write the number that
   comes before 216, 179, 205, 143, 200, 128,
   242, 164, 211, 217.**

3. Stand near the Number Line.
   a. Point to 10. **Listen.**

   | | | |
   |---|---|---|
   | 10+1, 11 | 10+4, 14 | 10+7, 17 |
   | 10+2, 12 | 10+5, 15 | 10+8, 18 |
   | 10+3, 13 | 10+6, 16 | 10+9, 19 |

   b. **Say them with me.**
      10+1, 11
      10+2, 12 . . .

Extra Activity

```
 1
+1
 2

 1     2
+2    +1
 3     3

 1     2     3
+3    +2    +1
 4     4     4

 1     2     3     4
+4    +3    +2    +1
 5     5     5     5

 1     2     3     4     5
+5    +4    +3    +2    +1
 6     6     6     6     6

 1     2     3     4     5     6
+6    +5    +4    +3    +2    +1
 7     7     7     7     7     7

 1     2     3     4     5     6     7
+7    +6    +5    +4    +3    +2    +1
 8     8     8     8     8     8     8

 1     2     3     4     5     6     7     8
+8    +7    +6    +5    +4    +3    +2    +1
 9     9     9     9     9     9     9     9

 1     2     3     4     5     6     7     8     9
+9    +8    +7    +6    +5    +4    +3    +2    +1
10    10    10    10    10    10    10    10    10
```

114

Fill in the whole and parts.
Trace and write the facts.
Make the twins take turns.

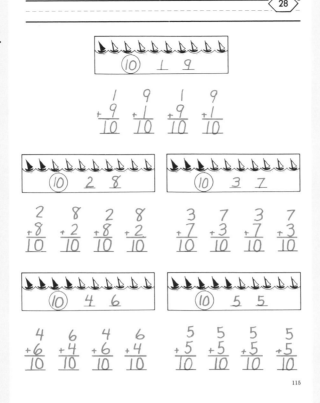

## Before Class

**Materials**

    10 sailboats

    Large coins—penny, nickel, dime

    *Addition 6–10 flash cards*

**Chalkboard**

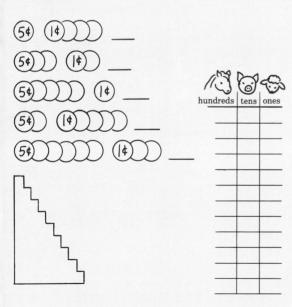

## Class Time

1. Call the children to the grid on the chalkboard.
   a. Motion: **Ones, tens, hundreds . . .**
   b. **When I call your name, come and write the number I say in the grid.** Use these numbers: **231, 6, 101, 47, 209, 185, 8, 212 250, 83, 154, 238.**

2. **Count by 5's to 200.**

3. a. Flash the large coins. **Penny, 1¢; nickel, 5¢; dime, 10¢ . . .**
   b. Have individuals count aloud as they do the Money samples.

4. Stand near the boats and waves.

   | 1 dark boat, 9 light boats |

   Circle the boats with your finger.
   **10 boats in the sea;**
   **10 is the whole number.**
   **What part of the 10 has dark sails?** 1
   **What part of the 10 has light sails?** 9
   **10 is the whole number.**
   **Its parts are 1 and 9 or 9 and 1.**

**28**

Answer these facts.

$$
\begin{array}{ccccccc}
5 & 4 & 4 & 3 & 5 & 7 & 5 \\
+5 & +6 & +5 & +5 & +4 & +3 & +3 \\
\hline
10 & 10 & 9 & 8 & 9 & 10 & 8
\end{array}
$$

$$
\begin{array}{ccccccc}
6 & 3 & 6 & 3 & 2 & 6 & 2 \\
+3 & +7 & +4 & +6 & +6 & +2 & +8 \\
\hline
9 & 10 & 10 & 9 & 8 & 8 & 10
\end{array}
$$

$$
\begin{array}{ccccccc}
8 & 6 & 2 & 9 & 4 & 3 & 2 & 7 \\
+2 & +4 & +7 & +1 & +3 & +6 & +4 & +3 \\
\hline
10 & 10 & 9 & 10 & 7 & 9 & 6 & 10
\end{array}
$$

$$
\begin{array}{cccccccc}
4 & 1 & 3 & 5 & 2 & 4 & 8 & 4 \\
+5 & +9 & +7 & +4 & +5 & +6 & +2 & +2 \\
\hline
9 & 10 & 10 & 9 & 7 & 10 & 10 & 6
\end{array}
$$

$$
\begin{array}{cccccccc}
2 & 3 & 5 & 3 & 6 & 3 & 4 & 4 \\
+8 & +4 & +5 & +5 & +3 & +7 & +6 & +5 \\
\hline
10 & 7 & 10 & 8 & 9 & 10 & 10 & 9
\end{array}
$$

$$
\begin{array}{cccccccc}
5 & 4 & 7 & 4 & 6 & 2 & 7 & 6 \\
+2 & +6 & +2 & +4 & +4 & +7 & +3 & +4 \\
\hline
7 & 10 & 9 & 8 & 10 & 9 & 10 & 10
\end{array}
$$

"He arose . . . and said unto the sea, Peace be still." Mark 4:39

116

a. Point to the flash cards: **These are twin facts: 1+9=10 and 9+1=10.**

b. **Say the twins with me. 1+9, 10; 9+1, 10; 1+9, 10.**

5. | 2 dark boats, 8 light boats |

Circle the boats . . .

**10 boats in the sea;**

**10 is the whole number.**

**What part of the 10 has dark sails?** 2

**What part of the 10 has light sails?** 8

**10 is the whole number.**

**Its parts are 2 and 8 or 8 and 2.**

a. Point to the flash cards: **These are twin facts: 2+8=10 and 8+2=10.**

b. **Say the twins with me: 2+8, 10; 8+2, 10; 2+8, 10.**

6. Proceed step by step through

| 3 dark boats, 7 light boats |

| 4 dark boats, 6 light boats |

| 5 dark boats, 5 light boats |

7. **Say Addition 2-10 facts as I fill in the steps.**

8. Do the Speed Drill in Lesson 28.

9. Assign Lesson 28.

28

Answer these problems.

| 226 | 765 | 457 | 364 | 583 |
|-----|-----|-----|-----|-----|
| +653 | +212 | +340 | +305 | +306 |
| 879 | 977 | 797 | 669 | 889 |

| 344 | 522 | 586 | 451 | 636 |
|-----|-----|-----|-----|-----|
| +545 | +147 | +211 | +526 | +243 |
| 889 | 669 | 797 | 977 | 879 |

Count the nickels and pennies.
Write the amount.

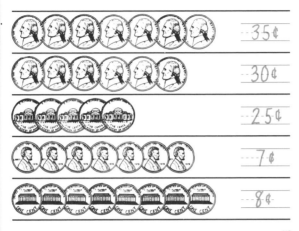

35¢

30¢

25¢

7¢

8¢

117

**Blacklines**

Fact Form I

Form B

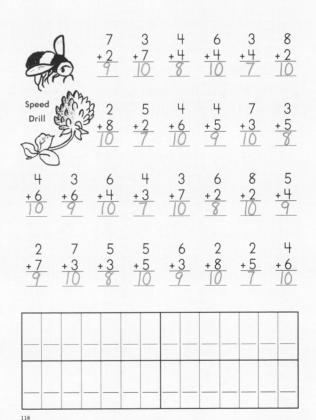

## After Class

| ↓↓ | ↓↓ | ↓↓ | ↓↓ | ↓↓ | ↓↓ | ↓↓ |
|-----|-----|-----|-----|-----|-----|-----|
| 423 | 624 | 145 | 236 | 343 | 562 | 557 |
| + 54 | + 35 | + 23 | + 33 | + 52 | + 27 | + 42 |

1. Circle Drill  Addition 6–10 flash cards. Select a spot in your room that can be circled with children. It may be your desk, a table, or your teaching corner.
   a. **You will quietly walk around and around. As you pass me, say the answer on my flash card.**
   b. **Use your fingers to keep count of your answers. As soon as you have given 10 answers, you may sit down.**
   c. **If your answer is wrong, you may not count it.**

2. Stand near the Addition samples.
   a. Trace the arrows. **Ones' place first; tens' place second . . .**
   b. **3+4=__.** Write 7.
      **2+5=__.** Write 7.
      **4+nothing=__.** Write 4.
   c. Have the children finish the samples.

Speed Drill

| 7 | 3 | 4 | 6 | 3 | 8 |
|-----|-----|-----|-----|-----|-----|
| +2 | +7 | +4 | +4 | +4 | +2 |
| 9 | 10 | 8 | 10 | 7 | 10 |

| 2 | 5 | 4 | 4 | 7 | 3 |
|-----|-----|-----|-----|-----|-----|
| +8 | +2 | +6 | +5 | +3 | +5 |
| 10 | 7 | 10 | 9 | 10 | 8 |

| 4 | 3 | 6 | 4 | 3 | 6 | 8 | 5 |
|-----|-----|-----|-----|-----|-----|-----|-----|
| +6 | +6 | +4 | +3 | +7 | +2 | +2 | +4 |
| 10 | 9 | 10 | 7 | 10 | 8 | 10 | 9 |

| 2 | 7 | 5 | 5 | 6 | 2 | 2 | 4 |
|-----|-----|-----|-----|-----|-----|-----|-----|
| +7 | +3 | +3 | +5 | +3 | +8 | +5 | +6 |
| 9 | 10 | 8 | 10 | 9 | 10 | 7 | 10 |

118

29

Fill in the whole and parts.
Trace and write the facts.
Make the twins take turns.

(10)  1  9

$$\begin{array}{r}1\\+9\\\hline 10\end{array}\quad\begin{array}{r}9\\+1\\\hline 10\end{array}\quad\begin{array}{r}1\\+9\\\hline 10\end{array}\quad\begin{array}{r}9\\+1\\\hline 10\end{array}$$

(10)  2  8

(10)  3  7

$$\begin{array}{r}2\\+8\\\hline 10\end{array}\quad\begin{array}{r}8\\+2\\\hline 10\end{array}\quad\begin{array}{r}2\\+8\\\hline 10\end{array}\quad\begin{array}{r}8\\+2\\\hline 10\end{array}\qquad\begin{array}{r}3\\+7\\\hline 10\end{array}\quad\begin{array}{r}7\\+3\\\hline 10\end{array}\quad\begin{array}{r}3\\+7\\\hline 10\end{array}\quad\begin{array}{r}7\\+3\\\hline 10\end{array}$$

(10)  4  6

(10)  5  5

$$\begin{array}{r}4\\+6\\\hline 10\end{array}\quad\begin{array}{r}6\\+4\\\hline 10\end{array}\quad\begin{array}{r}4\\+6\\\hline 10\end{array}\quad\begin{array}{r}6\\+4\\\hline 10\end{array}\qquad\begin{array}{r}5\\+5\\\hline 10\end{array}\quad\begin{array}{r}5\\+5\\\hline 10\end{array}\quad\begin{array}{r}5\\+5\\\hline 10\end{array}\quad\begin{array}{r}5\\+5\\\hline 10\end{array}$$

119

## Before Class

**Materials**

    10 sailboats

    *Addition 7–10 flash cards*

**Chalkboard**

| 625 | 452 | 165 | 344 | 753 | 664 |
|-----|-----|-----|-----|-----|-----|
| +73 | +37 | +32 | +33 | +46 | +24 |

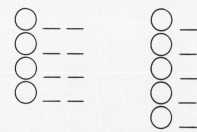

## Class Time

1. Stand near the boats and waves.

    2 dark boats, 8 light boats

    Circle the boats with your finger.

    **The whole number is __.**

    **Its parts are __ and __ or __ and __.** 2 and
    8 or 8 and 2

    **The facts are __.** 2+8, 10 and 8+2, 10

2. 3 dark boats, 7 light boats

    Circle the boats . . .

    **The whole number is __.**

    **Its parts are __ and __ or __ and __.**

    **The facts are __.** 3+7, 10 and 7+3, 10

3. 4 dark boats, 6 light boats

    Circle the boats . . .

    **The whole number is __.**

    **Its parts are __ and __ or __ and __.**

    **The facts are __.** 4+6, 10 and 6+4, 10

Answer these facts.

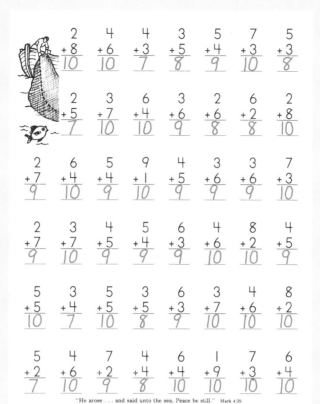

| | 2 | 4 | 4 | 3 | 5 | 7 | 5 |
|---|---|---|---|---|---|---|---|
| | +8 | +6 | +3 | +5 | +4 | +3 | +3 |
| | 10 | 10 | 7 | 8 | 9 | 10 | 8 |
| | 2 | 3 | 6 | 3 | 2 | 6 | 2 |
| | +5 | +7 | +4 | +6 | +6 | +2 | +8 |
| | 7 | 10 | 10 | 9 | 8 | 8 | 10 |

| 2 | 6 | 5 | 9 | 4 | 3 | 3 | 7 |
|---|---|---|---|---|---|---|---|
| +7 | +4 | +4 | +1 | +5 | +6 | +6 | +3 |
| 9 | 10 | 9 | 10 | 9 | 9 | 9 | 10 |

| 2 | 3 | 4 | 5 | 6 | 4 | 8 | 4 |
|---|---|---|---|---|---|---|---|
| +7 | +7 | +5 | +4 | +3 | +6 | +2 | +5 |
| 9 | 10 | 9 | 9 | 9 | 10 | 10 | 9 |

| 5 | 3 | 5 | 3 | 6 | 3 | 4 | 8 |
|---|---|---|---|---|---|---|---|
| +5 | +4 | +5 | +5 | +3 | +7 | +6 | +2 |
| 10 | 7 | 10 | 8 | 9 | 10 | 10 | 10 |

| 5 | 4 | 7 | 4 | 6 | 1 | 7 | 6 |
|---|---|---|---|---|---|---|---|
| +2 | +6 | +2 | +4 | +4 | +9 | +3 | +4 |
| 7 | 10 | 9 | 8 | 10 | 10 | 10 | 10 |

"He arose . . . and said unto the sea, Peace be still." Mark 4:39

120

4. | 5 dark boats, 5 light boats |

Circle the boats . . .

**The whole number is __.**

**Its parts are __ and __.**

**The fact is __.** 5+5, 10

5. **Say the whole and the parts for the 9 Family . . . 10 Family.** Write them in order.

    (9)   1   8
    (9)   2   7
    (9)   3   6
    (9)   4   5
    (10)   1   9
    (10)   2   8
    (10)   3   7
    (10)   4   6
    (10)   5   5

6. Do the Addition samples.

7. **Count by 5's to 250.**

8. Assign Lesson 29.

Answer these problems.

| | | | | |
|---|---|---|---|---|
| 626 | 725 | 457 | 434 | 345 |
| + 53 | + 62 | + 40 | + 55 | + 53 |
| 679 | 787 | 497 | 489 | 398 |

| | | | | |
|---|---|---|---|---|
| 453 | 542 | 626 | 461 | 536 |
| + 45 | + 47 | + 71 | + 26 | + 43 |
| 498 | 589 | 697 | 487 | 579 |

Count the nickels and pennies.
Write the amount.

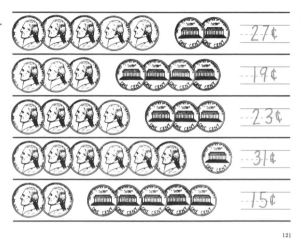

27¢

19¢

23¢

31¢

15¢

121

**Blacklines**

Fact Form I

Reading Problems #2

## *After Class*

| | | | |
|---|---|---|---|
| ___ 65 ___ | | ___ 115 ___ | |
| ___ 40 ___ | | ___ 130 ___ | |
| ___ 85 ___ | | ___ 155 ___ | |
| ___ 20 ___ | | ___ 170 ___ | |

1. Circle Drill: Addition 7–10 flash cards. Are the children moving quietly and answering quickly?

2. Fill in the Before and After samples by 5's.

3. Point to the Number Line.
   **Add with me.**

   | | | |
   |---|---|---|
   | 10+1, 11 | 10+4, 14 | 10+7, 17 |
   | 10+2, 12 | 10+5, 15 | 10+8, 18 |
   | 10+3, 13 | 10+6, 16 | 10+9, 19 |

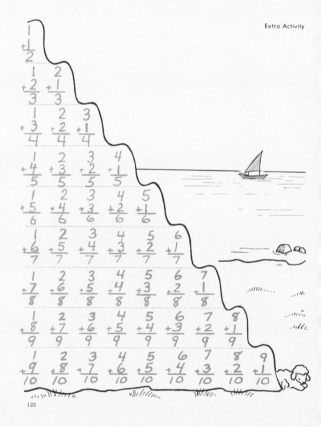

Extra Activity

122

Fill in the whole and parts.
Trace and write the facts.
Make the twins take turns.

⑩　1　9

$$\begin{array}{r}1\\+9\\\hline10\end{array}\qquad\begin{array}{r}9\\+1\\\hline10\end{array}\qquad\begin{array}{r}1\\+9\\\hline10\end{array}\qquad\begin{array}{r}9\\+1\\\hline10\end{array}$$

⑩　2　8　　　　⑩　3　7

$$\begin{array}{r}2\\+8\\\hline10\end{array}\ \begin{array}{r}8\\+2\\\hline10\end{array}\ \begin{array}{r}2\\+8\\\hline10\end{array}\ \begin{array}{r}8\\+2\\\hline10\end{array}\qquad\begin{array}{r}3\\+7\\\hline10\end{array}\ \begin{array}{r}7\\+3\\\hline10\end{array}\ \begin{array}{r}3\\+7\\\hline10\end{array}\ \begin{array}{r}7\\+3\\\hline10\end{array}$$

⑩　4　6　　　　⑩　5　5

$$\begin{array}{r}4\\+6\\\hline10\end{array}\ \begin{array}{r}6\\+4\\\hline10\end{array}\ \begin{array}{r}4\\+6\\\hline10\end{array}\ \begin{array}{r}6\\+4\\\hline10\end{array}\qquad\begin{array}{r}5\\+5\\\hline10\end{array}\ \begin{array}{r}5\\+5\\\hline10\end{array}\ \begin{array}{r}5\\+5\\\hline10\end{array}\ \begin{array}{r}5\\+5\\\hline10\end{array}$$

123

## Before Class

**Materials**

9, 10 sailboats
Addition 5–10 flash cards
*Addition 8–10 flash cards*
Form C

**Chalkboard**

| | | | | | |
|---|---|---|---|---|---|
| | | | 189 | 198 | 199 |
| | | | 102 | 120 | 112 |
| | | | 169 | 189 | 159 |
| 137 | 173 | 177 | 140 | 150 | 130 |
| 228 | 218 | 208 | 206 | 226 | 216 |

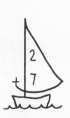

116

30

Answer these facts.

Speed Drill

| | | | | | | |
|---|---|---|---|---|---|---|
| 3<br>+7<br>10 | 4<br>+6<br>10 | 5<br>+3<br>8 | 3<br>+5<br>8 | 5<br>+4<br>9 | 7<br>+3<br>10 | 4<br>+5<br>9 |
| 2<br>+6<br>8 | 5<br>+5<br>10 | 6<br>+4<br>10 | 3<br>+6<br>9 | 2<br>+6<br>8 | 6<br>+3<br>9 | 2<br>+8<br>10 |
| 3<br>+7<br>10 | 6<br>+4<br>10 | 2<br>+7<br>9 | 9<br>+1<br>10 | 4<br>+6<br>10 | 3<br>+6<br>9 | 8<br>+2<br>10 | 7<br>+3<br>10 |
| 4<br>+5<br>9 | 6<br>+4<br>10 | 3<br>+7<br>10 | 5<br>+4<br>9 | 7<br>+3<br>10 | 4<br>+6<br>10 | 8<br>+2<br>10 | 1<br>+9<br>10 |
| 2<br>+8<br>10 | 4<br>+5<br>9 | 5<br>+5<br>10 | 3<br>+5<br>8 | 6<br>+3<br>9 | 3<br>+7<br>10 | 4<br>+6<br>10 | 4<br>+5<br>9 |
| 3<br>+6<br>9 | 4<br>+6<br>10 | 7<br>+2<br>9 | 4<br>+4<br>8 | 6<br>+4<br>10 | 2<br>+7<br>9 | 7<br>+3<br>10 | 6<br>+4<br>10 |

"Peter . . . walked on the water, to go to Jesus." Matthew 14:29

124

## Class Time

1. Stand near the sailboats on the board.
   a. Point to 4+5. **Look at the fact; then close your eyes and say it 3 times. 4+5, 9 . . .** Continue.

2. **Can you name one of Jesus' disciples who got out of a boat to walk on the sea?** Peter (Matthew 14:29)

3. Flash Addition 5–10 cards. **Answer together.**

4. Flash Card Drill: Addition 5–10 flash cards. Use Form C. **Are you ready to write the answers as I flash the cards? Flower Row: Box 1 . . .**

5. Ask a child to fill the steps as you say Addition 2–10 Facts.

6. **The bee buzzes down to the water lily and pokes his tongue into the lily. He sucks nectar up through his tongue as you suck milk up through a straw.** Circle the smallest number.

7. Have each child open his 1,000 book.
   a. **Count by 10's to 300.**
   b. **Count by 5's to 200.**

8. Do the Speed Drill in Lesson 30.

9. Assign Lesson 30.

Answer these problems.

| | | | | |
|---|---|---|---|---|
| 246 | 752 | 454 | 354 | 533 |
| + 53 | + 46 | + 44 | + 35 | + 56 |
| 299 | 798 | 498 | 389 | 589 |

| | | | | |
|---|---|---|---|---|
| 344 | 562 | 581 | 473 | 646 |
| + 45 | + 27 | + 17 | + 25 | + 53 |
| 389 | 589 | 598 | 498 | 699 |

Count the nickels and pennies.
Write the amount.

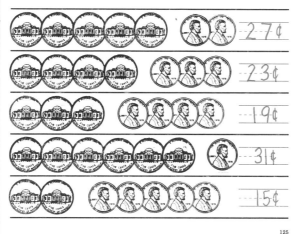

27¢

23¢

19¢

31¢

15¢

**Blacklines**

Form C (Class Time)

Fact Form I

Form B

125

## *After Class*

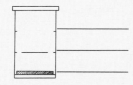

1. Drill individuals with Addition 8–10 flash cards.

2. Point to the Number Line. Review **10+1, 11 . . . 10+9, 19.**

3. Story Problems

   a. **A chipmunk found 6 brown nuts and 4 black nuts. How many nuts did he find altogether? Who can fill the beehive for us?**

   b. **Rhoda and Karen made paper dolls. Rhoda cut 4 dolls. Karen cut 5 dolls. How many dolls did both girls make? Who can . . . ?**

Speed Drill

| | | | | | |
|---|---|---|---|---|---|
| 6 | 4 | 2 | 5 | 7 | 5 |
| +4 | +5 | +8 | +3 | +3 | +5 |
| 10 | 9 | 10 | 8 | 10 | 10 |

| | | | | | |
|---|---|---|---|---|---|
| 3 | 8 | 3 | 5 | 2 | 4 |
| +6 | +2 | +7 | +4 | +7 | +6 |
| 9 | 10 | 10 | 9 | 9 | 10 |

| | | | | | | | |
|---|---|---|---|---|---|---|---|
| 2 | 3 | 6 | 5 | 6 | 7 | 4 | 8 |
| +8 | +6 | +4 | +5 | +2 | +3 | +5 | +2 |
| 10 | 9 | 10 | 10 | 8 | 10 | 9 | 10 |

| | | | | | | | |
|---|---|---|---|---|---|---|---|
| 6 | 6 | 3 | 5 | 7 | 8 | 4 | 6 |
| +3 | +4 | +7 | +4 | +2 | +2 | +6 | +3 |
| 9 | 10 | 10 | 9 | 9 | 10 | 10 | 9 |

126

Fill in the whole and parts.
Trace and write the facts.
Make the twins take turns.

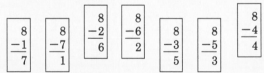

| | |
|---|---|
| ⑧ 1 7 | ⑧ 2 6 |

$$\begin{array}{cccc} 8 & 8 & 8 & 8 \\ -1 & -7 & -1 & -7 \\ \hline 7 & 1 & 7 & 1 \end{array} \qquad \begin{array}{cccc} 8 & 8 & 8 & 8 \\ -2 & -6 & -2 & -6 \\ \hline 6 & 2 & 6 & 2 \end{array}$$

$$\begin{array}{cccc} 8 & 8 & 8 & 8 \\ -1 & -7 & -1 & -7 \\ \hline 7 & 1 & 7 & 1 \end{array} \qquad \begin{array}{cccc} 8 & 8 & 8 & 8 \\ -2 & -6 & -2 & -6 \\ \hline 6 & 2 & 6 & 2 \end{array}$$

| | |
|---|---|
| ⑧ 3 5 | ⑧ 4 4 |

$$\begin{array}{cccc} 8 & 8 & 8 & 8 \\ -3 & -5 & -3 & -5 \\ \hline 5 & 3 & 5 & 3 \end{array} \qquad \begin{array}{cccc} 8 & 8 & 8 & 8 \\ -4 & -4 & -4 & -4 \\ \hline 4 & 4 & 4 & 4 \end{array}$$

$$\begin{array}{cccc} 8 & 8 & 8 & 8 \\ -3 & -5 & -3 & -5 \\ \hline 5 & 3 & 5 & 3 \end{array} \qquad \begin{array}{cccc} 8 & 8 & 8 & 8 \\ -4 & -4 & -4 & -4 \\ \hline 4 & 4 & 4 & 4 \end{array}$$

127

## Before Class

Mark the 25's on the Number Line.

See Patterns, page 213.

Tack Subtraction 8 flash cards above the waves
in this order:

| 8 | 8 | 8 | 8 | 8 | 8 | 8 |
|---|---|---|---|---|---|---|
| −1 | −7 | −2 | −6 | −3 | −5 | −4 |
| 7 | 1 | 6 | 2 | 5 | 3 | 4 |

### Materials

8 sailboats

Subtraction 8 flash cards

Chalkboard ___ 55 ___   ___ 140 ___
         ___ 90 ___   ___ 115 ___
         ___ 30 ___   ___ 185 ___
         ___ 75 ___   ___ 160 ___

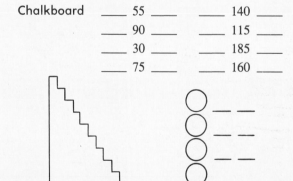

## Class Time

1. **The gray squirrel can collect five acorns at
   a time. We can count *5 numbers* at a time.**
   a. **Count by 5's to 200.**
   b. Fill in the Before and After samples by 5's.

2. Stand near the boats and waves.

   | 1 dark boat, 7 light boats |

   Circle the boats with your finger.
   **8 boats in the sea;**
   **8 is the whole number.**
   **What part of the 8 has dark sails?** 1
   **What part of the 8 has light sails?** 7
   **8 is the whole number.**
   **Its parts are 1 and 7 or 7 and 1.**
   a. Point to the flash cards. **These are twin
      facts: 8−1=7 and 8−7=1.**
   b. **Make the twins take turns as I write
      them and you say them.** (Write vertical-
      ly.) **8−1=7,  8−7=1 . . .**

3. | 2 dark boats, 6 light boats |

   Circle the boats . . .

Answer these facts.

| | | | | | | |
|---|---|---|---|---|---|---|
| 8<br>-5<br>**3** | 8<br>-3<br>**5** | 8<br>-4<br>**4** | 5<br>-3<br>**2** | 8<br>-7<br>**1** | 8<br>-1<br>**7** | 7<br>-1<br>**6** |
| 8<br>-6<br>**2** | 7<br>-3<br>**4** | 8<br>-3<br>**5** | 7<br>-4<br>**3** | 8<br>-2<br>**6** | 8<br>-1<br>**7** | 6<br>-5<br>**1** |

| | | | | | | | |
|---|---|---|---|---|---|---|---|
| 8<br>-6<br>**2** | 8<br>-4<br>**4** | 8<br>-3<br>**5** | 6<br>-3<br>**3** | 8<br>-6<br>**2** | 5<br>-2<br>**3** | 8<br>-3<br>**5** | 8<br>-2<br>**6** |
| 8<br>-5<br>**3** | 7<br>-2<br>**5** | 6<br>-2<br>**4** | 6<br>-4<br>**2** | 8<br>-2<br>**6** | 8<br>-3<br>**5** | 8<br>-5<br>**3** | 3<br>-1<br>**2** |
| 7<br>-5<br>**2** | 8<br>-7<br>**1** | 8<br>-4<br>**4** | 8<br>-5<br>**3** | 7<br>-5<br>**2** | 8<br>-4<br>**4** | 8<br>-7<br>**1** | 7<br>-4<br>**3** |
| 4<br>-2<br>**2** | 5<br>-1<br>**4** | 5<br>-4<br>**1** | 4<br>-1<br>**3** | 8<br>-6<br>**2** | 2<br>-1<br>**1** | 7<br>-3<br>**4** | 8<br>-5<br>**3** |

"Peter . . . walked on the water, to go to Jesus." Matthew 14:29

128

8 boats in the sea;

8 is the whole number.

**What part of the 8 has dark sails?** 2

**What part of the 8 has light sails?** 6

8 is the whole number.

**Its parts are 2 and 6 or 6 and 2.**

a. **These are twin facts: 8—2=6 and 8—6=2.**

b. **Make the twins take turns as I write them and you say them. 8—2=6, 8—6=2 . . .**

4. Proceed step by step through

> 3 dark boats, 5 light boats

> 4 dark boats, 4 light boats

5. Have the children fill in the whole and parts for the 8 Family.

6. **Say Subtraction 2–8 facts as I fill in the steps.**

7. Flash Subtraction 8 cards.

8. Assign Lesson 31.

**Reminder . . .**

In Lessons 31–40, you will be teaching Subtraction Families 8–10. During this time, review the corresponding addition facts daily.

**31**

**31**

Write the numbers in the correct places.

| | hundreds | tens | ones | | hundreds | tens | ones |
|---|---|---|---|---|---|---|---|
| 345 | 3 | 4 | 5 | 580 | 5 | 8 | 0 |
| 32 | | 3 | 2 | 7 | | | 7 |
| 495 | 4 | 9 | 5 | 83 | | 8 | 3 |
| 168 | 1 | 6 | 8 | 240 | 2 | 4 | 0 |
| 529 | 5 | 2 | 9 | 597 | 5 | 9 | 7 |

Write the numbers that come before and after when you count by 5's.

| Count by 5's | | | | |
|---|---|---|---|---|
| | | | 100 | 105 | 110 |

| | | | | | |
|---|---|---|---|---|---|
| 10 | 15 | 20 | 135 | 140 | 145 |
| 45 | 50 | 55 | 30 | 35 | 40 |
| 120 | 125 | 130 | 15 | 20 | 25 |
| 170 | 175 | 180 | 150 | 155 | 160 |

129

**Blacklines**

Form A: 200–299

Money Identification #3

### After Class

(ones) 108 423 200 519 244 367

(tens) 329 103 535 497 175 514

(hundreds) 245 350 527 136 489 301

1. Stand near the Place Value samples.
   a. Motion: **Ones, tens, hundreds . . .**
   b. Point to each digit in 108—**ones, tens, hundreds. Which numeral is in ones' place?** Circle it. 10⑧
   c. Point to each digit in 423—**ones, tens, hundreds. Which numeral is in ones' place?** Circle it. 42③
   d. Have each child say **ones, tens, hundreds** and then circle the correct numeral.

2. Point to the Number Line. **If we follow the green circles, we will be counting by __.** 25's
   **Count 3 times. 25 . . . 100.**

Extra Activity

130

Fill in the whole and parts.
Trace and write the facts.
Make the twins take turns.

⛵⛵⛵⛵⛵⛵⛵⛵  (8) 1 7

⛵⛵⛵⛵⛵⛵⛵⛵  (8) 2 6

| 8<br>−1<br>7 | 8<br>−7<br>1 | 8<br>−1<br>7 | 8<br>−7<br>1 | 8<br>−2<br>6 | 8<br>−6<br>2 | 8<br>−2<br>6 | 8<br>−6<br>2 |

| 8<br>−1<br>7 | 8<br>−7<br>1 | 8<br>−1<br>7 | 8<br>−7<br>1 | 8<br>−2<br>6 | 8<br>−6<br>2 | 8<br>−2<br>6 | 8<br>−6<br>2 |

⛵⛵⛵⛵⛵⛵⛵⛵  (8) 3 5

⛵⛵⛵⛵⛵⛵⛵⛵  (8) 4 4

| 8<br>−3<br>5 | 8<br>−5<br>3 | 8<br>−3<br>5 | 8<br>−5<br>3 | 8<br>−4<br>4 | 8<br>−4<br>4 | 8<br>−4<br>4 | 8<br>−4<br>4 |

| 8<br>−3<br>5 | 8<br>−5<br>3 | 8<br>−3<br>5 | 8<br>−5<br>3 | 8<br>−4<br>4 | 8<br>−4<br>4 | 8<br>−4<br>4 | 8<br>−4<br>4 |

131

## Before Class

### Materials

8 sailboats
Subtraction 5–8 flash cards
*1 quarter for each child*
*Subtraction 8 flash cards*

### Chalkboard

| (ones) | 273 | 187 | 348 | 462 | 515 |
| (tens) | 312 | 429 | 503 | 146 | 239 |
| (hundreds) | 107 | 432 | 290 | 329 | 555 |

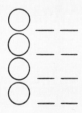

## Class Time

1. **An animal sneaks through the shadows at night. He hurries past the beans and tomatoes to the corn patch. Here he stops. He stands on his hind legs and reaches an ear of corn. *Ri-i-ip!* He jerks the husk back then sits down and eats. Suddenly he looks up. There are 25 kernels left on his cob.**

   a. **Can you name the animal?** Raccoon
   b. **Count 3 times.** 25, 50, 75, 100 . . .
   c. **Girls, count by 25's.**
   d. **Boys, count by 25's.**

2. Stand near the boats and waves.

   | 1 dark boat, 7 light boats |

   Circle the boats with your finger.
   **8 boats in the sea;**
   **8 is the whole number.**
   **What part of the 8 has dark sails?** 1
   **What part of the 8 has light sails?** 7
   **8 is the whole number.**

⟨ 32 ⟩

Answer these facts.

| | | | | | | |
|---|---|---|---|---|---|---|
| 8 −7 = 1 | 8 −5 = 3 | 7 −2 = 5 | 8 −4 = 4 | 7 −1 = 6 | 8 −6 = 2 | 8 −4 = 4 |
| 7 −3 = 4 | 8 −6 = 2 | 8 −2 = 6 | 6 −2 = 4 | 8 −3 = 5 | 8 −5 = 3 | 6 −5 = 1 |

| | | | | | | | |
|---|---|---|---|---|---|---|---|
| 8 −5 = 3 | 6 −1 = 5 | 6 −3 = 3 | 8 −3 = 5 | 7 −5 = 2 | 8 −2 = 6 | 6 −4 = 2 | 8 −2 = 6 |
| 8 −1 = 7 | 8 −5 = 3 | 5 −2 = 3 | 8 −1 = 7 | 8 −3 = 5 | 8 −4 = 4 | 7 −3 = 4 | 7 −2 = 5 |
| 8 −6 = 2 | 7 −4 = 3 | 8 −7 = 1 | 8 −3 = 5 | 8 −4 = 4 | 6 −4 = 2 | 8 −7 = 1 | 7 −4 = 3 |
| 7 −6 = 1 | 8 −5 = 3 | 7 −5 = 2 | 8 −6 = 2 | 7 −3 = 4 | 7 −2 = 5 | 8 −5 = 3 | 5 −4 = 1 |

"Peter . . . walked on the water, to go to Jesus." Matthew 14:29

132

**Its parts are 1 and 7 or 7 and 1.**

   a. Ask a child to fill in the whole and parts as everyone repeats: **8 is the . . . Its parts are . . .**

   b. **Point to the flash cards. 8—1, 7; 8—7, 1 . . .**

3. Proceed step by step through

   | 2 dark boats, 6 light boats |

   | 3 dark boats, 5 light boats |

   | 4 dark boats, 4 light boats |

4. Flash Subtraction 5–8 cards.

   **Answer together.**

5. Stand near the Place Value samples.

   a. Motion: **Ones, tens, hundreds . . .**

   b. Have the children do the samples.

   c. **Read the numbers with me.**

6. Do the Speed Drill in Lesson 32.

7. Assign Lesson 32.

32

Circle the numeral in ones' place, in tens' place, in hundreds' place.

ones  270  117  86  557  60  4

tens  468  59  302  6  599  30

hundreds  503  160  87  314  465  58

Write the numbers that come before and after when you count by 5's.

| Count by 5's | | | | | |
|---|---|---|---|---|---|
| | | | 140 | 145 | 150 |
| 20 | 25 | 30 | 155 | 160 | 165 |
| 125 | 130 | 135 | 130 | 135 | 140 |
| 190 | 195 | 200 | 5 | 10 | 15 |
| 165 | 170 | 175 | 145 | 150 | 155 |

133

**Blacklines**

2-Place Computation (−) #3

Form B

Money Identification #4

*After Class*

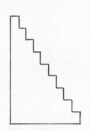

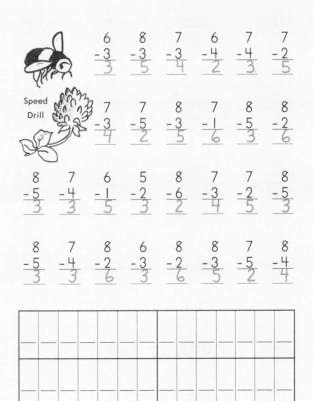

Speed Drill

| | | | | | |
|---|---|---|---|---|---|
| 6 | 8 | 7 | 6 | 7 | 7 |
| −3 | −3 | −3 | −4 | −4 | −2 |
| 3 | 5 | 4 | 2 | 3 | 5 |

| | | | | | |
|---|---|---|---|---|---|
| 7 | 7 | 8 | 7 | 8 | 8 |
| −3 | −5 | −3 | −1 | −5 | −2 |
| 4 | 2 | 5 | 6 | 3 | 6 |

| | | | | | | | |
|---|---|---|---|---|---|---|---|
| 8 | 7 | 6 | 5 | 8 | 7 | 7 | 8 |
| −5 | −4 | −1 | −2 | −6 | −3 | −2 | −5 |
| 3 | 3 | 5 | 3 | 2 | 4 | 5 | 3 |

| | | | | | | | |
|---|---|---|---|---|---|---|---|
| 8 | 7 | 8 | 6 | 8 | 8 | 7 | 8 |
| −5 | −4 | −2 | −3 | −2 | −3 | −5 | −4 |
| 3 | 3 | 6 | 3 | 6 | 5 | 2 | 4 |

1. **Say Subtraction 2–8 facts as I fill the steps.**

2. Give each child one quarter.
   a. **Do you recognize this coin? Whose picture is on the quarter?**
      George Washington
      **How much is a quarter worth?**
      **We count quarters by __. 25's**
   b. **Hold up your quarter and say "quarter, 25¢ . . ."**

3. Drill individuals with Subtraction 8 flash cards.

134

⬡ **33**

Fill in the whole and parts.
Trace and write the facts.
Make the twins take turns.

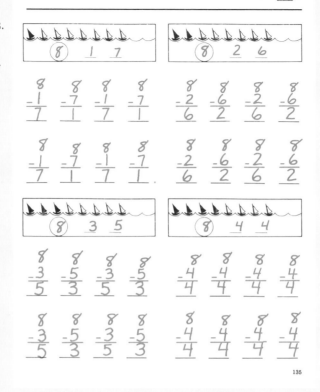

$$\begin{array}{cccc} 8 & 8 & 8 & 8 \\ -1 & -7 & -1 & -7 \\ \hline 7 & 1 & 7 & 1 \end{array}$$

$$\begin{array}{cccc} 8 & 8 & 8 & 8 \\ -2 & -6 & -2 & -6 \\ \hline 6 & 2 & 6 & 2 \end{array}$$

$$\begin{array}{cccc} 8 & 8 & 8 & 8 \\ -1 & -7 & -1 & -7 \\ \hline 7 & 1 & 7 & 1 \end{array}$$

$$\begin{array}{cccc} 8 & 8 & 8 & 8 \\ -2 & -6 & -2 & -6 \\ \hline 6 & 2 & 6 & 2 \end{array}$$

$$\begin{array}{cccc} 8 & 8 & 8 & 8 \\ -3 & -5 & -3 & -5 \\ \hline 5 & 3 & 5 & 3 \end{array}$$

$$\begin{array}{cccc} 8 & 8 & 8 & 8 \\ -4 & -4 & -4 & -4 \\ \hline 4 & 4 & 4 & 4 \end{array}$$

$$\begin{array}{cccc} 8 & 8 & 8 & 8 \\ -3 & -5 & -3 & -5 \\ \hline 5 & 3 & 5 & 3 \end{array}$$

$$\begin{array}{cccc} 8 & 8 & 8 & 8 \\ -4 & -4 & -4 & -4 \\ \hline 4 & 4 & 4 & 4 \end{array}$$

135

## Before Class

Materials

    8 sailboats

    *Subtraction 6–8 flash cards*

Chalkboard

## Class Time

1. Stand near the boats and waves.

   | 1 dark boat, 7 light boats |

   Circle the boats with your finger.

   **The whole number is __.**

   **Its parts are __ and __ or __ and __.**
   1 and 7 or 7 and 1.

   **The facts are __.** 8−1=7 and 8−7=1

2. | 2 dark boats, 6 light boats |

   Circle the boats . . .

   **The whole number is __.**

   **Its parts are __ and __ or __ and __.**

   **The facts are __.** 8−2=6 and 8−6=2

3. Proceed step by step through

   | 3 dark boats, 5 light boats |

   | 4 dark boats, 4 light boats |

4. **The raccoon left 25 kernels on the cob. Count by 25's 3 times.**

   a. **One quarter is worth __. We count quarters by __. Say "quarter, 25¢" as I**

Answer these facts.

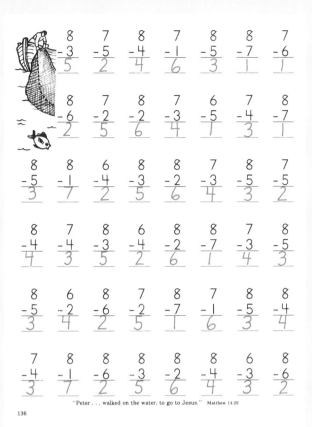

"Peter . . . walked on the water, to go to Jesus." Matthew 14:29

fill the circles.

b. **Count the quarters with me.** Write each amount.

5. Story Problems: **Close your eyes.**

a. **Beth had 8 grapes in her lunch. She ate 6. How many grapes are left for Beth's little sister? Who can give us the whole problem?**

   8 grapes − 6 grapes = 2 grapes.

b. **Thomas' dog had 8 pups. He gave 7 pups away. How many pups does Thomas have now? Who . . . ?**

   8 pups − 7 pups = 1 pup.

6. Point to the Number Line.

a. **Add with me.**

   | | |
   |---|---|
   | 10+1, 11 | 10+4, 14 |
   | 10+2, 12 | 10+5, 15 |
   | 10+3, 13 | 10+6, 16 . . . |

b. **Answer together.**

   | | | |
   |---|---|---|
   | 10+5 | 10+1 | 10+9 |
   | 10+2 | 10+6 | 10+3 |
   | 10+8 | 10+4 | 10+7 |

7. Assign Lesson 33.

33

Circle the numeral
in ones' place,
in tens' place,
in hundreds'
place.

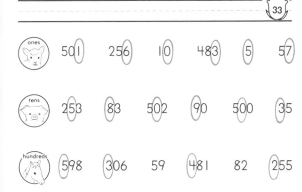

ones  50①  256  1⓪  48③  ⑤  5⑦

tens  2⑤3  ⑧3  5⓪2  ⑨0  5⓪0  ③5

hundreds  ⑤98  ③06  59  ④81  82  ②55

**Blacklines**

2-Place Computation (−) #3

Skip Counting (25's) #3

Count by 25's to 100.

Count by 25's

| 25 | 50 | 75 | 100 |
| 25 | 50 | 75 | 100 |
| 25 | 50 | 75 | 100 |
| 25 | 50 | 75 | 100 |

137

## After Class

1. Circle Drill: Subtraction 6–8 flash cards.

2. Chalkboard Drill: **Write the three numbers I say.**

    334    234    434
**Circle the largest number.**

    153    123    183
**Circle the smallest number.**

    365    360    369
**Circle the largest number.**

    400    200    300
**Circle the smallest number.**

    217    247    207
**Circle the largest number.**

Extra Activity

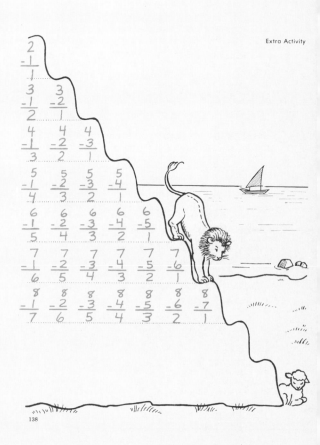

$$\begin{array}{c} 2 \\ -1 \\ \hline 1 \end{array}$$

$$\begin{array}{cc} 3 & 3 \\ -1 & -2 \\ \hline 2 & 1 \end{array}$$

$$\begin{array}{ccc} 4 & 4 & 4 \\ -1 & -2 & -3 \\ \hline 3 & 2 & 1 \end{array}$$

$$\begin{array}{cccc} 5 & 5 & 5 & 5 \\ -1 & -2 & -3 & -4 \\ \hline 4 & 3 & 2 & 1 \end{array}$$

$$\begin{array}{ccccc} 6 & 6 & 6 & 6 & 6 \\ -1 & -2 & -3 & -4 & -5 \\ \hline 5 & 4 & 3 & 2 & 1 \end{array}$$

$$\begin{array}{cccccc} 7 & 7 & 7 & 7 & 7 & 7 \\ -1 & -2 & -3 & -4 & -5 & -6 \\ \hline 6 & 5 & 4 & 3 & 2 & 1 \end{array}$$

$$\begin{array}{ccccccc} 8 & 8 & 8 & 8 & 8 & 8 & 8 \\ -1 & -2 & -3 & -4 & -5 & -6 & -7 \\ \hline 7 & 6 & 5 & 4 & 3 & 2 & 1 \end{array}$$

138

Fill in the whole and parts.
Trace and write the facts.
Make the twins take turns.

| ⑨ | 1 | 8 | | ⑨ | 2 | 7 |

$$\begin{array}{r}9\\-1\\\hline 8\end{array}\quad\begin{array}{r}9\\-8\\\hline 1\end{array}\quad\begin{array}{r}9\\-1\\\hline 8\end{array}\quad\begin{array}{r}9\\-8\\\hline 1\end{array}\qquad\begin{array}{r}9\\-2\\\hline 7\end{array}\quad\begin{array}{r}9\\-7\\\hline 2\end{array}\quad\begin{array}{r}9\\-2\\\hline 7\end{array}\quad\begin{array}{r}9\\-7\\\hline 2\end{array}$$

$$\begin{array}{r}9\\-1\\\hline 8\end{array}\quad\begin{array}{r}9\\-8\\\hline 1\end{array}\quad\begin{array}{r}9\\-1\\\hline 8\end{array}\quad\begin{array}{r}9\\-8\\\hline 1\end{array}\qquad\begin{array}{r}9\\-2\\\hline 7\end{array}\quad\begin{array}{r}9\\-7\\\hline 2\end{array}\quad\begin{array}{r}9\\-2\\\hline 7\end{array}\quad\begin{array}{r}9\\-7\\\hline 2\end{array}$$

| ⑨ | 3 | 6 | | ⑨ | 4 | 5 |

$$\begin{array}{r}9\\-3\\\hline 6\end{array}\quad\begin{array}{r}9\\-6\\\hline 3\end{array}\quad\begin{array}{r}9\\-3\\\hline 6\end{array}\quad\begin{array}{r}9\\-6\\\hline 3\end{array}\qquad\begin{array}{r}9\\-4\\\hline 5\end{array}\quad\begin{array}{r}9\\-5\\\hline 4\end{array}\quad\begin{array}{r}9\\-4\\\hline 5\end{array}\quad\begin{array}{r}9\\-5\\\hline 4\end{array}$$

$$\begin{array}{r}9\\-3\\\hline 6\end{array}\quad\begin{array}{r}9\\-6\\\hline 3\end{array}\quad\begin{array}{r}9\\-3\\\hline 6\end{array}\quad\begin{array}{r}9\\-6\\\hline 3\end{array}\qquad\begin{array}{r}9\\-4\\\hline 5\end{array}\quad\begin{array}{r}9\\-5\\\hline 4\end{array}\quad\begin{array}{r}9\\-4\\\hline 5\end{array}\quad\begin{array}{r}9\\-5\\\hline 4\end{array}$$

139

## Before Class

Tack Subtraction 9 flash cards above the waves
in this order:

| $\begin{array}{r}9\\-1\\\hline 8\end{array}$ | $\begin{array}{r}9\\-8\\\hline 1\end{array}$ | $\begin{array}{r}9\\-2\\\hline 7\end{array}$ | $\begin{array}{r}9\\-7\\\hline 2\end{array}$ | $\begin{array}{r}9\\-3\\\hline 6\end{array}$ | $\begin{array}{r}9\\-6\\\hline 3\end{array}$ | $\begin{array}{r}9\\-4\\\hline 5\end{array}$ | $\begin{array}{r}9\\-5\\\hline 4\end{array}$ |

### Materials

Large penny, nickel, dime, and quarter
9 sailboats
*Subtraction 9 flash cards*

### Chalkboard

6 dimes = _____     1 quarter = _____
3 quarters = _____     8 nickels = _____
10 nickels = _____     7 dimes = _____
26 pennies = _____     3 nickels = _____
4 quarters = _____     2 quarters = _____

## Class Time

1. Have the children bring *My 1,000 Book* to the
teaching corner.
   a. **Count by 25's to 100.**
   b. **Count on to 200 by 10's.**
   c. **Count on to 300 by 5's.**

2. a. Flash the large coins. **Dime, 10¢; Nickel,
   5¢ . . .**
   b. **Name the man on each coin.**

3. Do the Money samples.

4. Stand near the boats and waves.

   1 dark boat, 8 light boats

   Circle the boats with your finger.
   **9 boats in the sea;**
   **9 is the whole number.**
   **What part of the 9 has dark sails?** 1
   **What part of the 9 has light sails?** 8
   **9 is the whole number.**
   **Its parts are 1 and 8 or 8 and 1.**
   a. Point to the flash cards: **These are twin
   facts: 9—1, 8 and 9—8, 1.**

**34**

Answer these facts.

| | | | | | | |
|---|---|---|---|---|---|---|
| 9 −4 = 5 | 9 −6 = 3 | 9 −5 = 4 | 8 −6 = 2 | 8 −2 = 6 | 9 −8 = 1 | 8 −5 = 3 |
| 9 −6 = 3 | 8 −7 = 1 | 9 −3 = 6 | 9 −7 = 2 | 9 −5 = 4 | 7 −4 = 3 | 9 −4 = 5 |
| 9 −2 = 7 | 8 −1 = 7 | 9 −6 = 3 | 5 −2 = 3 | 7 −4 = 3 | 6 −3 = 3 | 9 −3 = 6 | 8 −2 = 6 |
| 6 −4 = 2 | 8 −3 = 5 | 9 −2 = 7 | 9 −7 = 2 | 9 −5 = 4 | 7 −5 = 2 | 9 −8 = 1 | 9 −4 = 5 |
| 9 −4 = 5 | 9 −8 = 1 | 9 −7 = 2 | 8 −4 = 4 | 9 −7 = 2 | 9 −2 = 7 | 9 −4 = 5 | 9 −7 = 2 |
| 9 −3 = 6 | 7 −1 = 6 | 9 −5 = 4 | 7 −3 = 4 | 6 −2 = 4 | 9 −5 = 4 | 9 −6 = 3 | 8 −5 = 3 |

"Peter . . . walked on the water, to go to Jesus."  Matthew 14:29

140

b. **Let's make the twins take turns as I write them and you say them.**
9−1=8;  9−8=1 . . .

5. Proceed step by step through

   | 2 dark boats, 7 light boats |
   | 3 dark boats, 6 light boats |
   | 4 dark boats, 5 light boats |

6. Point to the first flash card. **Say each fact twice.  9−1, 8;  9−1, 8 . . .**

7. Do the Speed Drill in Lesson 34.

8. Assign Lesson 34.

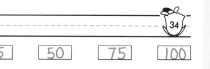

Count by 25's to 100.

 Count by 25's | 25 | 50 | 75 | 100 |

25 | 50 | 75 | 100

Count the quarters.
Write the amount.

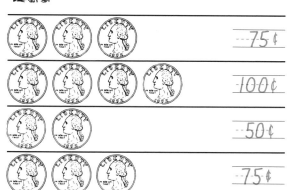

75¢

100¢

50¢

75¢

**Blacklines**

2-Place Computation (−) #3

Form B

Read the story.
Write the numbers
  in the beehive.
Write the label words
  on the lines.

Ross had nine mints.
He gave six of them to
his little sister. How many
mints did Ross have **left**?

```
  9    mints
- 6    mints
  3    mints
```

141

## *After Class*

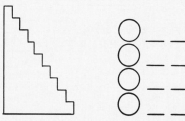

Speed
Drill

```
  5     8     7     6     5     7
- 3   - 3   - 2   - 4   - 2   - 3
  2     5     5     2     3     4

  6     8     8     8     8     8
- 2   - 4   - 3   - 6   - 2   - 5
  4     4     5     2     6     3

  7     8     7     8     6     8     7     7
- 2   - 1   - 3   - 5   - 4   - 3   - 2   - 5
  5     7     4     3     2     5     5     2

  8     7     6     8     7     8     7     8
- 1   - 2   - 3   - 2   - 5   - 3   - 3   - 4
  7     5     3     6     2     5     4     4
```

1. Have the children fill in the whole and parts for
   the Subtraction 9 facts.

2. Double Drill: Subtraction 9 flash cards.

3. Ask a child to fill in the steps as everyone says
   Subtraction 2–9 facts.

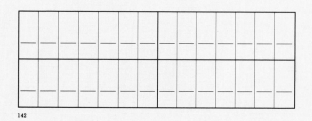

142

130

<35>

Fill in the whole and parts.
Trace and write the facts.
Make the twins take turns.

(9) 1 8          (9) 2 7

$$\frac{9}{-1}{8} \quad \frac{9}{-8}{1} \quad \frac{9}{-1}{8} \quad \frac{9}{-8}{1}$$   $$\frac{9}{-2}{7} \quad \frac{9}{-7}{2} \quad \frac{9}{-2}{7} \quad \frac{9}{-7}{2}$$

$$\frac{9}{-1}{8} \quad \frac{9}{-8}{1} \quad \frac{9}{-1}{8} \quad \frac{9}{-8}{1}$$   $$\frac{9}{-2}{7} \quad \frac{9}{-7}{2} \quad \frac{9}{-2}{7} \quad \frac{9}{-7}{2}$$

(9) 3 6          (9) 4 5

$$\frac{9}{-3}{6} \quad \frac{9}{-6}{3} \quad \frac{9}{-3}{6} \quad \frac{9}{-6}{3}$$   $$\frac{9}{-4}{5} \quad \frac{9}{-5}{4} \quad \frac{9}{-4}{5} \quad \frac{9}{-5}{4}$$

$$\frac{9}{-3}{6} \quad \frac{9}{-6}{3} \quad \frac{9}{-3}{6} \quad \frac{9}{-6}{3}$$   $$\frac{9}{-4}{5} \quad \frac{9}{-5}{4} \quad \frac{9}{-4}{5} \quad \frac{9}{-5}{4}$$

143

## Before Class

### Materials

Subtraction 6–9 flash cards

*Subtraction 6–9 flash cards*

### Chalkboard

| | 155 | |
|---|---|---|
| | 120 | |
| | 185 | |
| | 170 | |

| | 240 | |
|---|---|---|
| | 210 | |
| | 270 | |
| | 290 | |

$$789 \quad 678 \quad 479 \quad 597 \quad 569 \quad 489$$
$$-164 \quad -343 \quad -326 \quad -355 \quad -423 \quad -224$$

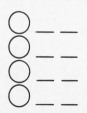

## Class Time

1. Have the children stand.
   a. **Count by 25's to 100.**
   b. **Count on to 300 by 10's.**
   c. **Count on to 350 by 5's.**

2. Do the Before and After samples.
   Fill in the first set counting by 5's.
   Fill in the second set counting by 10's.

3. Stand near the boats and waves.
   **Who was commanded by God to build a huge boat to save his family?**
   Noah (Genesis 6)

4. 1 dark boat, 8 light boats
   Circle the boats with your finger.
   **9 boats in the sea;**
   **9 is the whole number.**
   **What part of the 9 has dark sails?** 1
   **What part of the 9 has light sails?** 8
   **9 is the whole number.**
   **Its parts are 1 and 8 or 8 and 1.**

Answer these facts.

35   Extra Activity

| | | | | | | |
|---|---|---|---|---|---|---|
| 9<br>−7<br>2 | 9<br>−6<br>3 | 8<br>−4<br>4 | 9<br>−4<br>5 | 9<br>−2<br>7 | 9<br>−3<br>6 | 8<br>−5<br>3 |
| 9<br>−5<br>4 | 7<br>−4<br>3 | 7<br>−5<br>2 | 9<br>−3<br>6 | 8<br>−1<br>7 | 9<br>−4<br>5 | 9<br>−6<br>3 |

| | | | | | | | |
|---|---|---|---|---|---|---|---|
| 9<br>−5<br>4 | 6<br>−4<br>2 | 6<br>−2<br>4 | 9<br>−7<br>2 | 9<br>−7<br>2 | 9<br>−5<br>4 | 8<br>−6<br>2 | 7<br>−3<br>4 |
| 8<br>−2<br>6 | 9<br>−2<br>7 | 9<br>−1<br>8 | 9<br>−4<br>5 | 9<br>−6<br>3 | 9<br>−8<br>1 | 6<br>−1<br>5 | 7<br>−4<br>3 |
| 9<br>−6<br>3 | 9<br>−4<br>5 | 7<br>−6<br>1 | 6<br>−3<br>3 | 7<br>−2<br>5 | 9<br>−1<br>8 | 9<br>−2<br>7 | 9<br>−3<br>6 |
| 8<br>−3<br>5 | 9<br>−8<br>1 | 9<br>−4<br>5 | 8<br>−7<br>1 | 9<br>−3<br>6 | 9<br>−5<br>4 | 9<br>−3<br>6 | 7<br>−3<br>4 |

"Peter . . . walked on the water, to go to Jesus." Matthew 14:29

144

a. Ask a child to fill in the whole and parts as everyone says **9 is the . . . Its parts are . . .**

b. Point to the flash cards. **Say the twins with me. 9−1, 8; 9−8, 1 . . .**

5. Proceed step by step through

> 2 dark boats, 7 light boats

> 3 dark boats, 6 light boats

> 4 dark boats, 5 light boats

6. Flash Subtraction 6–9 cards.
   **Answer together.**

7. Stand near the Subtraction samples.

   a. Trace the arrows. **Ones' place *first;* tens' place *second* . . .**

   b. Have the children answer the problems.

8. Assign Lesson 35.

*Note:* Are you drilling the 0 facts with your flash cards?

$8−0=8; 8−8=0; 9−0=9; 9−9=0 . . .$

132

Answer these problems.

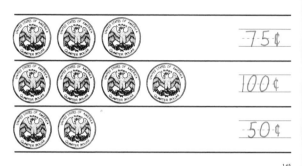

| 69 | 78 | 89 | 68 | 79 | 69 |
|---|---|---|---|---|---|
| - 5 | - 3 | - 7 | - 5 | - 4 | - 6 |
| 64 | 75 | 82 | 63 | 75 | 63 |

| 86 | 97 | 97 | 98 | 89 | 78 |
|---|---|---|---|---|---|
| -23 | -22 | -34 | -16 | -14 | -14 |
| 63 | 75 | 63 | 82 | 75 | 64 |

Count by 25's to 100.

Count by 25's

| 25 | 50 | 75 | 100 |
|---|---|---|---|
| 25 | 50 | 75 | 100 |

**Blacklines**

Number Facts (−) #7

Skip Counting (25's) #3

Count the quarters.
Write the amount.

75¢

100¢

50¢

145

*After Class*

1. Drill individuals with Subtraction 6–9 flash cards.

2. Stand near the Number Line.
   **Count by 25's, then by 1's.**
   **25, 50, 51, 52, 53, 54, 55, 56**
   **25, 26, 27, 28, 29, 30, 31, 32, 33**
   **25, 50, 75, 76, 77, 78, 79, 80**

3. Chalkboard Drill: **Write 486. Change it to 436, 536, 506, 509, 209, 279, 379, 370, 300, 500, 505.**

Extra Activity

146

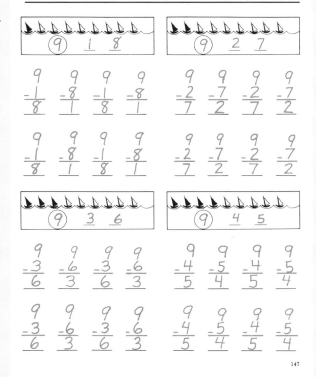

Fill in the whole and parts.
Trace and write the facts.
Make the twins take turns.

147

## Before Class

### Materials
Subtraction 5-9 flash cards
Use Form C

### Chalkboard

| 799 | 898 | 987 | 879 | 789 | 998 |
|-----|-----|-----|-----|-----|-----|
| −495 | −563 | −340 | −354 | −287 | −502 |

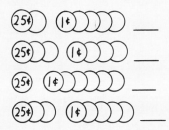

## Class Time

1. Stand near the boats and waves.

   2 dark boats, 7 light boats

   Circle the boats with your finger.
   **The whole number is __.**
   **Its parts are __ and __ or __ and __.**
   2 and 7 or 7 and 2
   **The facts are __.** 9−2=7 and 9−7=2

2. 3 dark boats, 6 light boats

   Circle the boats . . .
   **The whole number is __.**
   **Its parts are __ and __ or __ and __.**
   **The facts are __.** 9−3=6 and 9−6=3

3. 4 dark boats, 5 light boats

   Circle the boats . . .
   **The whole number is __.**
   **Its parts are __ and __ or __ and __.**
   **The facts are __.** 9−4=5 and 9−5=4

4. Flash Subtraction 5-9 cards. **Answer quickly!**

5. Flash Card Drill: Subtraction 5-9 flash cards.
   Use Form C. **Flower Row: Box 1 . . .**

134

Answer these facts.

| | 9 | 9 | 9 | 8 | 9 | 9 | 9 |
|---|---|---|---|---|---|---|---|
| | -8 | -6 | -4 | -6 | -5 | -3 | -2 |
| | 1 | 3 | 5 | 2 | 4 | 6 | 7 |

| | 9 | 8 | 8 | 9 | 9 | 7 | 7 |
|---|---|---|---|---|---|---|---|
| | -2 | -2 | -4 | -7 | -4 | -4 | -6 |
| | 7 | 6 | 4 | 2 | 5 | 3 | 1 |

| 9 | 8 | 9 | 8 | 9 | 8 | 9 | 8 |
|---|---|---|---|---|---|---|---|
| -5 | -5 | -7 | -3 | -7 | -7 | -5 | -2 |
| 4 | 3 | 2 | 5 | 2 | 1 | 4 | 6 |

| 9 | 9 | 9 | 9 | 9 | 7 | 9 | 7 |
|---|---|---|---|---|---|---|---|
| -3 | -5 | -8 | -7 | -4 | -5 | -6 | -3 |
| 6 | 4 | 1 | 2 | 5 | 2 | 3 | 4 |

| 9 | 9 | 7 | 9 | 9 | 8 | 9 | 9 |
|---|---|---|---|---|---|---|---|
| -6 | -1 | -2 | -3 | -6 | -6 | -3 | -8 |
| 3 | 8 | 5 | 6 | 3 | 2 | 6 | 1 |

| 9 | 9 | 9 | 8 | 7 | 9 | 9 | 8 |
|---|---|---|---|---|---|---|---|
| -8 | -3 | -7 | -5 | -1 | -4 | -1 | -5 |
| 1 | 6 | 2 | 3 | 6 | 5 | 8 | 3 |

"Peter . . . walked on the water, to go to Jesus." Matthew 14:29

148

Speed Drill

6. Do the 3-digit Subtraction samples.

7. Stand near the Number Line.
   **Count by 25's, then by 1's.**
   **25, 26, 27, 28**
   **25, 50, 75, 76, 77**
   **25, 50, 51, 52, 53, 54**

8. Have individuals count aloud as they
   do the Money samples.

9. Do the Speed Drill in Lesson 36.

10. Assign Lesson 36.

Answer these problems.

```
 799     977     878     997     899
-374    -354    -337    -360    -325
 425     623     541     637     574

 979     798     799     888     899
-405    -161    -258    -265    -474
 574     637     541     623     425
```

Read the story.
Write the numbers
  in the beehive.
Write the label words
  on the lines.
Answer the problem.

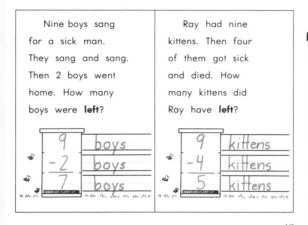

Nine boys sang for a sick man. They sang and sang. Then 2 boys went home. How many boys were **left**?

```
  9    boys
 -2    boys
  7    boys
```

Ray had nine kittens. Then four of them got sick and died. How many kittens did Ray have **left**?

```
  9    kittens
 -4    kittens
  5    kittens
```

**Blacklines**

Form C (Class Time)

Number Facts (−) #7

Form B

Skip Counting (25's) #3

149

---

## *After Class*

3 dimes + 2 pennies = ____
4 nickels + 3 pennies = ____
1 quarter + 1 penny = ____
5 dimes + 4 pennies = ____

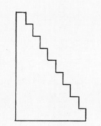

1. **Say Subtraction 2–9 facts as I fill in the steps.**

2. Do the Money samples.

3. Story Problems: **Close your eyes.**

   a. **Robert picked 9 pumpkins. He loaded 4 of them on his wagon. How many pumpkins are left? Who can give us the whole problem?**

      9 pumpkins − 4 pumpkins = 5 pumpkins.

   b. **8 apples lay on the ground. A deer ate 3 of them. How many apples are on the ground now? Who . . . ?**

      8 apples − 3 apples = 5 apples.

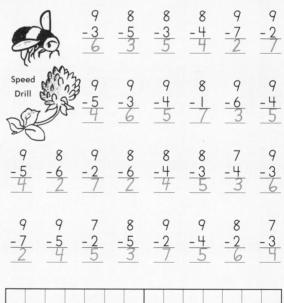

Speed Drill

```
  9    8    8    8    9    9
 -3   -5   -3   -4   -7   -2
  6    3    5    4    2    7

  9    9    9    8    9    9
 -5   -3   -4   -1   -6   -4
  4    6    5    7    3    5

  9    8    9    8    8    8    7    9
 -5   -6   -2   -6   -4   -3   -4   -3
  4    2    7    2    4    5    3    6

  9    9    7    8    9    9    8    7
 -7   -5   -2   -5   -2   -4   -2   -3
  2    4    5    3    7    5    6    4
```

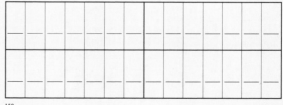

150

Fill in the whole and parts.
Trace and write the facts.
Make the twins take turns.

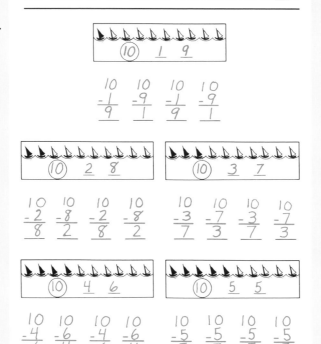

| | | | |
|---|---|---|---|
| 10 | 10 | 10 | 10 |
| −1 | −9 | −1 | −9 |
| 9 | 1 | 9 | 1 |

| | | | | | | | |
|---|---|---|---|---|---|---|---|
| 10 | 10 | 10 | 10 | 10 | 10 | 10 | 10 |
| −2 | −8 | −2 | −8 | −3 | −7 | −3 | −7 |
| 8 | 2 | 8 | 2 | 7 | 3 | 7 | 3 |

| | | | | | | | |
|---|---|---|---|---|---|---|---|
| 10 | 10 | 10 | 10 | 10 | 10 | 10 | 10 |
| −4 | −6 | −4 | −6 | −5 | −5 | −5 | −5 |
| 6 | 4 | 6 | 4 | 5 | 5 | 5 | 5 |

151

---

## Before Class

Tack Subtraction 10 flash cards above the waves
in this order:

| 10 | 10 | 10 | 10 | 10 | 10 | 10 | 10 | 10 |
|---|---|---|---|---|---|---|---|---|
| −1 | −9 | −2 | −8 | −3 | −7 | −4 | −6 | −5 |
| 9 | 1 | 8 | 2 | 7 | 3 | 6 | 4 | 5 |

### Materials

Subtraction 5–9 flash cards
10 sailboats
*Large coins*

### Chalkboard

| 589 | 678 | 897 | 796 | 578 | 898 |
|---|---|---|---|---|---|
| − 35 | − 40 | − 35 | − 92 | − 35 | −72 |

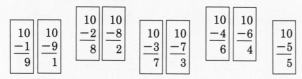

## Class Time

1. Circle Drill: Subtraction 5–9 flash cards. **As
   soon as you have given 10 answers you
   may sit down.**

2. Do the Subtraction samples.

3. Stand near the boats and waves.
   | 1 dark boat, 9 light boats |
   Circle the boats with your finger.
   **10 boats in the sea;**
   **10 is the whole number.**
   **What part of the 10 has dark sails?** 1
   **What part of the 10 has light sails?** 9
   **10 is the whole number.**
   **Its parts are 1 and 9 or 9 and 1.**
   a. Ask a child to fill in the whole and parts as
      everyone repeats: **10 is the . . . Its parts
      are . . .**
   b. Point to the flash cards: **Say the twins with
      me. 10−1, 9;  10−9, 1 . . .**

Answer these facts.

Extra Activity

| | | | | | | |
|---|---|---|---|---|---|---|
| 10<br>-4<br>6 | 10<br>-7<br>3 | 10<br>-5<br>5 | 9<br>-5<br>4 | 7<br>-5<br>2 | 9<br>-4<br>5 | 10<br>-3<br>7 |
| 10<br>-8<br>2 | 9<br>-6<br>3 | 10<br>-5<br>5 | 8<br>-5<br>3 | 10<br>-4<br>6 | 8<br>-6<br>2 | 10<br>-6<br>4 |
| 9<br>-7<br>2 | 10<br>-2<br>8 | 8<br>-3<br>5 | 10<br>-7<br>3 | 9<br>-3<br>6 | 10<br>-7<br>3 | 7<br>-3<br>4 | 10<br>-8<br>2 |
| 9<br>-1<br>8 | 10<br>-4<br>6 | 7<br>-4<br>3 | 7<br>-2<br>5 | 6<br>-2<br>4 | 6<br>-4<br>2 | 10<br>-5<br>5 | 10<br>-3<br>7 |
| 8<br>-2<br>6 | 10<br>-9<br>1 | 10<br>-6<br>4 | 10<br>-3<br>7 | 5<br>-3<br>2 | 7<br>-6<br>1 | 8<br>-4<br>4 | 10<br>-7<br>3 |
| 8<br>-7<br>1 | 10<br>-4<br>6 | 9<br>-2<br>7 | 5<br>-1<br>4 | 10<br>-9<br>1 | 10<br>-8<br>2 | 5<br>-2<br>3 | 10<br>-6<br>4 |

"Peter . . . walked on the water, to go to Jesus."   Matthew 14:29

152

4. Proceed step by step through

| 2 dark boats, 8 light boats |
|---|
| 3 dark boats, 7 light boats |
| 4 dark boats, 6 light boats |
| 5 dark boats, 5 light boats |

5. Point to the first flash card. **Look at the fact. Close your eyes and say it 3 times. 10—1, 9 . . .**

6. Have individuals count aloud as they do the Money samples.

7. Assign Lesson 37.

138

37

Answer these problems.

| 978 | 689 | 975 | 999 | 776 |
|---|---|---|---|---|
| -338 | -438 | -540 | -627 | -523 |
| 640 | 251 | 435 | 372 | 253 |

| 975 | 689 | 898 | 889 | 985 |
|---|---|---|---|---|
| -603 | -254 | -647 | -249 | -732 |
| 372 | 435 | 251 | 640 | 253 |

Count the quarters and pennies.
Write the amount.

78¢

54¢

77¢

31¢

55¢

153

**Blacklines**

Number Facts (−) #7

Form A: 300–399

## *After Class*

1. **Answer together.**

   | 10+1 | 10+5 | 10+9 |
   |---|---|---|
   | 10+2 | 10+6 | 10+4 |
   | 10+3 | 10+7 | 10+2 |
   | 10+4 | 10+8 | 10+6 |

2. Drill individuals with the large coins.
   **Dime, 10¢; quarter, 25¢ . . .**

3. Chalkboard Drill: **Write 564.**
   **Circle the numeral in tens' place.**
   Continue with
   **602** . . . hundreds' place.
   **439** . . . ones' place.
   **389** . . . hundreds' place.
   **717** . . . tens' place.
   **506** . . . ones' place.

Extra Activity

154

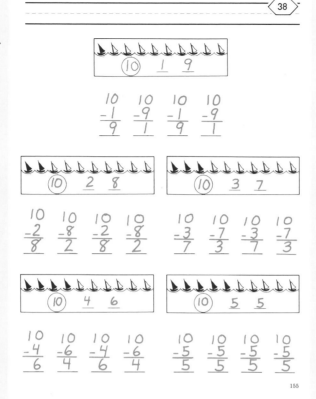

Fill in the whole and parts.
Trace and write the facts.
Make the twins take turns.

$$\boxed{10} \quad \underline{1} \quad \underline{9}$$

$$\begin{array}{cccc} 10 & 10 & 10 & 10 \\ -1 & -9 & -1 & -9 \\ \hline 9 & 1 & 9 & 1 \end{array}$$

$$\boxed{10} \quad \underline{2} \quad \underline{8} \qquad \boxed{10} \quad \underline{3} \quad \underline{7}$$

$$\begin{array}{cccc} 10 & 10 & 10 & 10 \\ -2 & -8 & -2 & -8 \\ \hline 8 & 2 & 8 & 2 \end{array} \qquad \begin{array}{cccc} 10 & 10 & 10 & 10 \\ -3 & -7 & -3 & -7 \\ \hline 7 & 3 & 7 & 3 \end{array}$$

$$\boxed{10} \quad \underline{4} \quad \underline{6} \qquad \boxed{10} \quad \underline{5} \quad \underline{5}$$

$$\begin{array}{cccc} 10 & 10 & 10 & 10 \\ -4 & -6 & -4 & -6 \\ \hline 6 & 4 & 6 & 4 \end{array} \qquad \begin{array}{cccc} 10 & 10 & 10 & 10 \\ -5 & -5 & -5 & -5 \\ \hline 5 & 5 & 5 & 5 \end{array}$$

155

## Before Class

**Materials**

    10 sailboats

    *Subtraction 10 flash cards*

**Chalkboard**

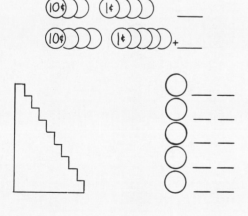

## Class Time

1. Stand near the boats and waves.

    | 1 dark boat, 9 light boats |

    Circle the boats with your finger.

    **10 boats in the sea;**

    **10 is the whole number.**

    **What part of the 10 has dark sails?** 1

    **What part of the 10 has light sails?** 9

    **10 is the whole number.**

    **Its parts are 1 and 9 or 9 and 1.**

    a. Ask a child to fill in the whole and parts as everyone repeats: **10 is the . . . Its parts are . . .**

    b. Point to the flash cards. **10−1, 9;**
       **10−9, 1 . . .**

2. Proceed step by step through

    | 2 dark boats, 8 light boats |

    | 3 dark boats, 7 light boats |

    | 4 dark boats, 6 light boats |

38

Answer these facts.

| | | | | | | |
|---|---|---|---|---|---|---|
| 10<br>−3<br>7 | 10<br>−6<br>4 | 10<br>−8<br>2 | 9<br>−4<br>5 | 8<br>−5<br>3 | 7<br>−5<br>2 | 6<br>−3<br>3 |
| 10<br>−7<br>3 | 10<br>−8<br>2 | 7<br>−4<br>3 | 10<br>−5<br>5 | 6<br>−4<br>2 | 9<br>−5<br>4 | 9<br>−2<br>7 |

| | | | | | | | |
|---|---|---|---|---|---|---|---|
| 10<br>−4<br>6 | 10<br>−2<br>8 | 10<br>−9<br>1 | 8<br>−4<br>4 | 10<br>−7<br>3 | 10<br>−8<br>2 | 9<br>−6<br>3 | 7<br>−3<br>4 |
| 10<br>−2<br>8 | 8<br>−2<br>6 | 10<br>−6<br>4 | 8<br>−7<br>1 | 9<br>−7<br>2 | 10<br>−7<br>3 | 6<br>−2<br>4 | 10<br>−7<br>3 |
| 10<br>−1<br>9 | 8<br>−6<br>2 | 7<br>−6<br>1 | 10<br>−5<br>5 | 10<br>−9<br>1 | 10<br>−3<br>7 | 10<br>−6<br>4 | 10<br>−4<br>6 |
| 10<br>−4<br>6 | 10<br>−6<br>4 | 10<br>−3<br>7 | 6<br>−5<br>1 | 10<br>−5<br>5 | 9<br>−8<br>1 | 10<br>−8<br>2 | 10<br>−1<br>9 |

"Peter . . . walked on the water, to go to Jesus." Matthew 14:29

156

5 dark boats, 5 light boats

3. **Say the subtraction facts as I fill the steps.**

4. Count by memory.
   a. **Count by 25's to 100.**
   b. **Count on to 200 by 5's.**
   c. **Count on to 300 by 10's.**

5. **We count pennies by __,** 1's
   **nickels by __,** 5's
   **dimes by __,** 10's
   **and quarters by __.** 25's

6. Point to the Money samples.
   a. **Count with me.**
      **10, 20, 30, 31, 32, 33, 34¢.** Write 34¢.
      **10, 20, 30, 40, 41, 42, 43, 44, 45¢.**
      Write 45¢.
   b. **Let's add to see how much we have altogether.**
      **4+5=__.** Write 9.
      **3+4=__.** Write 7.
      **We have 79¢.**

7. Do the Speed Drill in Lesson 38.

8. Assign Lesson 38.

Answer these problems.

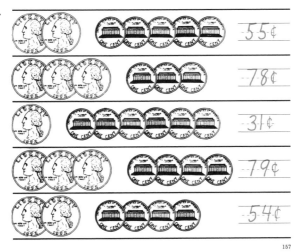

| | | | | |
|---|---|---|---|---|
| 897 | 989 | 698 | 769 | 979 |
| − 46 | − 43 | − 55 | − 65 | − 58 |
| 851 | 946 | 643 | 704 | 921 |
| 888 | 987 | 676 | 797 | 969 |
| − 73 | − 23 | − 42 | − 57 | − 57 |
| 815 | 964 | 634 | 740 | 912 |

Count the quarters and pennies.
Write the amount.

55¢

78¢

31¢

79¢

54¢

157

**Blacklines**

Fact Form II

Form B

---

## After Class

| 3 | 3 | 5 | 2 | 2 | 3 |
|---|---|---|---|---|---|
| 4 | 6 | 2 | 6 | 4 | 2 |
| +2 | +1 | +2 | +2 | +4 | +4 |

1. Drill Subtraction 10 flash cards.

2. Do the Column Addition samples.

   a. $3+4=$ ___. Write 7.

      $7+2=$ ___. Write 9.

      3
      4 7
     +2

   b. Have the children finish
   the samples.

Speed
Drill

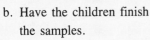

| 9 | 8 | 9 | 9 | 9 | 8 |
|---|---|---|---|---|---|
| −6 | −3 | −5 | −3 | −7 | −5 |
| 3 | 5 | 4 | 6 | 2 | 3 |
| 8 | 9 | 8 | 6 | 9 | 8 |
| −4 | −1 | −5 | −4 | −4 | −2 |
| 4 | 8 | 3 | 2 | 5 | 6 |
| 9 | 7 | 9 | 8 | 9 | 9 | 8 | 9 |
| −2 | −2 | −6 | −6 | −3 | −5 | −3 | −6 |
| 7 | 5 | 3 | 2 | 6 | 4 | 5 | 3 |
| 9 | 9 | 8 | 7 | 7 | 9 | 9 | 9 |
| −4 | −2 | −2 | −2 | −5 | −6 | −1 | −5 |
| 5 | 7 | 6 | 5 | 2 | 3 | 8 | 4 |

*Note:* Initially, we write the partial sum in column addition.

   By midyear some children will quietly exchange writing it for mentally holding it. Other children must continue to write it to be accurate.

   The question is **not** when shall the child stop writing it? But rather, is his work **accurate**?

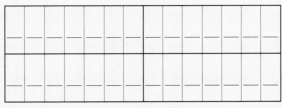

158

**39**

Fill in the whole and parts.
Trace and write the facts.
Make the twins take turns.

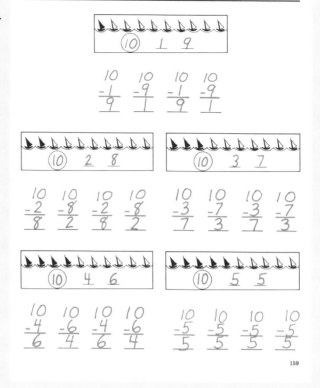

159

**Before Class**

Chalkboard

| 696 | 759 | 879 | 988 | 899 | 976 |
|---|---|---|---|---|---|
| − 64 | − 20 | − 32 | − 63 | − 53 | − 73 |

| 5 | 2 | 4 | 3 | 2 | 2 |
|---|---|---|---|---|---|
| 3 | 6 | 2 | 4 | 5 | 4 |
| +2 | +1 | +4 | +3 | +2 | +2 |

**Class Time**

1. Stand near the boats and waves.

   2 dark boats, 8 light boats

   Circle the boats . . .

   **The whole number is __.**

   **Its parts are __ and __ or __ and __.**
   2 and 8 or 8 and 2

   **The facts are __.** 10−2=8 and 10-8=2

2. 3 dark boats, 7 light boats

   Circle the boats . . .

   **The whole number is __.**

   **Its parts are __ and __ or __ and __.**

   **The facts are __.** 10−3=7 and 10−7=3

3. 4 dark boats, 6 light boats

   Circle the boats . . .

   **The whole number is __.**

   **Its parts are __ and __ or __ and __.**

   **The facts are __.** 10−4=6 and 10−6=4

Answer these facts.

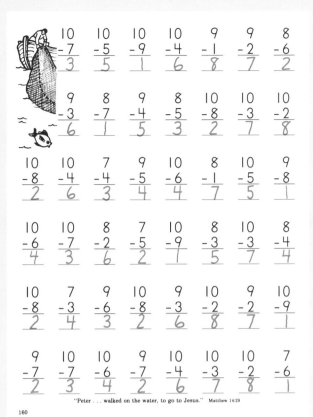

| 10 | 10 | 10 | 10 | 9 | 9 | 8 |
|---|---|---|---|---|---|---|
| -7 | -5 | -9 | -4 | -1 | -2 | -6 |
| 3 | 5 | 1 | 6 | 8 | 7 | 2 |

| 9 | 8 | 9 | 8 | 10 | 10 | 10 |
|---|---|---|---|---|---|---|
| -3 | -7 | -4 | -5 | -8 | -3 | -2 |
| 6 | 1 | 5 | 3 | 2 | 7 | 8 |

| 10 | 10 | 7 | 9 | 10 | 8 | 10 | 9 |
|---|---|---|---|---|---|---|---|
| -8 | -4 | -4 | -5 | -6 | -1 | -5 | -8 |
| 2 | 6 | 3 | 4 | 4 | 7 | 5 | 1 |

| 10 | 10 | 8 | 7 | 10 | 8 | 10 | 8 |
|---|---|---|---|---|---|---|---|
| -6 | -7 | -2 | -5 | -9 | -3 | -3 | -4 |
| 4 | 3 | 6 | 2 | 1 | 5 | 7 | 4 |

| 10 | 7 | 9 | 10 | 9 | 10 | 9 | 10 |
|---|---|---|---|---|---|---|---|
| -8 | -3 | -6 | -8 | -3 | -2 | -2 | -9 |
| 2 | 4 | 3 | 2 | 6 | 8 | 7 | 1 |

| 9 | 10 | 10 | 9 | 10 | 10 | 10 | 7 |
|---|---|---|---|---|---|---|---|
| -7 | -7 | -6 | -7 | -4 | -3 | -2 | -6 |
| 2 | 3 | 4 | 2 | 6 | 7 | 8 | 1 |

"Peter . . . walked on the water, to go to Jesus." Matthew 14:29

160

4. 5 dark boats, 5 light boats

   Circle the boats . . .

   **The whole number is __.**

   **Its parts are __ and __.**

   **The fact is __.** 10−5=5

5. **One dark stormy night an angel stood beside a man on a boat. Who was the man?**

   Paul (Acts 27:23)

6. Do the Subtraction samples.

7. Point to the Number Line.

   a. **Add with me.**

   | 10+1 | 10+4 |
   |---|---|
   | 10+2 | 10+5 |
   | 10+3 | 10+6 . . . |

   b. **Answer together.**

   | 10+5 | 10+1 | 10+7 |
   |---|---|---|
   | 10+2 | 10+6 | 10+3 |
   | 10+8 | 10+4 | 10+9 |

8. Do the Column Addition samples.

9. Assign Lesson 39.

39

Answer these problems.

| | | | | |
|---|---|---|---|---|
| 799 | 898 | 978 | 978 | 799 |
| − 74 | − 36 | − 40 | − 63 | − 82 |
| 725 | 862 | 938 | 915 | 717 |

| | | | | |
|---|---|---|---|---|
| 788 | 999 | 999 | 889 | 779 |
| − 71 | − 85 | − 61 | − 27 | − 54 |
| 717 | 914 | 938 | 862 | 725 |

Count the quarters
and pennies.
Write the amount.

77¢

31¢

55¢

78¢

54¢

161

**Blacklines**

Fact Form II

Reading Problems #3

*After*
*Class*

| 9 | 4 | 10 | 9 | 2 | 5 |
|---|---|---|---|---|---|
| −7 | +6 | −3 | −6 | +7 | +4 |
| 10 | 3 | 4 | 10 | 9 | 9 |
| −5 | +7 | +5 | −2 | −5 | −2 |
| 8 | 9 | 10 | 7 | 10 | 6 |
| +2 | −4 | −6 | +3 | −7 | +4 |
| 10 | 9 | 9 | 2 | 6 | 10 |
| −8 | −8 | −3 | +8 | +3 | −4 |

*Note:* You will use this grid in Lesson 40 too.

1. Call the children to the Addition and Subtraction
   Grid on the board.

   a. **Answer together.**

   b. **Boys, answer the subtraction.**
      **Girls, answer the addition.**

2. Stand near the Number Line. **We have count-**
   **ed by 1's, 5's, 10's and 25's. Can you think**
   **of another way to count?** By 2's.

   a. **Do you remember the key numbers for**
      **counting by 2's?**
      2, 4, 6, 8, 0

   b. **Count by 2's to 100.**

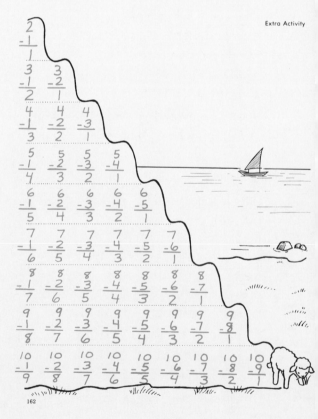

162

Fill in the whole and parts.
Trace and write the facts.
Make the twins take turns.

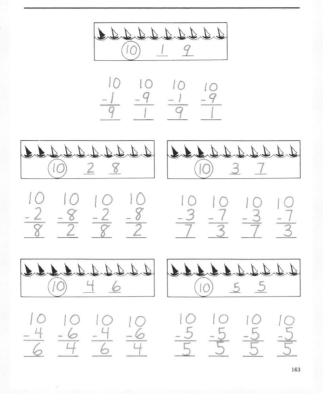

```
 10    10    10    10
 -1    -9    -1    -9
 ─     ─     ─     ─
  9     1     9     1
```

```
 10    10    10    10        10    10    10    10
 -2    -8    -2    -8        -3    -7    -3    -7
 ─     ─     ─     ─         ─     ─     ─     ─
  8     2     8     2         7     3     7     3
```

```
 10    10    10    10        10    10    10    10
 -4    -6    -4    -6        -5    -5    -5    -5
 ─     ─     ─     ─         ─     ─     ─     ─
  6     4     6     4         5     5     5     5
```

163

## Before Class

**Materials**

Subtraction 5–10 flash cards

Form C

**Chalkboard**

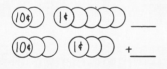

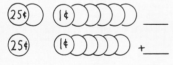

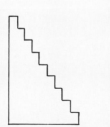

## Class Time

1. Stand near the Addition and Subtraction Grid on the board.
   a. Drill the facts right and left, down and up.
   b. **Answer together!** Are you finished in 30 seconds?

2. Flash Card Drill: Subtraction 5–10 flash cards. Use Form C.
   **Flower Row: Box 1 . . .**

3. **A small brown chipmunk is hungry. He sniffs and looks. Then he spies his favorite fruit—raspberries. His tough little toes do not mind the thorny twigs as he scampers toward the *two* berries. He stuffs one berry in his right cheek and one berry in his left cheek. Then he hurries to a sunny spot on a rock to eat. God prepared the tasty meal for the hungry chipmunk—*two* black raspberries.**
   **Count by 2's to 100.**

Answer these facts.

Speed Drill

| | | | | | | |
|---|---|---|---|---|---|---|
| 10<br>−1<br>9 | 10<br>−8<br>2 | 10<br>−6<br>4 | 10<br>−3<br>7 | 10<br>−7<br>3 | 9<br>−4<br>5 | 8<br>−5<br>3 |
| 10<br>−7<br>3 | 8<br>−3<br>5 | 9<br>−6<br>3 | 9<br>−2<br>7 | 8<br>−4<br>4 | 8<br>−6<br>2 | 10<br>−1<br>9 |
| 10<br>−2<br>8 | 10<br>−4<br>6 | 10<br>−2<br>8 | 9<br>−3<br>6 | 10<br>−9<br>1 | 10<br>−7<br>3 | 9<br>−8<br>1 | 10<br>−7<br>3 |
| 10<br>−4<br>6 | 10<br>−3<br>7 | 9<br>−2<br>7 | 8<br>−2<br>6 | 10<br>−6<br>4 | 10<br>−8<br>2 | 9<br>−7<br>2 | 10<br>−6<br>4 |
| 10<br>−5<br>5 | 8<br>−7<br>1 | 10<br>−6<br>4 | 10<br>−4<br>6 | 10<br>−3<br>7 | 10<br>−9<br>1 | 9<br>−1<br>8 | 10<br>−6<br>4 |
| 9<br>−5<br>4 | 10<br>−9<br>1 | 10<br>−5<br>5 | 10<br>−9<br>1 | 8<br>−1<br>7 | 9<br>−3<br>6 | 9<br>−5<br>4 | 10<br>−2<br>8 |

"Peter . . . walked on the water, to go to Jesus."   Matthew 14:29

164

4. Have the children count and add the Money samples with you.

5. **Say Subtraction 2–10 facts as I fill the steps.**

6. Do the Speed Drill in Lesson 40.

7. Assign Lesson 40.

*Note:* See the *Overview*, page 13, for the directions to make a Clover Patch Poster. Beginning in lesson 41, the Clover Patch Poster replaces the Boat Poster.

40

Answer these problems.

```
 989      999      898      999      899
- 34     - 76     - 57     - 61     - 25
 955      923      841      938      874

 889      988      889      988      899
- 15     - 50     - 48     - 65     - 74
 874      938      841      923      825
```

Read the story.
Write the numbers
 in the beehive.
Write the label words
 on the lines.
Answer the problem.

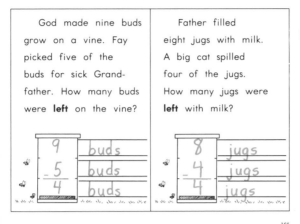

God made nine buds grow on a vine. Fay picked five of the buds for sick Grand-father. How many buds were **left** on the vine?

```
 9   buds
-5   buds
 4   buds
```

Father filled eight jugs with milk. A big cat spilled four of the jugs. How many jugs were **left** with milk?

```
 8   jugs
-4   jugs
 4   jugs
```

165

**Blacklines**

Form C (Class Time)

Fact Form II

Form B

*After Class*

1. Drill individuals at the grid on the chalkboard.

2. Review money.

   a. **Tell how many dimes would make**

   70¢      40¢      80¢      30¢

   b. **Tell how many nickels would make**

   15¢      25¢      40¢      50¢

   c. **Tell how many quarters would make**

   50¢      100¢      25¢      75¢

Speed Drill

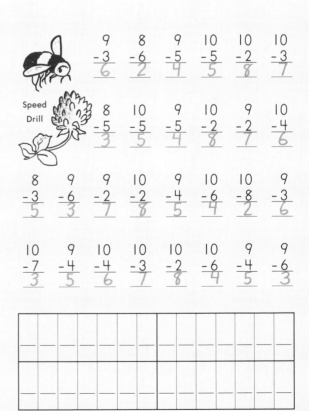

```
  9    8    9   10   10   10
 -3   -6   -5   -5   -2   -3
  6    2    4    5    8    7

  8   10    9   10    9   10
 -5   -5   -5   -2   -2   -4
  3    5    4    8    7    6

  8    9    9   10    9   10   10    9
 -3   -6   -2   -2   -4   -6   -8   -3
  5    3    7    8    5    4    2    6

 10    9   10   10   10   10    9    9
 -7   -4   -4   -3   -2   -6   -4   -6
  3    5    6    7    8    4    5    3
```

# Unit 2    Lessons 41–60

**Explaining Lesson 41:** the *whole* and *parts* at the clover patch.

1. Stand near the clover patch.

    (11)  9  2

**See it.**

a. **How many pink clovers are in the patch?** 10 ⟨ You are recalling your base number.

   **We think—10 pink.** ⟨ You are standing on your base number.

   **1 more makes __ altogether.** 11 ⟨ You are determining the *whole* by looking beyond your base number.

   **We think—10 pink.** ⟨ You are standing on your base number.

   **1 less makes __ clovers with bees.** 9 ⟨ You are determining a *part* by looking behind your base number.

   At this point, you are not subtracting or adding (11)  9  2.
   You are seeing the *whole* and *parts*.

**Say it.**

b. Circle the clover with your finger.
   **11 clovers in the patch;**
   **11 is the whole number.**
   **What part of the 11 has bees?** 9
   **What part of the 11 has no bees?** 2
   **11 is the whole number.**
   **Its parts are 9 and 2.**
c. **The triplet is (11)  9  2;  (11)  9  2 . . .**
d. Point to the flash cards. **The facts are**
   **11−9, 2; 11−2, 9; 9+2, 11; 2+9, 11 . . .**

**Write it.**

2. **Say the triplet as I fill the clover and bees. (11)  9  2;  (11)  9  2 . . .**

## Understanding the Ten Pink Clovers in the Patch.

A family of ten plans to invite eight guests for Sunday dinner. As Mother plans the meal, she thinks, "Ten in our family. One quart of peas for us. So I will use __ quarts for Sunday dinner." Mother measured with ten and determined the *whole* amount of peas she would need.

Monday comes. Mother decides to make egg sandwiches for lunch. She thinks, "Ten in our family. Four are at school. So I'll fry eggs for __ persons." She measured with ten and determined the *part* that would eat at home.

Mother's base number was ten. She used her base number to determine how much food she should prepare—how much more or less than ten. (A mother in a family of six would use a base number of six.) In a similar way, our system of numbers has a base of ten. We think of twelve as ten and two more (12), and eighteen as ten and eight more (18). This is the reason that ten of the clovers in the patch are pink.

On the Clover Patch Chart, these ten pink clovers show your base number. You find the *whole* number by measuring with the ten pink clovers. You find the *part* with bees by measuring with these ten pink clovers. Ten is your base number. It helps you to determine the *whole* or *part* without counting one by one.

Why not count the pink clovers one by one to find the *whole* number? That will lead to counting one by one to find the *parts*.

If a child is in the habit of counting one by one, do not assume that he will automatically quit counting when he studies the facts. A counting child does not find the sum of 9+2 by adding 2 and getting 11. Rather, he finds it by counting: 10, 11. The counting habit is so deeply ingrained that he does not grasp the concept of adding numbers.

## Using the Clover Patch Poster

1. *Always* begin at the left end to put clovers in the patch.
2. *Always* have the bees on the first pink clovers. *Never* mix the clovers with the bees and the clovers without bees.
3. There will *always* be 10 pink clovers in the patch. Use these 10 pink clovers to measure how many clovers there are in all. Use them to measure how many clovers have bees.
4. When you want to exchange a clover with a bee for a clover without a bee, pull the clover out, flip it over, and slide it back into the same slot.

## Why are subtraction facts first?

The (11) 9 2 facts are taught, drilled, and written in this order:

$$\begin{array}{cccc} 11 & 11 & 9 & 2 \\ -9 & -2 & +2 & +9 \end{array}$$

We begin with 11−9=2 because

- the numbers in the problem are in the same order as the triplet.
- we say the *whole* number first, 11.
- we say the greater *part* next, 9.
- the Clover Patch Poster illustrates the greater *part* and then the lesser *part*.

## Using the Blossom Charts

1. Blossom 11 Chart is first used in Lesson 47.
2. The Teacher's Manual tells you when to add each new bee.
3. The Teacher's Manual tells you when to mount a new Blossom Chart.
4. *Drill, drill, drill the triplets.* Always say the *whole* number first, the greater *part* second, the smaller *part* last: (11) 9 2.
5. Add bee after bee to a Blossom Chart. Add chart after chart to the wall until Blossom Charts 11–18 are all displayed.

## 41

Trace and fill in the whole and parts.

Trace, answer, and write the facts.

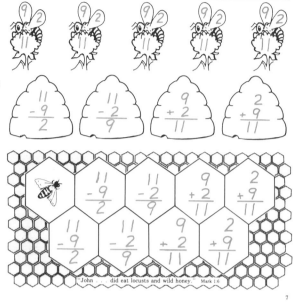

"John . . . . did eat locusts and wild honey."  Mark 1:6

7

---

### Before Class

Exchange the Boat Poster for the Clover Patch Poster.

Make  (11)  9  2  flash cards for each child.

Tack your  (11)  9  2  flash cards above the clover patch in this order:

| 11 | 11 | 9 | 2 |
|---|---|---|---|
| −9 | −2 | +2 | +9 |
| 2 | 9 | 11 | 11 |

### Materials

11 blossoms, 9 with bees.

*1 reclosable sandwich bag for each child*

*Addition and Subtraction 2–10 flash cards*

### Chalkboard

| ones | 520 | 386 | 419 | 634 | 247 | 568 |
|---|---|---|---|---|---|---|
| tens | 375 | 463 | 104 | 591 | 350 | 228 |
| hundreds | 142 | 280 | 447 | 301 | 563 | 294 |

### Class Time

1. Stand near the Number Line.
   a. **What did the chipmunk eat?**
      2 raspberries
   b. **What are our key numbers for counting by 2's?**  2, 4, 6, 8, 0
   c. **Count by 2's to 120.**

2. Stand near the clover patch.
   a. **How many pink clovers are in the patch?** 10
      We think—10 pink.
      **1 more makes __ clovers in all.**  11
      We think—10 pink.
      **1 less makes __ clovers with bees.**  9
   b. Circle the clovers with your finger.
      **11 clovers in the patch;**
      **11 is the whole number.**
      **What part of the 11 has bees?**  9
      **What part of the 11 has no bees?**  2
      **11 is the whole number.**
      **Its parts are 9 and 2.**

Answer these facts.

```
  9    11     2    11    11    11     9    11
+ 2   - 9   + 9   - 2   - 9   - 2   + 2   - 9
 11     2    11     9     2     9    11     2

  2    11     9    11    11     2    11    11
+ 9   - 2   + 2   - 9   - 2   + 9   - 9   - 2
 11     9    11     2     9    11     2     9

 11     9    11     2    11    11     9    11
- 9   + 2   - 2   + 9   - 2   - 9   + 2   - 9
  2    11     9    11     9     2    11     2

 11    11    11    11     9    11     2    11
- 2   - 9   - 2   - 9   + 2   - 9   + 9   - 9
  9     2     9     2    11     2    11     2

 11     2    11    11    11     9    11
- 9   + 9   - 2   - 9   - 2   + 2   - 9
  2    11     9     2     9    11     2

  2    11     9    11    11     9    11
+ 9   - 2   + 2   - 2   - 2   + 2   - 2
 11     9    11     9     9    11     9
```

8

c. **The triplet is (11) 9 2;**
  **(11) 9 2 . . .**

d. Point to the flash cards. **The facts are**
  **11−9, 2;  11−2, 9;  9+2, 11;**
  **2+9, 11 . . .**

3. **Say the triplet as I fill the clover and**
  **bees. (11) 9 2 . . .**

4. Point to the (11) 9 2 flash cards.
  **Say the triplet, then the answer.**
  Card 11−9=2: **(11) 9 2; the answer is 2.**
  Card 11−2=9: **(11) 9 2; the answer is 9.**
  Card 9+2=11: **(11) 9 2; the answer is 11.**
  Card 2+9=11: **(11) 9 2; the answer is 11.**

5. Stand near the Place Value samples.
  a. **Read the numbers together.**
  b. Have the children circle the correct numerals.

6. Assign Lesson 41.

152

41

41

| Count by 2's | 2 | 4 | 6 | 8 |
|---|---|---|---|---|
| | 10 | 12 | 14 | 16 |
| 18 | 20 | 22 | 24 | 26 |
| 28 | 30 | 32 | 34 | 36 |
| 38 | 40 | 42 | 44 | 46 |
| 48 | 50 | 52 | 54 | 56 |

31  78  20

Circle the largest number.

| 200 | (300) | 100 |
|---|---|---|
| 173 | (193) | 183 |

| 217 | 207 | (247) | (179) | 175 | 174 |
|---|---|---|---|---|---|
| (359) | 350 | 355 | 234 | 134 | (334) |
| 357 | 354 | (358) | (352) | 332 | 312 |

9

**Blacklines**

Fact Hives #1

Form A: 400–499

Money Identification #5

## After Class

$$
\begin{array}{cccc}
\downarrow & \downarrow & \downarrow & \downarrow \\
23 & 96 & 24 & 23 \\
+94 & +22 & +95 & +93 \\
\end{array}
$$

$$
\begin{array}{cccc}
\downarrow & \downarrow & \downarrow & \downarrow \\
117 & 118 & 117 & 119 \\
-23 & -24 & -95 & -93 \\
\end{array}
$$

1. Give each child his (11) 9 2 flash cards and a reclosable sandwich bag to store them in.

2. Call the children to the Addition and Subtraction samples.
   a. Trace the arrows. **Ones' place first; ones' place first . . .**
   b. $3+4=$__. Write 7.
      $2+9=$__. Write 11.
   c. $7-3=$__. Write 4.
      Circle $11-2=$__.
      Write 9.

3. Flash Addition and Subtraction 2–10 cards.

Extra Activity

"His eye seeth every precious thing." Job 28:10

10

Trace and fill in the whole and parts.

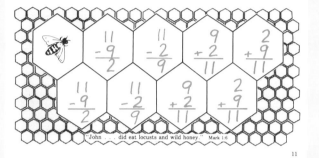

Trace, answer, and write the facts.

"John . . . did eat locusts and wild honey." Mark 1:6

11

---

## Before Class

### Materials

Large coins

(11) 9 2 flash cards

### Chalkboard

| 27 | 93 | 20 | 98 | 117 | 119 | 110 | 118 |
|---|---|---|---|---|---|---|---|
| +92 | +25 | +94 | +21 | −93 | −22 | −90 | −26 |

## Class Time

1. Stand near the clover patch.

   **There is a special name for bees that fly out of the hive to gather nectar. Their name is worker bees.**

   **God's eye sees each worker bee as it sucks nectar from a clover blossom. Yes, "His eye seeth every precious thing."** (Job 28:10)

2. (11) 9 2

   Circle the clovers . . .

   **11 clovers in the patch;**
   **11 is the whole number.**
   **What part of the 11 has bees?** 9
   **What part of the 11 has no bees?** 2
   **11 is the whole number.**
   **Its parts are 9 and 2.**
   a. **The triplet is (11) 9 2;**
      **(11) 9 2 . . .**
   b. Point to the flash cards. **The facts are 11−9, 2; 11−2, 9; 9+2, 11; 2+9, 11 . . .**

3. Ask a child to fill in the bees as everyone says **(11) 9 2;    (11) 9 2 . . .**

42

Answer these problems.

```
  114      115      118      119      117      118
 - 93     - 22     - 93     - 95     - 27     - 25
   21       93       25       24       90       93

  116      112      118      117      117      113
 - 23     - 22     - 94     - 92     - 24     - 92
   93       90       24       25       93       21

  115      119      116      118      115      118
 - 20     - 93     - 21     - 92     - 93     - 96
   95       26       95       26       22       22

   92       25       94       25       26       91
 + 22     + 93     + 25     + 94     + 92     + 23
  114      118      119      119      118      114
```

```
   26       23       94       23       91
 + 93     + 93     + 23     + 94     + 27
  119      116      117      117      118

   23       96       22       24       28
 + 95     + 21     + 95     + 92     + 91
  118      117      117      116      119
```

12

4. Do the Addition and Subtraction samples.

   a. **Be careful to add in ones'
   place and in tens' place.**

   $$\overset{\frown}{27}$$
   $$\oplus 92$$

   b. **Be careful to subtract in
   ones' place and in tens'
   place.**

   $$\overset{\frown}{117}$$
   $$\ominus 93$$

5. Flash the large coins. **Penny, 1¢; quarter,
   25¢** . . .

6. Have individuals count aloud as they do the
   Money samples.

7. Have each child get his 1,000 book. **The chipmunk ate two raspberries. Count by 2's to
   130.**

8. Do the Speed Drill in Lesson 42.

9. Assign Lesson 42.

*Note:* Triplet (11) **9 2** brings many new exercises:
   • 3-digit with 2-digit computation
   • Counting and adding money
   • Missing whole or parts
It will take many days for these exercises to
become routine.

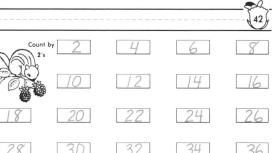

Count by 2's

| 2 | 4 | 6 | 8 |
|---|---|---|---|
| 10 | 12 | 14 | 16 |

| 18 | 20 | 22 | 24 | 26 |
|----|----|----|----|----|
| 28 | 30 | 32 | 34 | 36 |
| 38 | 40 | 42 | 44 | 46 |
| 48 | 50 | 52 | 54 | 56 |

**Blacklines**

Fact Hives #1

Money Identification #5

Circle the numeral
in ones' place,
in tens' place,
in hundreds' place.

ones    503  160  58  483  5  57

tens    599  87  582  90  500  35

hundreds  302  465  59  481  82  314

13

---

*After Class*

| ___ 16 ___ | ___ 70 ___ |
|---|---|
| ___ 28 ___ | ___ 86 ___ |
| ___ 52 ___ | ___ 74 ___ |
| ___ 44 ___ | ___ 38 ___ |

1. Flash Card Drill: (11) 9 2 cards. **Say the triplet; then say the answer.**

2. Fill in the Before and After numbers by 2's.

3. Point to the Number Line.
   **Add with me.**
   | 10+1 | 10+4 | 10+7 |
   |------|------|------|
   | 10+2 | 10+5 | 10+8 |
   | 10+3 | 10+6 | 10+9 |

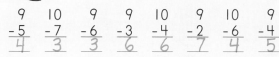

Speed Drill

| 9  | 10 | 10 | 10 | 9  | 10 |
|----|----|----|----|----|----|
| -4 | -6 | -3 | -4 | -3 | -7 |
| 5  | 4  | 7  | 6  | 6  | 3  |

| 9  | 10 | 10 | 10 | 10 | 10 |
|----|----|----|----|----|----|
| -7 | -5 | -2 | -7 | -6 | -4 |
| 2  | 5  | 8  | 3  | 4  | 6  |

| 9  | 10 | 9  | 9  | 10 | 9  | 10 | 9  |
|----|----|----|----|----|----|----|----|
| -5 | -7 | -6 | -3 | -4 | -2 | -6 | -4 |
| 4  | 3  | 3  | 6  | 6  | 7  | 4  | 5  |

| 9  | 10 | 10 | 9  | 10 | 10 | 9  | 10 |
|----|----|----|----|----|----|----|----|
| -6 | -6 | -4 | -5 | -7 | -2 | -4 | -8 |
| 3  | 4  | 6  | 4  | 3  | 8  | 5  | 2  |

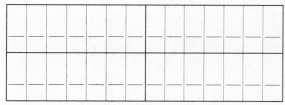

"Whatsoever thy hand findeth to do, do it with thy might." Ecclesiastes 9:10

14

156

Trace and fill in the whole and parts.

Trace, answer, and write the facts.

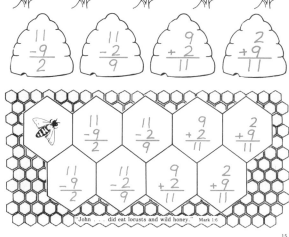

"John . . . did eat locusts and wild honey." Mark 1:6

15

## Before Class

### Materials

(11)  9  2   flash cards

Large clock

*Addition and Subtraction 2-10 flash cards*

### Chalkboard

| | | |
|---|---|---|
| ___ 64 ___ | ___ 88 ___ |
| ___ 36 ___ | ___ 46 ___ |
| ___ 20 ___ | ___ 70 ___ |
| ___ 58 ___ | ___ 98 ___ |

| | |
|---|---|
| 9+2=__ | 11−9=__ |
| __+9=11 | 11−__=9 |
| 2+__=11 | 11−2=__ |
| 9+__=11 | __−9=2 |

## Class Time

1. Have each child bring his 1,000 book to the teaching corner. **Begin at 50. Count to 150 by 2's.**

2. Fill in the Before and After numbers by 2's.

3. Stand near the clover patch.

   > (11)  9  2

   Circle the clover . . .

   **11 clovers in the patch;**

   **11 is the whole number.**

   **What part of the 11 has bees?** 9

   **What part of the 11 has no bees?** 2

   **11 is the whole number.**

   **Its parts are 9 and 2.**

   a. **The triplet is (11)  9  2;**
      **(11)  9  2 . . .**

   b. **Say the facts. 11−9, 2;**
      **11−2, 9;  9+2, 11;  2+9, 11 . . .**

4. Flash (11)  9  2 cards. **Say the triplet; then say the answer.**

Count the first row.
　Write the amount.
Count the second row.
　Write the amount.
Add.

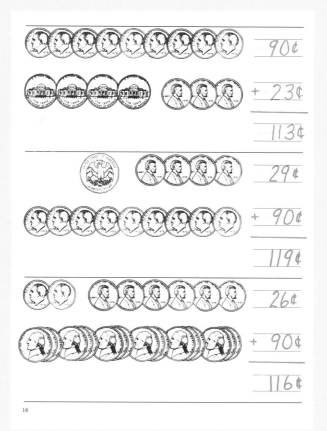

90¢
+ 23¢
113¢

29¢
+ 90¢
119¢

26¢
+ 90¢
116¢

16

5. Have the children fill in the Missing Whole or
　Parts samples.

6. Hold the large clock.
　a. **Can you name the hands?**
　　Minute hand and hour hand.
　b. **Read the time together as I set the
　　hands. 4:00, 9:00, 11:00, 2:00, 6:00, 10:00,
　　12:00, 3:00.**

7. Assign Lesson 43.

43

43

Count by 2's

| 32 | 34 | 36 | 38 |
| 40 | 42 | 44 | 46 |
| 48 | 50 | 52 | 54 | 56 |
| 58 | 60 | 62 | 64 | 66 |
| 68 | 70 | 72 | 74 | 76 |
| 78 | 80 | 82 | 84 | 86 |

85 (31) 76

Circle the smallest number.

| 234 | (134) | 334 |
| (173) | 193 | 183 |
| 247 | (207) | 217 | 179 | 175 | (174) |
| 352 | 332 | (312) | (100) | 300 | 200 |
| 357 | (354) | 358 | 359 | (350) | 355 |

17

**Blacklines**

Fact Hives #1

Missing Whole or Parts #1

## After Class

$$
\begin{array}{cccccccc}
3 & 2 & 1 & 1 & 3 & 4 & 2 & 5 \\
6 & 6 & 1 & 8 & 4 & 5 & 0 & 2 \\
+2 & +2 & +9 & +2 & +3 & +2 & +9 & +3 \\
\end{array}
$$

1. Do the Column Addition samples.

2. Circle Drill: Addition and Subtraction 2–10 flash cards.

3. Chalkboard Drill: **You can read the time. Let's see if you can write the time. Write 5:00, 8:00, 1:00, 7:00, 12:00, 4:00, 10:00.**

Extra Activity

"His eye seeth every precious thing." Job 28:10

$$
\begin{array}{cccc}
11 & 11 & 9 & 2 \\
-9 & -2 & +2 & +9 \\
\hline
2 & 9 & 11 & 11 \\
\end{array}
$$

18

Fill in the whole and parts.

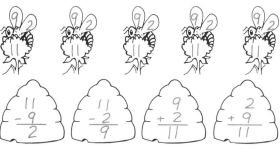

Write the facts.

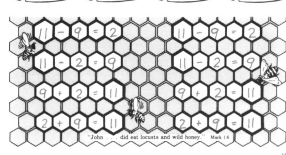

Trace, answer, and write the facts.

"John . . . did eat locusts and wild honey." Mark 1:6

19

## Before Class

### Materials

Mix Addition and Subtraction 8–10 and
  (11) 9 2 flash cards.
Form C
Large clock

### Chalkboard

| hundreds | tens | ones |
| --- | --- | --- |
| | | |
| | | |
| | | |
| | | |
| | | |
| | | |
| | | |
| | | |
| | | |
| | | |

## Class Time

1. Stand near the clover patch.
    a. **Say the triplet. (11) 9 2 . . .**
    b. **Can we say the four facts in order?**
       $11-9=2$;   $11-2=9$;   $9+2=11$;
       $2+9=11$

2. Story Problems: **Close your eyes.**
    a. **9 red hens and 2 black hens scratched in the barnyard. How many is that altogether? Who can give us the whole problem?**
       9 hens+2 hens=11 hens.
    b. **11 lamps are in the store window. The storekeeper lit 2 of them. How many lamps were not lit? Who . . . ?**
       11 lamps−2 lamps=9 lamps.

3. Double Drill: Flash Addition and Subtraction 8–10 and (11) 9 2 cards.

4. Flash Card Drill: Addition and Subtraction 8–10 and (11) 9 2 cards. Use Form C. **Flower Row: Box 1 . . .**

Fill in the missing whole or parts.

| | | |
|---|---|---|
| 9 + _2_ = 11 | 11 - _9_ = 2 | _11_ - 2 = 9 |
| 2 + _9_ = 11 | _2_ + 9 = 11 | 2 + _9_ = 11 |
| 11 - _9_ = 2 | _11_ - 9 = 2 | 11 - 9 = _2_ |
| 11 - _2_ = 9 | 11 - 2 = _9_ | _11_ - 2 = 9 |
| _2_ + 9 = 11 | 2 + _9_ = 11 | 2 + _9_ = 11 |
| _11_ - 9 = 2 | 9 + 2 = _11_ | _11_ - 9 = 2 |

Speed Drill

Answer these problems.

$$
\begin{array}{cccccccc}
6 & 5 & 6 & 4 & 8 & 5 & 7 & 1 \\
3 & 4 & 0 & 5 & 1 & 2 & 2 & 1 \\
+2 & +2 & +4 & +2 & +2 & +3 & +2 & +9 \\
\hline
11 & 11 & 10 & 11 & 11 & 10 & 11 & 11
\end{array}
$$

$$
\begin{array}{cccccccc}
3 & 2 & 2 & 4 & 5 & 1 & 1 & 2 \\
2 & 2 & 7 & 2 & 3 & 8 & 6 & 1 \\
+5 & +6 & +2 & +4 & +2 & +2 & +3 & +7 \\
\hline
10 & 10 & 11 & 10 & 10 & 11 & 10 & 10
\end{array}
$$

20

5. **Begin at 32. Count by 2's to 130.**

6. Review place value.
   Have the children fill the grid as you say **8, 205, 63, 140, 301, 256, 38, 15, 414, 192, 520, 79.**

7. Hold the large clock.
   a. **Name the hands.**
   b. Set the clock at 5:00. Write 5:00. **The hour is 5. Read the hour as I move the hands around the clock. 6:00, 7:00, 8:00 . . .**
   Continue around the clock to 5:00.

8. Do the Speed Drill in Lesson 44.

9. Assign Lesson 44.

**44**

Write the numbers that come before and after when you count by 2's.

| Count by 2's | | | | |
|---|---|---|---|---|
| 32 | _34_ | _22_ | 24 | _26_ |
| 58 | _60_ | _74_ | 76 | _78_ |
| _80_ | 82 | _84_ | _82_ | 84 | _86_ |
| _18_ | 20 | _22_ | _38_ | 40 | _42_ |
| _14_ | 16 | _18_ | _66_ | 68 | _70_ |

**Blacklines**

Form C (Class Time)

Skip Counting (2's) #4

Fact Form I

Write the time.

11:00  5:00  9:00  2:00  6:00

4:00  10:00  3:00  7:00  12:00

21

*After Class*

1. Have each child bring his 1,000 book to the teaching corner.
   a. **Count by 2's to 150.**
   b. **Count on to 300 by 5's.**

2. **If Sarah has 30¢, how many nickels does she have?** Continue with

   | 10¢ | 25¢ | 15¢ |
   |---|---|---|
   | 40¢ | 50¢ | 35¢ |

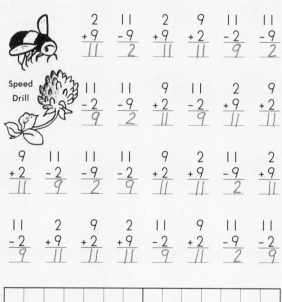

Speed Drill

| | | | | | |
|---|---|---|---|---|---|
| 2<br>+9<br>11 | 11<br>-9<br>2 | 2<br>+9<br>11 | 9<br>+2<br>11 | 11<br>-2<br>9 | 11<br>-9<br>2 |
| 11<br>-2<br>9 | 11<br>-9<br>2 | 9<br>+2<br>11 | 11<br>-2<br>9 | 2<br>+9<br>11 | 9<br>+2<br>11 |
| 9<br>+2<br>11 | 11<br>-2<br>9 | 11<br>-9<br>2 | 11<br>-2<br>9 | 9<br>+2<br>11 | 2<br>+9<br>11 | 11<br>-9<br>2 | 2<br>+9<br>11 |
| 11<br>-2<br>9 | 2<br>+9<br>11 | 9<br>+2<br>11 | 2<br>+9<br>11 | 11<br>-2<br>9 | 9<br>+2<br>11 | 11<br>-9<br>2 | 11<br>-2<br>9 |

"Whatsoever thy hand findeth to do, do it with thy might." Ecclesiastes 9:10

⟨ **45** ⟩

Fill in the whole and parts.

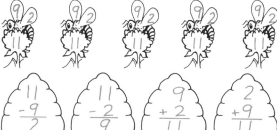

Write the facts.

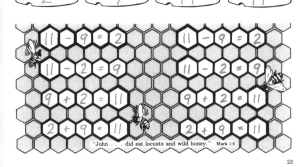

Trace, answer, and write the facts.

"John . . . did eat locusts and wild honey." Mark 1:6

23

---

## Before Class

### Materials

Large clock

### Chalkboard

| | |
|---|---|
| 11−2=__ | 2+9=__ |
| 11−9=__ | 9+2=__ |
| __−2=9 | __+9=11 |
| 11−__=2 | 9+__=11 |

11 mice played in the clover patch. Then 2 of them ran away. How many mice are left?

Nine cars were parked at church. Then two more came. How many cars is that in all?

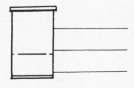

## Class Time

1. Stand near the clover patch.

   (11) 9 2

   Circle the clover . . .
   **11 clovers in the patch;**
   **11 is the whole number.**
   **What part of the 11 has bees?** 9
   **What part of the 11 has no bees?** 2
   **11 is the whole number.**
   **Its parts are 9 and 2.**
   a. **The triplet is (11) 9 2;**
      **(11) 9 2 . . .**
   b. **The facts are 11−9, 2; 11−2, 9;**
      **9+2, 11; 2+9, 11 . . .**

2. Do the Missing Whole or Parts samples.

3. **Read the first story problem to me.**
   a. Circle 11. Underline 2.
      **What is our triplet?** (11) 9 2
      **We must subtract to find the missing part.**

Read the story.
Write the numbers
  in the beehive.
Write the label words
  on the lines.
Answer the problem.

Extra
Activity

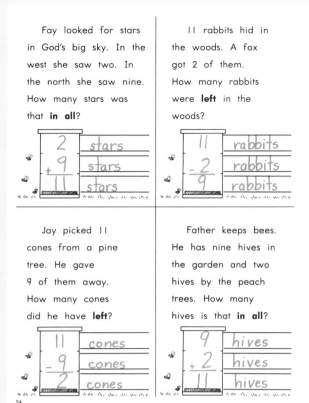

Fay looked for stars in God's big sky. In the west she saw two. In the north she saw nine. How many stars was that **in all**?

| 2 | stars |
| + 9 | stars |
| 11 | stars |

11 rabbits hid in the woods. A fox got 2 of them. How many rabbits were **left** in the woods?

| 11 | rabbits |
| - 2 | rabbits |
| 9 | rabbits |

Jay picked 11 cones from a pine tree. He gave 9 of them away. How many cones did he have **left**?

| 11 | cones |
| - 9 | cones |
| 2 | cones |

Father keeps bees. He has nine hives in the garden and two hives by the peach trees. How many hives is that **in all**?

| 9 | hives |
| + 2 | hives |
| 11 | hives |

24

  b. **What shall I write in the beehive?**
      11 mice−2 mice=9 mice.

4. **Read the second story problem to me.**
  a. Underline *nine* and *two*.
    **What is our triplet?** (11) 9 2
    **We must add to find the whole number.**
  b. **What shall I write in the beehive?**
      9 cars+2 cars=11 cars.

5. Hold the large clock. Station a child at the chalk-board. **I will set the clock.** (Student) **will write the time. You read the time. 4:00, 9:00, 1:00, 5:00, 10:00, 12:00, 6:00.**

6. Assign Lesson 45.

**45**

Write the numbers that come before and after when you count by 2's

| Count by 2's | | | | | |
|---|---|---|---|---|---|
| 26 | *28* | *36* | 38 | *40* |
| 74 | *76* | *48* | 50 | *52* |
| *84* | 86 | *88* | *90* | 92 | *94* |
| *20* | 22 | *24* | *78* | 80 | *82* |
| *62* | 64 | *66* | *86* | 88 | *90* |

**Blacklines**

Missing Whole or Parts #1

Skip Counting (2's) #4

Write the time.

1:00  5:00  8:00  2:00  6:00

12:00  10:00  4:00  7:00  3:00

25

---

## After Class

|  |  |  |
|---|---|---|
| 351 | 531 | 153 |
| 244 | 442 | 424 |
| 301 | 310 | 103 |

|  |  |  |
|---|---|---|
| 515 | 155 | 551 |
| 423 | 324 | 243 |
| 121 | 112 | 211 |
| 140 | 401 | 104 |

1. **Count by 10's to 400.**

2. **If Charles saved 8 dimes, he has __¢.**
   Continue with

   **4 dimes**  **7 dimes**

   **10 dimes**  **6 dimes**

   **3 dimes and 2 pennies**

   **5 dimes and 5 pennies**

3. Circle the smallest number.

Extra Activity

"His eye seeth every precious thing."
Job 28:10

$$\begin{array}{r}11\\-9\\\hline2\end{array}\qquad\begin{array}{r}11\\-2\\\hline9\end{array}\qquad\begin{array}{r}9\\+2\\\hline11\end{array}\qquad\begin{array}{r}2\\+9\\\hline11\end{array}$$

26

Trace and fill in the whole and parts.

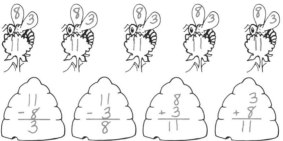

(11)  8  3

Trace, answer, and write the facts.

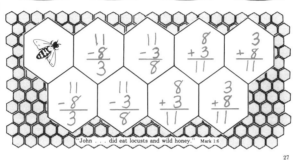

"John . . . did eat locusts and wild honey."  Mark 1:6

27

## Before Class

Make  (11)  8  3  flash cards for each child.

Tack your  (11)  8  3  flash cards above the clover patch in this order:

| 11<br>−8<br>3 | 11<br>−3<br>8 | 8<br>+3<br>11 | 3<br>+8<br>11 |
|---|---|---|---|

**Materials**

11 clovers, 8 with bees

Large coins

*Large clock*

**Chalkboard**

| | |
|---|---|
| 8 nickels =__ | 9 dimes =__ |
| 2 quarters =__ | 3 quarters =__ |
| 5 dimes =__ | 7 nickels =__ |
| 4 nickels + 3 pennies =__ | |
| 2 dimes + 2 pennies =__ | |

## Class Time

1. Call the children to the clover patch.

   (11)  8  3

   a. **How many pink clovers are in the patch?** 10

   **We think—10 pink.**

   **1 more makes __ clovers in all.** 11

   **We think—10 pink.**

   **2 less makes __ clovers with bees.** 8

   b. **Circle the clovers with your finger.**

   **11 clovers in the patch;**

   **11 is the whole number.**

   **What part of the 11 has bees?** 8

   **What part of the 11 has no bees?** 3

   **11 is the whole number.**

   **Its parts are 8 and 3.**

   c. **The triplet is  (11)  8  3;**

   **(11)  8  3 . . .**

   d. **Point to the flash cards. The facts are**

   **11−8, 3;  11−3, 8;  8+3, 11;**

   **3+8, 11 . . .**

46

Answer these facts.

Speed Drill

| | | | | | | | |
|---|---|---|---|---|---|---|---|
| 3<br>+8<br>11 | 11<br>−8<br>3 | 8<br>+3<br>11 | 11<br>−3<br>8 | 11<br>−8<br>3 | 11<br>−3<br>8 | 8<br>+3<br>11 | 11<br>−8<br>3 |
| 3<br>+8<br>11 | 11<br>−3<br>8 | 8<br>+3<br>11 | 11<br>−8<br>3 | 11<br>−3<br>8 | 3<br>+8<br>11 | 11<br>−8<br>3 | 11<br>−3<br>8 |
| 11<br>−8<br>3 | 8<br>+3<br>11 | 11<br>−3<br>8 | 3<br>+8<br>11 | 11<br>−3<br>8 | 11<br>−8<br>3 | 8<br>+3<br>11 | 11<br>−3<br>8 |
| 11<br>−3<br>8 | 11<br>−8<br>3 | 11<br>−3<br>8 | 11<br>−8<br>3 | 8<br>+3<br>11 | 11<br>−8<br>3 | 3<br>+8<br>11 | 11<br>−8<br>3 |
| 11<br>−8<br>3 | 3<br>+8<br>11 | 11<br>−3<br>8 | 11<br>−8<br>3 | 11<br>−3<br>8 | 8<br>+3<br>11 | 11<br>−8<br>3 | |
| 3<br>+8<br>11 | 11<br>−8<br>3 | 8<br>+3<br>11 | 11<br>−8<br>3 | 11<br>−3<br>8 | 8<br>+3<br>11 | 11<br>−3<br>8 | |

28

2. Point to the first flash card again. **Say the triplet; then say the answer. (11) 8 3; the answer is 3.**

3. Fill in the bees and clovers as everyone repeats: **(11) 8 3 . . .**

4. **Begin at 82. Count by 2's to 150.**

5. Flash the large coins. **Answer together.**
   a. **Nickel, quarter, dime . . .**
   b. **5¢, 25¢, 10¢, 1¢ . . .**

6. Do the Money samples.

7. Do the Speed Drill in Lesson 46.

8. Assign Lesson 46.

*Note:* Make Blossom 11 Chart. You will begin to use it in Lesson 47. See the *Overview*, page 14, for directions.

46

Count by 2's

| 82 | 84 | 86 | 88 |
| 90 | 92 | 94 | 96 |
| 98 | 100 | 102 | 104 | 106 |
| 108 | 110 | 112 | 114 | 116 |
| 118 | 120 | 122 | 124 | 126 |
| 128 | 130 | 132 | 134 | 136 |

**Blacklines**

Fact Hives #2

Fact Form III

Write the time.

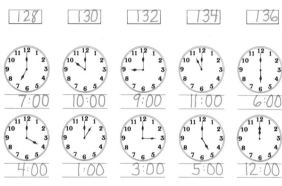

7:00   10:00   9:00   11:00   6:00

4:00   1:00   3:00   5:00   12:00

29

## After Class

1. Give each child his (11) 8 3 flash cards.

2. Oral Drill  Have the children line up in two rows. **Whoever says the correct answer first may go to the back of his line.**

   8+2    10−3    11−2    9+2    9−6
   3+6    10−5    2+9     3+7    10−7
   6+4    9−4     11−9    4+5    9−5

3. Hold the large clock. Ask individuals to set the clock at **3:00, 7:00, 10:00, 4:00, 9:00** . . .

Speed Drill

| 10 | 10 | 10 | 10 | 11 | 10 |
| −7 | −3 | −8 | −5 | −2 | −6 |
| 3 | 7 | 2 | 5 | 9 | 4 |

| 10 | 10 | 11 | 10 | 10 | 11 |
| −4 | −7 | −9 | −2 | −3 | −2 |
| 6 | 3 | 2 | 8 | 7 | 9 |

| 11 | 10 | 10 | 11 | 10 | 11 | 10 | 10 |
| −9 | −8 | −6 | −2 | −5 | −9 | −3 | −7 |
| 2 | 2 | 4 | 9 | 5 | 2 | 7 | 3 |

| 10 | 11 | 11 | 10 | 10 | 11 | 10 | 10 |
| −8 | −9 | −2 | −3 | −2 | −9 | −7 | −4 |
| 2 | 2 | 9 | 7 | 8 | 2 | 3 | 6 |

30

"Whatsoever thy hand findeth to do, do it with thy might." Ecclesiastes 9:10

**47**

Fill in the whole and parts.

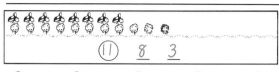

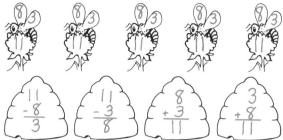

Trace, answer, and write the facts.

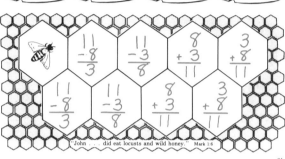

---

### Before Class

Paste bees (11) 9 2 and (11) 8 3 on
the Blossom Chart.
Mount it on the wall.

#### Materials

Addition and Subtraction 7–10 flash cards

*(11) 9 2 and (11) 8 3 flash cards*

*Large clock*

#### Chalkboard

| 37 | 83 | 85 | 32 | 117 | 119 | 118 | 119 |
|----|----|----|----|-----|-----|-----|-----|
| +82 | +32 | +34 | +86 | −83 | −36 | −35 | −87 |

| | | 102 | 104 | | |
|---|---|---|---|---|---|
| | 25 | | | 40 | |
| | | 60 | | 80 | |
| | 42 | | | | 50 |
| 90 | | 100 | | | |

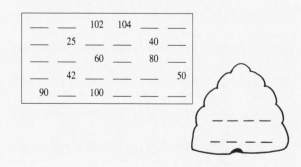

### Class Time

1. Stand near the clover patch.

   (11)  8  3

   Circle the clovers with your finger.

   **11 clovers in the patch;**

   **11 is the whole number.**

   **What part of the 11 has bees?** 8

   **What part of the 11 has no bees?** 3

   **11 is the whole number.**

   **Its parts are 8 and 3.**

   a. **The triplet is (11) 8 3;**
      **(11) 8 3 . . .**

   b. Point to the flash cards. **11−8, 3;**
      **11−3, 8; 8+3, 11; 3+8, 11 . . .**

2. Point to Blossom 11 Chart. **Say the triplets.**

   **(11) 9 2**

   **(11) 9 2 . . .**

   **(11) 8 3**

   **(11) 8 3 . . .**

Answer these problems.

Extra Activity

| 119 | 117 | 118 | 119 | 117 | 118 |
|---|---|---|---|---|---|
| -84 | -36 | -83 | -85 | -37 | -35 |
| 35 | 81 | 35 | 34 | 80 | 83 |

| 116 | 116 | 118 | 117 | 116 | 119 |
|---|---|---|---|---|---|
| -33 | -36 | -84 | -82 | -35 | -84 |
| 83 | 80 | 34 | 35 | 81 | 35 |

| 118 | 119 | 119 | 118 | 117 | 118 |
|---|---|---|---|---|---|
| -30 | -83 | -31 | -82 | -85 | -86 |
| 88 | 36 | 88 | 36 | 32 | 32 |

| 82 | 35 | 84 | 35 | 36 | 81 |
|---|---|---|---|---|---|
| +33 | +83 | +35 | +84 | +82 | +34 |
| 115 | 118 | 119 | 119 | 118 | 115 |

| | 33 | 32 | 84 | 33 | 82 |
|---|---|---|---|---|---|
| | +86 | +84 | +33 | +84 | +36 |
| | 119 | 116 | 117 | 117 | 118 |

| | 33 | 86 | 32 | 34 | 32 |
|---|---|---|---|---|---|
| | +85 | +31 | +85 | +82 | +87 |
| | 118 | 117 | 117 | 116 | 119 |

32

3. **Say the (11) 9 2 and (11) 8 3 facts as I fill the beehive.**

4. Flash Addition and Subtraction 7–10 flash cards.

5. Do the Addition and Subtraction samples.
   a. **Be careful to add in ones' place and in tens' place.**

   $\begin{array}{r} 37 \\ \oplus 82 \end{array}$

   b. **Be careful to subtract in ones' place and in tens' place.**

   $\begin{array}{r} 117 \\ \ominus 83 \end{array}$

6. Have each child get his 1,000 book.
   a. **Count by 10's to 200.**
   b. **Count on to 300 by 5's.**
   c. **Count on to 350 by 2's.**

7. Fill in the Missing Number samples.
   **Decide if you should count by 2's, 5's, or 10's.**

8. Assign Lesson 47.

170

**47**

Circle the numeral
  in ones' place,
  in tens' place,
  in hundreds' place.

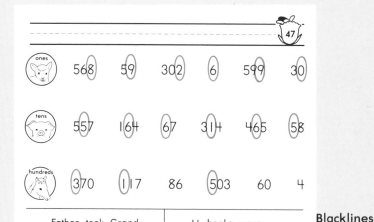

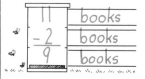47

| ones | 568 | 59 | 302 | 6 | 599 | 30 |
| tens | 557 | 164 | 67 | 314 | 465 | 58 |
| hundreds | 370 | 117 | 86 | 503 | 60 | 4 |

Read the story.
Write the numbers
  in the beehive.
Write the label words
  on the lines.
Answer the problem.

Father took Grand-
mother to church. He
drove 8 miles to her
house and then 3 miles
to church. How many
miles was that in all?

```
  8    miles
+ 3    miles
 11    miles
```

11 books were
on the shelf. Lee took
two of them to his
desk. How many books
were left on the shelf?

```
 11    books
- 2    books
  9    books
```

33

**Blacklines**

Fact Hives #2

Skip Counting (2's) #4

### After Class

1. Flash (11) 9 2 and (11) 8 3 cards.
   **Answer together.**

2. Point to the Number Line.

   | | | |
   |---|---|---|
   | 10+4 | 10+5 | 10+8 |
   | 10+2 | 10+1 | 10+3 |
   | 10+7 | 10+6 | 10+9 |

3. Set the large clock at 9:00.

   a. Quietly move the hands around to 10:00. **It
      is one hour from 9:00 to 10:00.**

   b. **In one hour it will be __.**  11:00
      **In two hours it will be __.**  12:00
      **One hour ago it was __.**  9:00

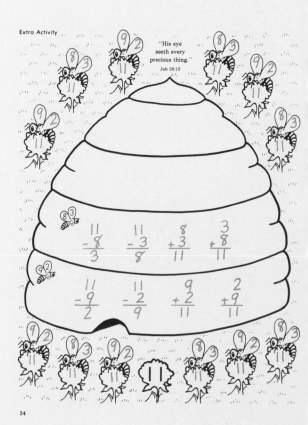

Extra Activity

"His eye
seeth every
precious thing."
Job 28:10

34

**Fill in the whole and parts.**

**Trace, answer, and write the facts.**

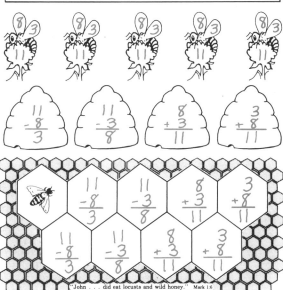

"John . . . did eat locusts and wild honey." Mark 1:6

35

---

### Before Class

**Materials**

Large clock

(11) 9 2; (11) 8 3  flash cards

*Addition and Subtraction 7–10 flash cards*

**Chalkboard**

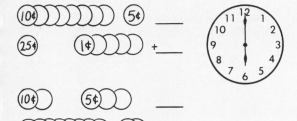

When you say **60 minutes = 1 hour** in 1e, make the clock on the board look like the one below. Keep it on the board for several days.

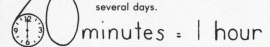

minutes = 1 hour

### Class Time

1. Set the large clock at 6:00.

   a. **The small hand is the __.**  Hour hand.
      **The hour hand tells us the hour.**

   b. **The large hand is the __.** Minute hand.
      **The minute hand tells us the minutes.**

   c. Slowly move the minute hand from
      • 12 to 1—**1, 2, 3, 4, 5 minutes**
      • 1 to 2—**1, 2, 3, 4, 5 minutes**
      • 2 to 3—**1, 2, 3, 4, 5 minutes**
      Continue around the clock.

   d. **There are 5 minutes between each number. Count by 5's to find out how many minutes are in one hour. 5, 10, 15 . . . 60.**

   e. Write 60 minutes = 1 hour.
      **60 minutes = 1 hour or**
      **60 minutes make 1 hour.**

48

Count the first row.
  Write the amount.
Count the second row.
  Write the amount.
Add.

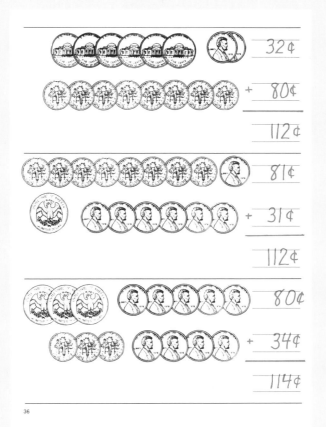

| | 32¢ |
| | + 80¢ |
| | 112¢ |
| | 81¢ |
| | + 31¢ |
| | 112¢ |
| | 80¢ |
| | + 34¢ |
| | 114¢ |

**Speed Drill**

36

2. Stand near the clover patch.

   (11)  8  3

   **11 clovers in the patch;**
   **11 is the whole number.**
   **What part of the 11 has bees?** 8
   **What part of the 11 has no bees?** 3
   **11 is the whole number.**
   **Its parts are 8 and 3.**
   a. **The triplet is (11) 8 3;**
      **(11) 8 3 . . .**
   b. **The facts are 11−8, 3;  11−3, 8;**
      **8+3, 11;  3+8, 11 . . .**

3. Point to the Blossom 11 Chart.
   **Say both triplets.**
       **(11) 9  2**
       **(11) 8  3**
       **(11) 9  2 . . .**

4. Flash (11) 9 2 and (11) 8 3 cards.
   **Answer together.**

5. Have individuals count aloud as they do the
   Money samples.

6. Do the Speed Drill in Lesson 48.

7. Assign Lesson 48.

48

Answer the facts.

| 3<br>+ 8<br>11 | 11<br>- 3<br>8 | 11<br>- 9<br>2 | 11<br>- 8<br>3 | 11<br>- 3<br>8 | 2<br>+ 9<br>11 | 11<br>- 8<br>3 | 11<br>- 2<br>9 |
|---|---|---|---|---|---|---|---|
| 11<br>- 8<br>3 | 11<br>- 9<br>2 | 11<br>- 3<br>8 | 3<br>+ 8<br>11 | 11<br>- 2<br>9 | 11<br>- 8<br>3 | 9<br>+ 2<br>11 | 11<br>- 3<br>8 |
| 11<br>- 3<br>8 | 2<br>+ 9<br>11 | 11<br>- 3<br>8 | 9<br>+ 2<br>11 | 11<br>- 2<br>9 | 11<br>- 8<br>3 | 11<br>- 2<br>9 | 11<br>- 8<br>3 |

Write the time.

12:00   5:00   9:00   2:00   6:00

11:00   10:00   3:00   7:00   4:00

37

**Blacklines**

Fact Hives #2

Missing Whole or Parts #2

Money Identification #6

## After Class

1. Circle Drill: Addition and Subtraction 7–10 flash cards.

2. Stand near the Number Line.
   **Count by 10's, then by 5's.**
   10, 20, 30, 40, 45, 50, 55
   10, 15, 20, 25, 30, 35, 40
   10, 20, 30, 40, 50, 60, 65, 70, 75

3. Chalkboard Drill: **When I stop counting, write the number that would come next.**
   20, 30, 40, ___        132, 134, 136, ___
   75, 80, 85, ___        200, 210, 220, ___
   94, 96, 98, ___        115, 120, 125, ___

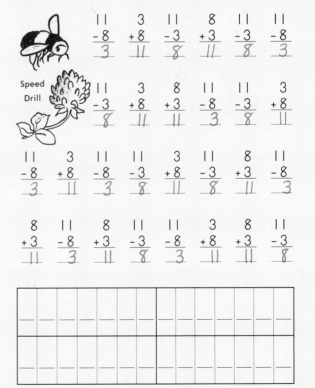

Speed Drill

| 11<br>- 8<br>3 | 3<br>+ 8<br>11 | 11<br>- 3<br>8 | 8<br>+ 3<br>11 | 11<br>- 3<br>8 | 11<br>- 8<br>3 |
|---|---|---|---|---|---|
| 11<br>- 3<br>8 | 3<br>+ 8<br>11 | 8<br>+ 3<br>11 | 11<br>- 8<br>3 | 11<br>- 3<br>8 | 3<br>+ 8<br>11 |
| 11<br>- 8<br>3 | 3<br>+ 8<br>11 | 11<br>- 8<br>3 | 11<br>- 3<br>8 | 3<br>+ 8<br>11 | 11<br>- 3<br>8 | 8<br>+ 3<br>11 | 11<br>- 8<br>3 |
| 8<br>+ 3<br>11 | 11<br>- 8<br>3 | 8<br>+ 3<br>11 | 11<br>- 3<br>8 | 11<br>- 8<br>3 | 3<br>+ 8<br>11 | 8<br>+ 3<br>11 | 11<br>- 3<br>8 |

"Whatsoever thy hand findeth to do, do it with thy might." Ecclesiastes 9:10

**49**

Fill in the whole and parts.

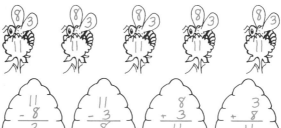

(11)  8  3

Write the facts.

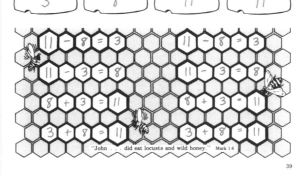

|  11  |  11  |  8  |  3  |
| - 8 | - 3 | + 3 | + 8 |
|  3  |  8  | 11  | 11  |

Trace, answer, and write the facts.

11 − 8 = 3   11 − 8 = 3
11 − 3 = 8   11 − 3 = 8
8 + 3 = 11   8 + 3 = 11
3 + 8 = 11   3 + 8 = 11

"John . . . did eat locusts and wild honey."  Mark 1:6

39

## Before Class

**Materials**

*(11) 9 2 and (11) 8 3 flash cards*

Chalkboard

| 8+__=11 | __+9=11 |
| 2+__=11 | __−3=8 |
| 11−8=__ | 11−__=9 |
| __+3=11 | 8+__=11 |

___ 108 ___
___ 120 ___
___ 134 ___
___ 116 ___
___ 92 ___

## Class Time

1. Stand near the clover patch.

(11)  9  2

**11 clovers in the patch;**
**11 is the whole number.**
**What part of the 11 has bees?** 9
**What part of the 11 has no bees?** 2
**11 is the whole number.**
**Its parts are 9 and 2.**
a. **The triplet is (11) 9 2;**
   **(11) 9 2 . . .**
b. Ask a child to write the facts in the bottom row of the beehive as everyone says **11−9=2; 11−2=9; 9+2=11; 2+9=11.**

2. (11)  8  3

**11 clovers in the patch;**
**11 is the whole number.**
**What part of the 11 has bees?** 8
**What part of the 11 has no bees?** 3
**11 is the whole number.**
**Its parts are 8 and 3.**

Fill in the missing whole or
  parts.

| | | |
|---|---|---|
| 11 − 8 = _3_ | 11 − _3_ = 8 | _8_ + 3 = 11 |
| 11 − 3 = _8_ | _8_ + 3 = 11 | _3_ + 8 = 11 |
| 3 + _8_ = 11 | 3 + 8 = _11_ | 11 − _8_ = 3 |
| _11_ − 8 = 3 | 11 − _3_ = 8 | _11_ − 3 = 8 |
| 8 + _3_ = 11 | _8_ + 3 = 11 | 3 + 8 = _11_ |
| 11 − _8_ = 3 | 3 + 8 = _11_ | 11 − _8_ = 3 |

Answer these problems.

```
  2    3    1    4    5    1    1    4
  2    5    2    2    3    7    6    4
+ 6  + 3  + 8  + 4  + 2  + 3  + 3  + 3
 10   11   11   10   10   11   10   11

  7    2    5    2    4    3    3    6
  1    1    2    6    5    2    0    0
+ 3  + 8  + 3  + 3  + 1  + 5  + 8  + 4
 11   11   10   11   10   10   11   10
```
40

a. **The triplet is (11) 8 3;**
   **(11) 8 3 . . .**
b. Ask a child to write the facts in the beehive
   as everyone says **11−8=3; 11−3=8;**
   **8+3=11; 3+8=11.**

3. Do the Missing Whole or Parts samples.

4. Point to the real clock in your classroom.
   a. **The hour hand is near the __.**
      **The minute hand is near the __.**
   b. **How many minutes are between each**
      **number? 5**
   c. **Begin at 12. Count the minutes. 5, 10,**
      **15 . . . 60.**
   d. **60 minutes=1 hour. . . .**

5. **Count by 2's from 50–150.**

6. Fill in the Before and After numbers by 2's.

7. Assign Lesson 49.

176

Write the numbers that come before and after when you count by 2's.

| Count by 2's | | | | | |
|---|---|---|---|---|---|
| 52 | *54* | | *44* | 46 | *48* |
| 94 | *96* | | *68* | 70 | *72* |
| *26* | 28 | *30* | *42* | 44 | *46* |
| *70* | 72 | *74* | *16* | 18 | *20* |
| *34* | 36 | *38* | *88* | 90 | *92* |

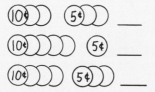

Circle the smallest number.

| | | | (172) | 175 | 174 |
|---|---|---|---|---|---|
| | | | (302) | 332 | 312 |
| (354) | 357 | 358 | 334 | (134) | 234 |
| (207) | 217 | 247 | (173) | 193 | 183 |
| (352) | 353 | 355 | 203 | 300 | (130) |

41

**Blacklines**

Fact Hives #3

2-Place Computation #4

Missing Whole or Parts #2

*After Class*

(10¢)(  )(  )  (5¢)(  )(  )  ___

(10¢)(  )(  )(  )  (5¢)(  )  ___

(10¢)(  )(  )  (5¢)(  )(  )  ___

1. Drill individuals with (11) 9 2 and (11) 8 3 flash cards.

2. Have individuals count aloud as they do the Money samples.

3. Chalkboard Drill: **Write the number you hear.**
   • **King Darius had 120 princes.** (Daniel 6:1)
   • **Abraham had 318 servants.** (Genesis 14:14)
   • **The disciples caught 153 great fishes in a net.** (John 21:11)
   • **Joseph gave his brother Benjamin 300 pieces of silver.** (Genesis 45:22)
   • **King Solomon had 550 rulers.** (1 Kings 9:23)

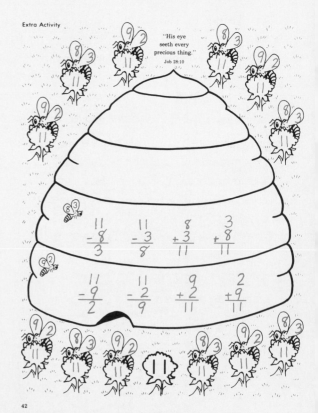

42

Fill in the whole and parts.

(11) 8 3

Write the facts.

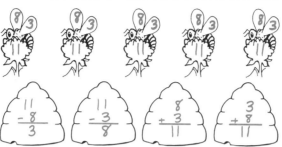

$$\begin{array}{r} 11 \\ -\ 8 \\ \hline 3 \end{array} \qquad \begin{array}{r} 11 \\ -\ 3 \\ \hline 8 \end{array} \qquad \begin{array}{r} 8 \\ +\ 3 \\ \hline 11 \end{array} \qquad \begin{array}{r} 3 \\ +\ 8 \\ \hline 11 \end{array}$$

Trace, answer, and write the facts.

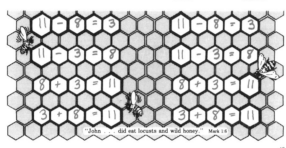

11 − 8 = 3    11 − 8 = 3
11 − 3 = 8    11 − 3 = 8
8 + 3 = 11    8 + 3 = 11
3 + 8 = 11    3 + 8 = 11

"John . . . did eat locusts and wild honey." Mark 1:6

43

---

## Before Class

**Materials**

(11) 9 2 and (11) 8 3 flash cards

**Chalkboard**

(10¢) ⊙⊙ (5¢)⊙⊙⊙ ___

(10¢)⊙ (5¢)⊙⊙ +___

(10¢)⊙⊙⊙ (5¢) ___

(10¢)⊙⊙ (5¢)⊙⊙⊙ +___

## Class Time

1. Stand near the clover patch.

   **The worker bees dart from clover to clover, sipping nectar. They store the nectar in a special honey stomach that God made in them. Then straight back to the beehive they go—all in a beeline.**

2. ☐ (11) 9 2 ☐

   **11 is the whole number.
   Its parts are 9 and 2.**
   a. **The triplet is (11) 9 2;
      (11) 9 2 . . .**
   b. **The facts are 11−9=2 . . .**

3. ☐ (11) 8 3 ☐

   **11 is the whole number.
   Its parts are 8 and 3.**
   a. **The triplet is (11) 8 3,
      (11) 8 3 . . .**
   b. **The facts are 11−8=3 . . .**

4. Flash the 11's cards. **Say the triplet; then say the answer.**

50

Read the story.
Write the numbers
  in the beehive.
Write the label words
  on the lines.
Answer the problem.

God sent rain.
8 drops fell on
Mae's hand. Three
drops fell on her
cheek. How many
drops was that?

```
  8    drops
+ 3    drops
 11    drops
```

Mark went on a
bug hunt. He found
3 bugs in a log and
eight bugs on a rock.
How many bugs did
Mark find?

```
  3    bugs
+ 8    bugs
 11    bugs
```

11 jets were on the
ground. Eight of them
went up into the sky.
How many jets were
on the ground then?

```
 11    jets
- 8    jets
  3    jets
```

Mother made 11
pies. She gave three of
them to the preacher's
wife. How many pies
did Mother have left?

```
 11    pies
- 3    pies
  8    pies
```

44

5. Drill the triplets on the Blossom Chart.
   **(11) 9 2; (11) 8 3 . . .**

6. Point to the Number Line.
   **Count by 10's, then by 5's.**
   **10, 20, 30, 35, 40, 45, 50, 55**
   **10, 15, 20, 25, 30**
   **10, 20, 30, 40, 50, 60, 70, 80, 85, 90**

7. Have individuals count aloud as they do the
   money samples.

8. Do the Speed Drill in Lesson 50.

9. Assign Lesson 50.

*After Class*

| hundreds | tens | ones |
|---|---|---|
|  |  | 0 |
|  |  | 1 |
|  |  | 2 |

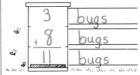
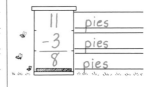

Answer these facts.

| | | | | | | | |
|---|---|---|---|---|---|---|---|
| 11<br>−3<br>**8** | 11<br>−9<br>**2** | 11<br>−8<br>**3** | 11<br>−3<br>**8** | 9<br>+2<br>**11** | 11<br>−8<br>**3** | 8<br>+3<br>**11** | 11<br>−8<br>**3** |
| 11<br>−3<br>**8** | 11<br>−2<br>**9** | 3<br>+8<br>**11** | 11<br>−2<br>**9** | 11<br>−3<br>**8** | 11<br>−9<br>**2** | 11<br>−9<br>**2** | 2<br>+9<br>**11** |
| 11<br>−8<br>**3** | 8<br>+3<br>**11** | 11<br>−8<br>**3** | 3<br>+8<br>**11** | 11<br>−3<br>**8** | 11<br>−8<br>**3** | 11<br>−9<br>**2** | 11<br>−3<br>**8** |

Count the dimes and nickels.
Write the amount.

60¢
55¢
65¢
45¢

**Blacklines**

Fact Hives #3

Missing Whole or Parts #2

2-Place Computation #4

45

1. Review time.
   **60 minutes=1 hour. . . .**
   a. **Kevin raked leaves for 1 hour or Kevin raked leaves for __.** 60 minutes
   b. **The children sang for crippled Mrs. Smith for 60 minutes or they sang for __.** 1 hour

2. Stand near the grid and the apples on the board.
   a. **Count with me as I fill the apples and the grid.**
   > 0 apples—0 ones
   > 1 apple—1 one
   > 1, 2 apples—2 ones
   > 1, 2, 3 apples—3 ones
   > 1, 2, 3, 4 apples—4 ones
   Continue to 9 apples.
   b. **We counted the apples by 1's. Is there a faster way to count apples? You will find out tomorrow.**

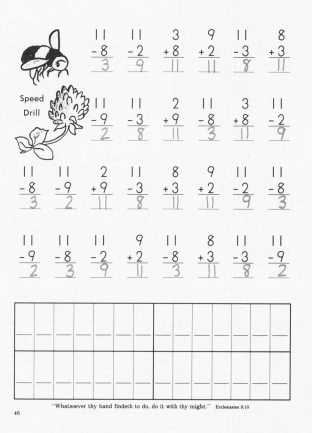

Speed Drill

| | | | | | |
|---|---|---|---|---|---|
| 11<br>−8<br>**3** | 11<br>−2<br>**9** | 3<br>+8<br>**11** | 9<br>+2<br>**11** | 11<br>−3<br>**8** | 8<br>+3<br>**11** |
| 11<br>−9<br>**2** | 11<br>−3<br>**8** | 2<br>+9<br>**11** | 11<br>−8<br>**3** | 3<br>+8<br>**11** | 11<br>−2<br>**9** |

| | | | | | | | |
|---|---|---|---|---|---|---|---|
| 11<br>−8<br>**3** | 11<br>−9<br>**2** | 2<br>+9<br>**11** | 11<br>−3<br>**8** | 8<br>+3<br>**11** | 9<br>+2<br>**11** | 11<br>−2<br>**9** | 11<br>−8<br>**3** |
| 11<br>−9<br>**2** | 11<br>−8<br>**3** | 11<br>−2<br>**9** | 9<br>+2<br>**11** | 11<br>−8<br>**3** | 8<br>+3<br>**11** | 11<br>−3<br>**8** | 11<br>−9<br>**2** |

"Whatsoever thy hand findeth to do, do it with thy might." Ecclesiastes 9:10

46

51

Trace and fill in the whole and parts.

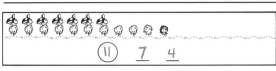

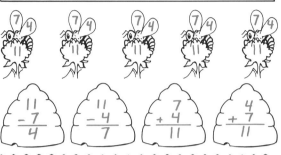

Trace, answer, and write the facts.

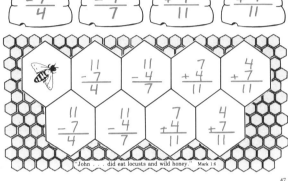

"John . . . did eat locusts and wild honey." Mark 1:6

47

## Before Class

Make (11) 7 4 flash cards for each child.

Tack (11) 7 4 flash cards above the clover patch in this order:

| 11 | 11 | 7 | 4 |
|----|----|----|----|
| −7 | −4 | +4 | +7 |
| 4 | 7 | 11 | 11 |

### Materials

Mix Addition and Subtraction 9–11 flash cards. Form C

11 clovers, 7 with bees

### Chalkboard

## Class Time

1. Flash Addition and Subtraction 9–11 cards for 1 minute. **Answer together.**

2. Flash Card Drill: Addition and Subtraction 9–11 cards. Use Form C.
   **Flower Row: Box 1 . . .**

3. Stand near the clover patch.

   (11)  7  4

   a. **How many pink clovers are in the patch?** 10
      **We think—10 pink.**
      **1 more makes __ altogether.** 11
      **We think—10 pink.**
      **3 less makes __ clovers with bees.** 7
   b. **Circle the clovers with your finger.**
      **11 clovers in the patch;**
      **11 is the whole number.**
      **What part of the 11 has bees?** 7
      **What part of the 11 has no bees?** 4
      **11 is the whole number.**
      **Its parts are 7 and 4.**

Answer these facts.

Extra Activity

| | | | | | | | |
|---|---|---|---|---|---|---|---|
| 7<br>+4<br>11 | 4<br>+7<br>11 | 11<br>-4<br>7 | 11<br>-7<br>4 | 7<br>+4<br>11 | 11<br>-4<br>7 | 11<br>-7<br>4 | 11<br>-4<br>7 |
| 11<br>-7<br>4 | 11<br>-7<br>4 | 11<br>-4<br>7 | 7<br>+4<br>11 | 11<br>-7<br>4 | 11<br>-4<br>7 | 4<br>+7<br>11 | 11<br>-7<br>4 |
| 4<br>+7<br>11 | 11<br>-4<br>7 | 7<br>+4<br>11 | 11<br>-4<br>7 | 4<br>+7<br>11 | 11<br>-7<br>4 | 11<br>-7<br>4 | 11<br>-4<br>7 |
| 11<br>-7<br>4 | 11<br>-7<br>4 | 11<br>-7<br>4 | 7<br>+4<br>11 | 11<br>-4<br>7 | 4<br>+7<br>11 | 11<br>-4<br>7 | 11<br>-7<br>4 |
| 7<br>+4<br>11 | 11<br>-4<br>7 | 11<br>-7<br>4 | 11<br>-4<br>7 | 4<br>+7<br>11 | 11<br>-7<br>4 | 11<br>-4<br>7 | |
| 11<br>-7<br>4 | 7<br>+4<br>11 | 11<br>-4<br>7 | 11<br>-7<br>4 | 11<br>-4<br>7 | 4<br>+7<br>11 | 11<br>-4<br>7 | |

48

c. **The triplet is (11) 7 4;**
(11) 7 4 . . .

d. Point to the flash cards. **The facts are**
**11−7, 4; 11−4, 7; 7+4, 11;**
**4+7, 11 . . .**

4. Point to the flash cards again. **Say the triplet;**
**then say the answer. (11) 7 4; the an-**
**swer is 4 . . .**

5. Ask a child to fill the bees as everyone
says **(11) 7 4 . . .**

6. Stand near the beehive. **Say the 11's facts as**
**I fill the beehive. 11−9, 2; 11−2, 9 . . .**

7. **Count by 5's to 100.**
**Count on to 150 by 2's.**

8. Story Problems

a. **Willis worked in the barn. He fed 7**
**calves milk and 4 calves grain. How**
**many calves is that altogether?**
**Who can give us the whole problem?**
7 calves+4 calves=11 calves.

b. **11 papers were on a desk. God sent a**
**wind puff. 4 papers sailed to the floor.**
**How many papers are on the desk?**
**Who can . . . ?**
11 papers−4 papers=7 papers.

9. Assign Lesson 51.

182

51

Write the numbers that come before and after when you count by 2's.

51

| Count by 2's | | | | |
|---|---|---|---|---|
| 100 | *102* | *110* | 112 | *114* |
| 102 | *104* | *130* | 132 | *134* |
| *104* | 106 | *108* | *102* | 104 | *106* |
| *114* | 116 | *118* | *120* | 122 | *124* |
| *124* | 126 | *128* | *126* | 128 | *130* |

Count the dimes and nickels. Write the amount.

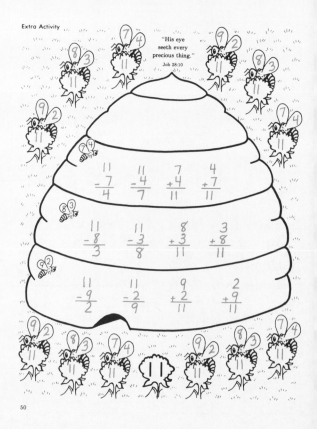

*50¢*

*70¢*

*45¢*

*65¢*

49

**Blacklines**

Form C (Class Time)

Fact Hives #4

Triplets With Facts #1

## After Class

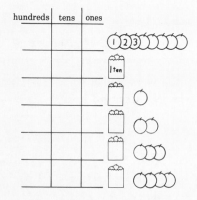

| hundreds | tens | ones |
|---|---|---|
|  |  |  |
|  |  |  |
|  |  |  |
|  |  |  |
|  |  |  |

1. Give each child his (11) 7 4 flash cards.

2. Stand near the grid on the board.

   a. **Help me count the apples and fill the grid.**

      **1, 2, 3 . . . 9 apples—9 ones.**

   b. **10 apples in a bag—1 ten.**

      **1 ten and 0 ones make 10.**

      **1 ten and 1 one make 11.**

      **1 ten and 2 ones make 12 . . .**

Extra Activity

"His eye seeth every precious thing." Job 28:10

$$\begin{array}{r} 11 \\ -7 \\ \hline 4 \end{array} \quad \begin{array}{r} 11 \\ -4 \\ \hline 7 \end{array} \quad \begin{array}{r} 7 \\ +4 \\ \hline 11 \end{array} \quad \begin{array}{r} 4 \\ +7 \\ \hline 11 \end{array}$$

$$\begin{array}{r} 11 \\ -8 \\ \hline 3 \end{array} \quad \begin{array}{r} 11 \\ -3 \\ \hline 8 \end{array} \quad \begin{array}{r} 8 \\ +3 \\ \hline 11 \end{array} \quad \begin{array}{r} 3 \\ +8 \\ \hline 11 \end{array}$$

$$\begin{array}{r} 11 \\ -9 \\ \hline 2 \end{array} \quad \begin{array}{r} 11 \\ -2 \\ \hline 9 \end{array} \quad \begin{array}{r} 9 \\ +2 \\ \hline 11 \end{array} \quad \begin{array}{r} 2 \\ +9 \\ \hline 11 \end{array}$$

50

52 | 52

**Fill in the whole and parts.**

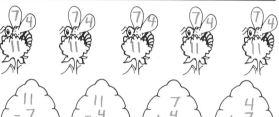

**Trace, answer, and write the facts.**

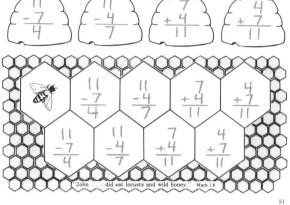

"John . . . did eat locusts and wild honey."  Mark 1:6

51

## Before Class

Add  (11)  7  4  bee to the Blossom 11 Chart.

**Materials**

Large clock

Large coins

*(11)  9  2;  (11)  8  3;  (11)  7  4 flash cards*

**Chalkboard**

| 73 | 43 | 75 | 42 | 117 | 118 | 116 | 119 |
|----|----|----|----|-----|-----|-----|-----|
| +44 | +76 | +43 | +77 | −73 | −42 | −94 | −35 |

## Class Time

1. Point to Blossom 11 Chart.

   **Say each triplet 3 times.**

3. Stand near the clover patch.

   (11)  7  4

   **11 clovers in the patch;**

   **11 is the whole number.**

   **What part of the 11 has bees?** 7

   **What part of the 11 has no bees?** 4

   **11 is the whole number.**

   **Its parts are 7 and 4.**

   a. **Say the triplet. (11)  7  4 . . .**

   b. Point to the first flash card.

   **Close your eyes and say it 3 times.**

   **11—7, 4 . . .** Drill each fact.

3. Do the Addition and Subtraction samples.

   a. **Be careful to add in ones' place and in tens' place.**

184

<52>

Answer these problems.

Speed Drill

| | | | | | |
|---|---|---|---|---|---|
| 114<br>-42<br>72 | 115<br>-74<br>41 | 118<br>-41<br>77 | 119<br>-76<br>43 | 119<br>-79<br>40 | 119<br>-47<br>72 |
| 119<br>-72<br>47 | 114<br>-71<br>43 | 117<br>-43<br>74 | 119<br>-76<br>43 | 118<br>-71<br>47 | 116<br>-42<br>74 |
| 113<br>-41<br>72 | 114<br>-74<br>40 | 119<br>-76<br>43 | 119<br>-42<br>77 | 119<br>-78<br>41 | 116<br>-44<br>72 |
| 71<br>+45<br>116 | 47<br>+72<br>119 | 74<br>+44<br>118 | 73<br>+41<br>114 | 45<br>+72<br>117 | 76<br>+43<br>119 |
|  | 41<br>+78<br>119 | 78<br>+40<br>118 | 41<br>+76<br>117 | 44<br>+74<br>118 | 73<br>+46<br>119 |
| | 74<br>+45<br>119 | 42<br>+75<br>117 | 74<br>+40<br>114 | 47<br>+71<br>118 | 42<br>+77<br>119 |

52

b. **Be careful to subtract in ones' place and in tens' place.**

⟳117
⊖73

4. Set the large clock at 7:00.
   a. **Name the hands.**
   b. **In one hour it will be __.**
      Slowly push the hands to 8:00. **It takes *one hour* for the hour hand to move to the *next number*.**
   c. **In one hour it will be __.**
      Glide the hands around to 9:00. **The minute hand can pass *all the numbers* in *one hour*.**

5. Review money.
   a. **We count quarters by __, dimes by __, nickels by __, and pennies by __.**
   b. **Flash the coins. 10¢, 25¢, 1¢, 5¢ . . .**
   c. **Which is more**
      •**5 nickels or 2 dimes?**
      •**20 pennies or 1 quarter?**
      •**2 quarters or 4 dimes?**
      •**6 nickels or 1 quarter?**

6. Do the Speed Drill in Lesson 52.

7. Assign Lesson 52.

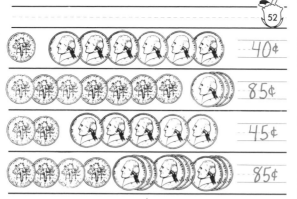

Count the dimes and nickels.
Write the amount.

40¢

85¢

45¢

85¢

Read the story.
Write the numbers
   in the beehive.
Write the label words
   on the lines.
Answer the problem.

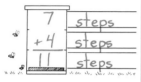

Baby Sister tries to walk. She takes 7 steps. Step, step! She takes four more steps. How many steps is that **altogether**?

```
   7   steps
 + 4   steps
  11   steps
```

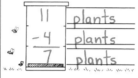

Mother likes plants. She planted 11 plants in pots. Four plants died. How many plants did Mother have left?

```
  11   plants
 - 4   plants
   7   plants
```

**Blacklines**

Fact Hives #4

Triplets With Facts #1

Money Identification #6

53

## After Class

| hundreds | tens | ones |
|----------|------|------|
|          |      |      |
|          |      |      |
|          |      |      |
|          |      |      |
|          |      |      |

1. Flash the 11's cards. **Say the triplet; then say the answer.**

2. Review place value.
   Stand near the grid on the board.

   a. **How many apples are in a bag?** 10
      **10 apples—1 ten; 1 apple—1 one.**
      **1 ten and 1 one make 11.**

   b. Have the children count aloud as they number the items and fill the grid.

Speed Drill

```
  4    11    7    11    7    11
 +7   -4   +4   -7   +4   -4
 11    7   11    4   11    7

  7     4   11     4   11    11
 +4    +7   -7    +7   -4   -7
 11    11    4    11    7    4

 11    11   11     4   11     7   11     7
 -4    -7   -4    +7   -7    +4   -4    +4
  7     4    7    11    4    11    7    11

 11    11   11    11    4    11    7     4
 -7    -4   -7    -4   +7    -7   +4    +7
  4     7    4     7   11     4   11    11
```

| | | | | | | | | | |
|--|--|--|--|--|--|--|--|--|--|
| | | | | | | | | | |
| | | | | | | | | | |

"Whatsoever thy hand findeth to do, do it with thy might." Ecclesiastes 9:10

54

53

Fill in the whole and parts.

Trace, answer, and write the facts.

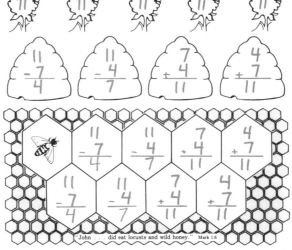

(11) 7 4

"John . . . did eat locusts and wild honey." Mark 1:6

55

## Before Class

### Chalkboard

| 53 | 25 | 62 | 42 | 12 |
|----|----|----|----|----|
| 24 | 23 | 23 | 36 | 14 |
| +42 | +71 | +32 | +41 | +92 |

(10¢) (5¢)  ___

(10¢) (5¢) +___

(10¢) (5¢)  ___

(10¢) (5¢)  +___

| 11 | 11 | 2 | 11 |
|----|----|----|----|
| −3 | −7 | +9 | −8 |
| 4 | 11 | 3 | 7 |
| +7 | −9 | +8 | +4 |
| 11 | 11 | 11 | 11 |
| −2 | −4 | −9 | −4 |
| 8 | 11 | 9 | 11 |
| +3 | −7 | +2 | −3 |

## Class Time

1. **Count by 5's to 155.**

2. Stand near the clover patch.

   (11) 7 4

   **11 clovers in the patch;**
   **11 is the whole number.**
   **What part of the 11 has bees?** 7
   **What part of the 11 has no bees?** 4
   **11 is the whole number.**
   **Its parts are 7 and 4.**
   a. **Say the triplet.** (11) 7 4 . . .
   b. Point to the flash cards. **Say the facts.**
      11−7, 4;  11−4, 7 . . .

3. Point to Blossom 11 Chart. **Say the triplets.**
   Drill 3 times.

4. **Answer together. What number belongs**
   **on the blank?** (Say *blank* for each blank.)

   | 11, 7 __ | 11 __ 3 | __ 8, 3 |
   |----------|---------|---------|
   | 11, 9 __ | 11 __ 4 | __ 7, 4 |
   | 11, 8 __ | 11 __ 2 | __ 9, 2 |

Count the first row.
  Write the amount.
Count the second row.
  Write the amount.
Add.

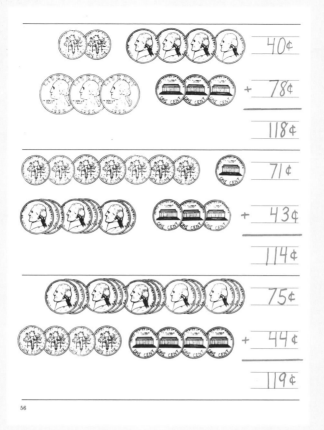

40¢
+ 78¢
‾‾‾‾‾
118¢

71¢
+ 43¢
‾‾‾‾‾
114¢

75¢
+ 44¢
‾‾‾‾‾
119¢

56

Extra Activity

5. Stand near the grid on the board.
   a. **Boys, answer the first column. Girls, answer the second column.**
   b. Drill the facts down and up, right and left. Save the grid for *After Class*.

6. Do the Column Addition samples. **Ones' place first, ones' place . . .**

7. Have the children count with you as you do the Money samples.

8. Assign Lesson 53.

188

**53**

Answer these facts.

| | | | | | | | |
|---|---|---|---|---|---|---|---|
| 11<br>−7<br>**4** | 11<br>−2<br>**9** | 11<br>−8<br>**3** | 11<br>−9<br>**2** | 4<br>+7<br>**11** | 7<br>+4<br>**11** | 11<br>−4<br>**7** | 11<br>−3<br>**8** |
| 11<br>−8<br>**3** | 11<br>−2<br>**9** | 11<br>−7<br>**4** | 8<br>+3<br>**11** | 9<br>+2<br>**11** | 11<br>−9<br>**2** | 11<br>−3<br>**8** | 11<br>−4<br>**7** |
| 11<br>−4<br>**7** | 3<br>+8<br>**11** | 11<br>−3<br>**8** | 11<br>−7<br>**4** | 9<br>+2<br>**11** | 11<br>−8<br>**3** | 8<br>+3<br>**11** | 11<br>−9<br>**2** |
| 11<br>−3<br>**8** | 2<br>+9<br>**11** | 11<br>−4<br>**7** | 11<br>−8<br>**3** | 3<br>+8<br>**11** | 11<br>−7<br>**4** | 11<br>−9<br>**2** | 4<br>+7<br>**11** |

Count the dimes and nickels.
Write the amount.

70¢

45¢

57

**Blacklines**

Fact Hives #4

Missing Whole or Parts #3

Fact Form I

### After Class

1. Drill individuals at the Addition and Subtraction grid on the board.

2. Chalkboard Drill: **Write the three numbers I say.**

    537    375    573
**Circle the smallest number.**

    268    682    628
**Circle the largest number.**

    504    540    405
**Circle the smallest number.**

    301    103    310
**Circle the largest number.**

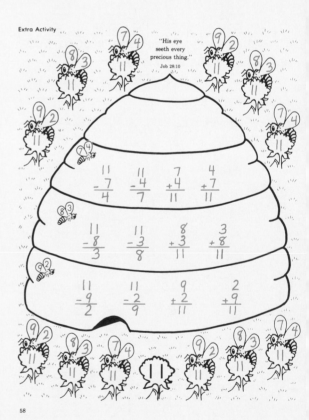

Extra Activity

"His eye seeth every precious thing."
Job 28:10

58

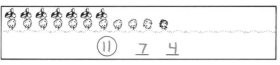

Fill in the whole and parts.

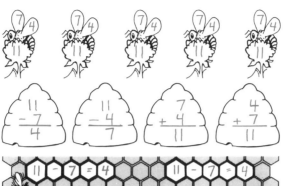

Write the facts.

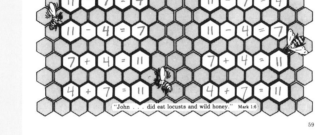

Trace and write
   the facts.

"John . . . did eat locusts and wild honey." Mark 1:6

59

## Before Class

### Materials
   Addition and Subtraction 9–11 flash cards
   Large clock
   *(11)  9  2; (11)  8  3; (11)  7  4 flash cards*

### Chalkboard

| 25 | 62 | 23 | 34 | 42 |
|----|----|----|----|----|
| 12 | 33 | 53 | 52 | 33 |
| +81 | +23 | +43 | +32 | +42 |

## Class Time

1. Circle Drill: Addition and Subtraction 9–11 flash cards.

2. Point to Blossom 11 Chart.
   **Say the triplets. (11) 9 2 . . .**

3. Stand near the beehive.
   a. **While the older worker bees are busy in the clover patch, the younger worker bees are busy in the hive. They are making tiny wax cups called cells. The wax cells will be filled with honey. The honey and wax is called honeycomb.**
   b. Have individuals write the (11) 9 2; (11) 8 3; and (11) 7 4 facts in the beehive as everyone says them together.

4. Do the Column Addition samples.

⟨ 54 ⟩

Fill in the missing whole or parts.

| | | |
|---|---|---|
| 4 + 7 = _11_ | 11 – _7_ = 4 | 4 + 7 = _11_ |
| 11 – 7 = _4_ | 11 – 4 = _7_ | 11 – 7 = _4_ |
| 11 – _4_ = 7 | 7 + 4 = _11_ | _11_ – 4 = 7 |
| _7_ + 4 = 11 | 4 + _7_ = 11 | 7 + 4 = _11_ |
| 11 – _4_ = 7 | _4_ + 7 = 11 | 4 + _7_ = 11 |
| _7_ + 4 = 11 | 11 – _7_ = 4 | _11_ – 7 = 4 |

Answer these problems.

$$\begin{array}{r} 2 \\ 2 \\ +7 \\ \hline 11 \end{array} \quad \begin{array}{r} 3 \\ 2 \\ +5 \\ \hline 10 \end{array} \quad \begin{array}{r} 4 \\ 3 \\ +4 \\ \hline 11 \end{array} \quad \begin{array}{r} 2 \\ 6 \\ +2 \\ \hline 10 \end{array} \quad \begin{array}{r} 3 \\ 5 \\ +2 \\ \hline 10 \end{array} \quad \begin{array}{r} 5 \\ 2 \\ +4 \\ \hline 11 \end{array} \quad \begin{array}{r} 1 \\ 6 \\ +4 \\ \hline 11 \end{array} \quad \begin{array}{r} 7 \\ 0 \\ +4 \\ \hline 11 \end{array}$$

$$\begin{array}{r} 3 \\ 1 \\ +7 \\ \hline 11 \end{array} \quad \begin{array}{r} 2 \\ 2 \\ +6 \\ \hline 10 \end{array} \quad \begin{array}{r} 1 \\ 3 \\ +7 \\ \hline 11 \end{array} \quad \begin{array}{r} 6 \\ 1 \\ +4 \\ \hline 11 \end{array} \quad \begin{array}{r} 5 \\ 3 \\ +2 \\ \hline 10 \end{array} \quad \begin{array}{r} 5 \\ 4 \\ +1 \\ \hline 10 \end{array} \quad \begin{array}{r} 1 \\ 6 \\ +4 \\ \hline 11 \end{array} \quad \begin{array}{r} 2 \\ 5 \\ +4 \\ \hline 11 \end{array}$$

60

5. Set the large clock at 4:00.
   a. **One hour ago it was __.** 3:00
      **In one hour it will be __.** 5:00
   b. **Name the hands.**
   c. **60 minutes=1 hour. . . .**

6. Do the Speed Drill in Lesson 54.

7. Assign Lesson 54.

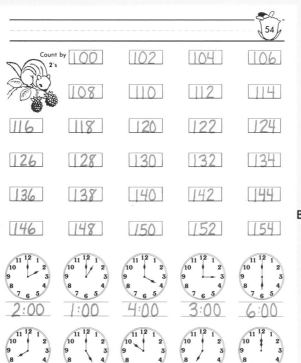

**Count by 2's.**

Count by 2's

| 100 | 102 | 104 | 106 |
| 108 | 110 | 112 | 114 |
| 116 | 118 | 120 | 122 | 124 |
| 126 | 128 | 130 | 132 | 134 |
| 136 | 138 | 140 | 142 | 144 |
| 146 | 148 | 150 | 152 | 154 |

**Blacklines**

Fact Hives #5

Missing Whole or Parts #3

**Write the time.**

2:00  1:00  4:00  3:00  6:00

8:00  5:00  10:00  7:00  12:00

61

---

## After Class

Use the bushel
of 1 hundred
apples for each number.

1. Drill individuals with the 11's flash cards.

2. Stand near the grid.

  a. **1 apple—1 one**

    **10 apples—1 ten**

  b. Point to the bushel.

    **1 hundred apples in a bushel—**

    **1 hundred.** Write 1 hundred on the bushel
basket.

  c. **1 hundred, 1 ten, and 3 ones make 113.**

    Continue with the rest of the samples. Have
the children repeat each one with you.

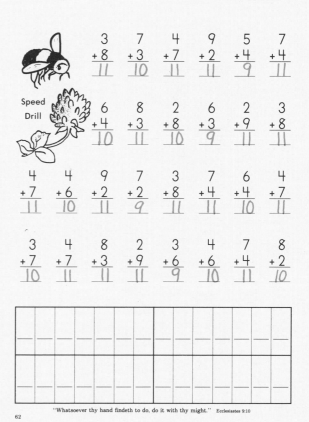

Speed Drill

| 3 +8 = 11 | 7 +3 = 10 | 4 +7 = 11 | 9 +2 = 11 | 5 +4 = 9 | 7 +4 = 11 |
| 6 +4 = 10 | 8 +3 = 11 | 2 +8 = 10 | 6 +3 = 9 | 2 +9 = 11 | 3 +8 = 11 |
| 4 +7 = 11 | 4 +6 = 10 | 9 +2 = 11 | 7 +2 = 9 | 3 +8 = 11 | 7 +4 = 11 | 6 +4 = 10 | 4 +7 = 11 |
| 3 +7 = 10 | 4 +7 = 11 | 8 +3 = 11 | 2 +9 = 11 | 3 +6 = 9 | 4 +6 = 10 | 7 +4 = 11 | 8 +2 = 10 |

"Whatsoever thy hand findeth to do, do it with thy might." Ecclesiastes 9:10

62

55

Fill in the whole and parts.

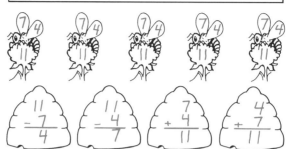

Write the facts.

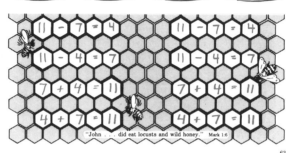

Trace, answer, and write the facts.

"John . . . did eat locusts and wild honey." Mark 1:6

63

## Before Class

### Materials

*Large clock*

### Chalkboard

| | |
|---|---|
| __−2=9 | 7+__=11 |
| 3+__=11 | __−8=3 |
| 9+2=__ | __+7=11 |
| __+3=11 | 11−__=4 |
| __+4=11 | 11−__=9 |

## Class Time

1. Stand near the clover patch.
   **The Bible tells about a preacher who ate wild honey and locusts. Do you know his name?**
   John the Baptist (Matthew 3:4)

2. (11)  9  2
   **11 is the whole number.**
   **Its parts are __ and __.**
   a. **The triplet is (11) 9 2 . . .**
   b. **The facts are 11−9, 2;  11−2, 9; 9+2, 11;  2+9, 11.**

3. (11)  8  3
   **11 is the whole number.**
   **Its parts are __ and __.**
   a. **The triplet is (11) 8 3 . . .**
   b. **The facts are 11−8, 3;  11−3, 8; 8+3, 11;  3+8, 11.**

Read the story.
Write the numbers
  in the beehive.
Write the label words
  on the lines.
Answer the problem.

At church we sang 7 songs about God and four songs about the Bible. How many songs was that **altogether**?

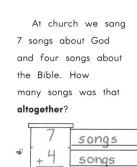

11 apples hang on a tree. Plop, plop! Plop, plop! Four apples fall down. How many apples are on the tree now?

Fay looked at a group of trees. Four trees were big and 7 trees were little. How many trees was that **altogether**?

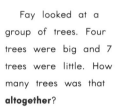

Mark helped Mother rake leaves. They made 11 heaps. A wind blew 7 heaps away. How many heaps were left?

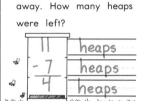

64

4.   (11)  7  4

   **11 is the whole number.**
   **Its parts are __ and __.**
   a. **The triplet is (11) 7 4 . . .**
   b. **The facts are 11−7, 4;  11−4, 7;  7+4, 11;  4+7, 11.**

5. Point to Blossom 11 Chart.
   a. **Say the triplets in order.**
        **(11) 9 2**
        **(11) 8 3**
        **(11) 7 4 . . .**
   b. **Can we say the triplets without looking at the chart?**

6. Do the Missing Whole or Parts samples.

7. Have responsive counting by 2's to 150. **You say the first number; I will say the next number.**

8. **Answer together.**
   | | | |
   |---|---|---|
   | 10+3 | 10+1 | 10+7 |
   | 10+5 | 10+8 | 10+2 |
   | 10+9 | 10+4 | 10+6 |

9. Assign Lesson 55.

Answer these problems.

```
  34     44     25     53     35     61
  23     30     43     32     22     15
+ 52   + 42   + 31   + 21   + 20   + 42
 109    116     99    106     77    118
```

```
  22     32     33     54     23     27
  23     12     51     12     21     50
+ 64   + 33   + 22   + 33   + 72   + 41
 109     77    106     99    116    118
```

```
  11     11     11      8      9     11     11     11
 - 4    - 3    - 7    + 3    + 2    - 7    - 3    - 4
   7      8      4     11     11      4      8      7
```

```
  11      3     11     11      9     11      8     11
 - 4    + 8    - 3    - 7    + 2    - 8    + 3    - 9
   7     11      8      4     11      3     11      2
```

```
  11      2     11     11      3     11     11      4
 - 3    + 9    - 4    - 8    + 8    - 7    - 9    + 7
   8     11      7      3     11      4      2     11
```

65

**Blacklines**

Fact Hives #5

Missing Whole or Parts #3

Fact Form II

---

## After Class

```
  63     32     52     21     72     42
  32     41     32     83     41     64
+ 23   + 46   + 35   +  5   +  5   +  3
```

When you say **30 minutes = 1/2 hour** in 2d, make the clock on the board look like the one below. Keep it on the board for several days.

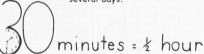
**30 minutes = ½ hour**

1. Do the Column Addition samples.

2. Set the large clock at 1:00.

   a. **How many minutes is it from 12 to 1?** 5

   b. **How many minutes are in one hour?** 60

   c. **How many minutes are in one-half hour? Count with me.** 5, 10 . . . 30 **minutes.**

   d. Write 30 minutes = ½ hour.

     **30 minutes = ½ hour, or**

     **30 minutes make ½ hour.**

**Extra Activity**

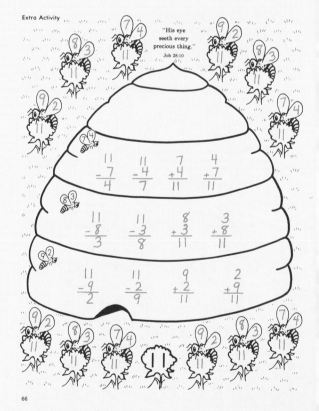

"His eye seeth every precious thing."
Job 28:10

66

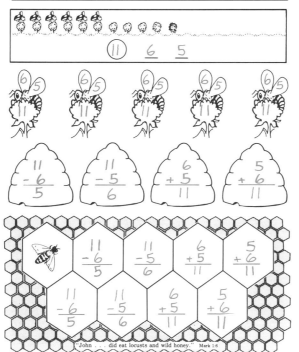

Trace and fill in the whole and parts.

Trace, answer, and write the facts.

"John . . . . did eat locusts and wild honey." Mark 1:6

## Before Class

Make (11) 6 5 flash cards for each child.

Tack (11) 6 5 flash cards above the clover patch in this order:

| 11 | 11 | 6 | 5 |
|---|---|---|---|
| −6 | −5 | +5 | +6 |
| 5 | 6 | 11 | 11 |

### Materials

Large clock

11 blossoms, 6 with bees

### Chalkboard

| 62 | 53 | 72 | 34 | 42 |
|---|---|---|---|---|
| 55 | 63 | 43 | 82 | 70 |
| +2 | +3 | +3 | +3 | +5 |

## Class Time

1. Set the large clock at 2:00.

   a. **Count the minutes. 5, 10 . . .**
      **30 minutes = ½ hour.**

   b. **It is half past 2—2:30.**
      Write 2:30.

   c. Ask a child to write the time as his classmates say the time. Set the clock.
      **half past 5—5:30**
      **half past 8—8:30**
      **half past 10—10:30**
      **half past 12—12:30**
      **half past 3—3:30**

2. Stand near the clover patch.

   a. **How many pink clovers are in the patch?** 10
      **We think—10 pink.**
      **1 more makes __ clovers in all.** 11
      **We think—10 pink.**
      **4 less makes __ clovers with bees.**

   b. Circle the clover with your finger.
      **11 clovers in the patch;**

56

Answer these facts.

| 11 | 6 | 11 | 5 | 11 | 11 | 5 | 11 |
|---|---|---|---|---|---|---|---|
| -6 | +5 | -5 | +6 | -6 | -5 | +6 | -6 |
| 5 | 11 | 6 | 11 | 5 | 6 | 11 | 5 |

| 11 | 11 | 6 | 5 | 11 | 11 | 11 | 5 |
|---|---|---|---|---|---|---|---|
| -5 | -6 | +5 | +6 | -6 | -5 | -5 | +6 |
| 6 | 5 | 11 | 11 | 5 | 6 | 6 | 11 |

| 11 | 5 | 11 | 11 | 5 | 11 | 6 | 11 |
|---|---|---|---|---|---|---|---|
| -6 | +6 | -5 | -6 | +6 | -5 | +5 | -6 |
| 5 | 11 | 6 | 5 | 11 | 6 | 11 | 5 |

| 6 | 11 | 11 | 5 | 11 | 11 | 6 | 11 |
|---|---|---|---|---|---|---|---|
| +5 | -5 | -6 | +6 | -5 | -6 | +5 | -5 |
| 11 | 6 | 5 | 11 | 6 | 5 | 11 | 6 |

| | 5 | 11 | 11 | 11 | 5 | 6 | 11 |
|---|---|---|---|---|---|---|---|
| | +6 | -5 | -5 | -6 | +6 | +5 | -6 |
| | 11 | 6 | 6 | 5 | 11 | 11 | 5 |

| 11 | 6 | 11 | 11 | 5 | 11 | 11 |
|---|---|---|---|---|---|---|
| -5 | +5 | -6 | -5 | +6 | -6 | -5 |
| 6 | 11 | 5 | 6 | 11 | 5 | 6 |

68

11 is the whole number.

**What part of the 11 has bees?** 6

**What part of the 11 has no bees?** 5

11 is the whole number.

**Its parts are 6 and 5.**

c. **The triplet is (11) 6 5 . . .**

d. **The facts are 11—6, 5; 11—5, 6;**
   **6+5, 11; 5+6, 11.**

3. Ask a child to fill the bees as everyone says
   (11) 6 5, (11) 6 5 . . .

4. **Say the 11's facts as I fill the beehive.**

5. Do the Column Addition samples.

6. Do the Speed Drill in Lesson 56.

7. Assign Lesson 56.

56

Answer these problems.

| 24 | 35 | 45 | 63 | 41 | 23 |
|---|---|---|---|---|---|
| 53 | 23 | 12 | 12 | 45 | 21 |
| +42 | +51 | +30 | +41 | +32 | +62 |
| 119 | 109 | 87 | 116 | 118 | 106 |

| 34 | 47 | 23 | 32 | 54 | 52 |
|---|---|---|---|---|---|
| 50 | 30 | 21 | 22 | 32 | 13 |
| +22 | +41 | +72 | +33 | +23 | +34 |
| 106 | 118 | 116 | 87 | 109 | 99 |

**Blacklines**

Fact Hives #6

Triplets With Facts #2

Write the time.

1:00    6:00    3:00    8:00    5:00

7:00    10:00    9:00    12:00    11:00

69

*After Class*

153    315    531

1. Give each child his (11) 6 5 flash cards.
2. Review place value.
   a. **1 apple is __.** 1 one
      **1 bag of apples is __.** 1 ten
      **1 bushel of apples is __.** 1 hundred
   b. Underline 1 in each number. **1 one, 1 ten, 1 hundred. Which 1 is the greatest?** 1 hundred

Speed Drill

| 11 | 11 | 11 | 11 | 11 | 11 |
|---|---|---|---|---|---|
| -8 | -2 | -3 | -9 | -4 | -3 |
| 3 | 9 | 8 | 2 | 7 | 8 |

| 11 | 11 | 11 | 11 | 11 | 11 |
|---|---|---|---|---|---|
| -7 | -8 | -4 | -3 | -9 | -2 |
| 4 | 3 | 7 | 8 | 2 | 9 |

| 11 | 11 | 11 | 11 | 11 | 11 | 11 | 11 |
|---|---|---|---|---|---|---|---|
| -4 | -7 | -3 | -4 | -9 | -3 | -2 | -8 |
| 7 | 4 | 8 | 7 | 2 | 8 | 9 | 3 |

| 11 | 11 | 11 | 11 | 11 | 11 | 11 | 11 |
|---|---|---|---|---|---|---|---|
| -7 | -4 | -2 | -9 | -3 | -4 | -8 | -7 |
| 4 | 7 | 9 | 2 | 8 | 7 | 3 | 4 |

"Whatsoever thy hand findeth to do, do it with thy might." Ecclesiastes 9:10

**57**

Fill in the whole and parts.

Trace, answer, and write the facts.

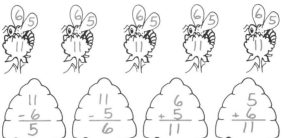

"John . . . did eat locusts and wild honey."  Mark 1:6

71

## Before Class

Add   (11)  6  5   bee to the Blossom 11 Chart.

**Materials**

Addition and Subtraction 9–11 flash cards

*Addition and Subtraction 9–11 flash cards*

Large clock

**Chalkboard**

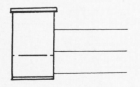

## Class Time

1. Flash Addition and Subtraction 9–11 cards. **Answer together.**

2. Stand near the clover patch.

   | (11)  6  5 |

   **11 clovers in the patch;**
   **11 is the whole number.**
   **What part of the 11 has bees?** 6
   **What part of the 11 has no bees?** 5
   **11 is the whole number.**
   **Its parts are 6 and 5.**
   a. **The triplet is  (11)  6  5 . . .**
   b. **The facts are 11—6, 5;   11—5, 6;**
      **6+5, 11;   5+6, 11.**

3. Point to the Blossom 11 Chart. Drill the triplets.

4. Story Problems
   a. **Philip has 5 short nails and 6 long nails in his pocket. How many nails is that?**
      Ask a child to fill the beehive.
   b. **Philip does not know that his pocket has a hole in it. The 11 nails slide down.**

Answer these problems.

| | | | | | |
|---|---|---|---|---|---|
| 61<br>+52<br>113 | 113<br>-62<br>51 | 53<br>+64<br>117 | 67<br>+51<br>118 | 113<br>-53<br>60 | 57<br>+62<br>119 |
| 119<br>-57<br>62 | 119<br>-63<br>56 | 65<br>+51<br>116 | 119<br>-51<br>68 | 56<br>+60<br>116 | 119<br>-65<br>54 |
| 65<br>+54<br>119 | 114<br>-54<br>60 | 55<br>+63<br>118 | 65<br>+52<br>117 | 119<br>-68<br>51 | 53<br>+60<br>113 |
| 118<br>-55<br>63 | 117<br>-54<br>63 | 118<br>-67<br>51 | 61<br>+57<br>118 | 119<br>-57<br>62 | 56<br>+63<br>119 |
| | 118<br>-64<br>54 | 61<br>+55<br>116 | 118<br>-50<br>68 | 64<br>+52<br>116 | 118<br>-62<br>56 |
| | 51<br>+68<br>119 | 117<br>-55<br>62 | 52<br>+66<br>118 | 118<br>-67<br>51 | 115<br>-52<br>63 |

72

**5 nails drop out. How many nails are left?** Ask a child to fill the beehive.

5. Do the Money samples.

6. Ask a child to write the time as his classmates read the clock. Set the clock at **7:30, 9:30, 11:30, 1:30, 5:30, 6:30** . . .

7. Assign Lesson 57.

200

57

Answer these problems.

| 32 | 23 | 33 | 54 | 44 | 12 |
|----|----|----|----|----|----|
| 23 | 12 | 50 | 12 | 21 | 54 |
| +64 | +31 | +25 | +33 | +52 | +53 |
| 119 | 66 | 108 | 99 | 117 | 119 |

| 34 | 43 | 25 | 53 | 35 | 72 |
|----|----|----|----|----|----|
| 13 | 31 | 42 | 32 | 22 | 15 |
| +22 | +42 | +31 | +24 | +60 | +32 |
| 69 | 116 | 98 | 109 | 117 | 119 |

Write the time.

1:30   2:30   5:30   6:30   9:30

3:30   4:30   7:30   8:30   11:30

73

**Blacklines**

Fact Hives #6

Number Triplets #1

## After Class

1. a. Flash the 9–11 cards once. As you flash them, lay the 9's and 10's on one pile and the 11's on another pile.

   b. Pick up the 11's. **Say the triplet; then say the answer.**

2. Chalkboard Drill: **Write the three numbers I say.**

   246    462    624

   **Circle the number with 6 tens.**

   104    401    410

   Circle . . . **0 ones.**

   375    537    753

   Circle . . . **3 hundreds.**

   789    897    978

   Circle . . . **7 tens.**

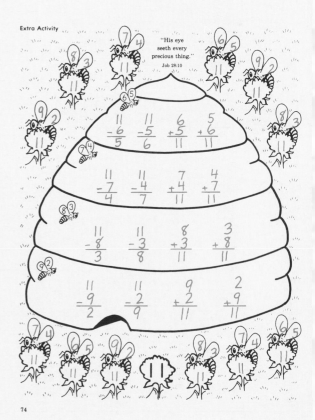

Extra Activity

"His eye seeth every precious thing."
Job 28:10

74

Fill in the whole and parts.

Trace, answer, and write the facts.

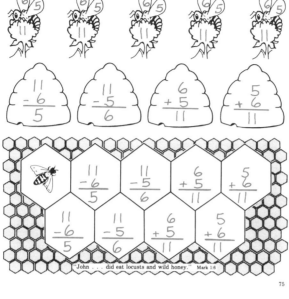

(11) 6 5

11
−6
 5

11
−5
 6

6
+5
11

5
+6
11

"John . . . did eat locusts and wild honey." Mark 1:6

75

## Before Class

**Materials**

11's flash cards

**Chalkboard**

__ 214 216 __ __ __
__ 155 __ 165 __ __
__ __ 300 __ 320 __
286 __ 290 __ __ __

## Class Time

1. Have each child bring *My 1,000 Book* to the teaching corner.
   a. **Count to 100 by 25's.**
   b. **Count on to 200 by 10's.**
   c. **Count on to 300 by 5's.**
   d. **Count on to 350 by 2's.**

2. Do the Missing Number samples.

3. Stand near the clover patch.

   | (11) 6 5 |

   **11 clovers in the patch;**
   **11 is the whole number.**
   **What part of the 11 has bees?** 6
   **What part of the 11 has no bees?** 5
   **11 is the whole number.**
   **Its parts are 6 and 5.**
   a. **The triplet is (11) 6 5 . . .**
   b. Point to the first flash card. **Close your eyes and say it 3 times.** Drill each fact.

4. Flash the 11's cards for 1 minute.
   **Answer together.**

Count the first row.
  Write the amount.
Count the second row.
  Write the amount.
Add.

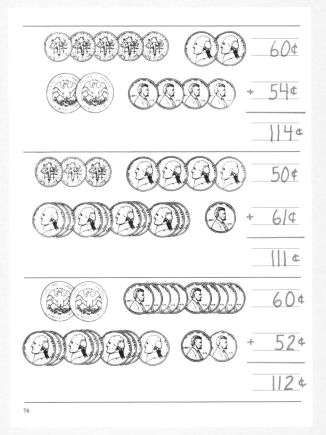

60¢
+ 54¢
114¢

50¢
+ 61¢
111¢

60¢
+ 52¢
112¢

76

Speed
Drill

5. Review ½ hour.
  a. **30 minutes = ½ hour.** . . .
  b. **Mother read Bible stories to the children for 30 minutes, or she read for __. ½ hour**
  c. **Father visited blind Mr. Edwards for 30 minutes, or he visited for __. ½ hour**

6. Do the Speed Drill in Lesson 58.

7. Assign Lesson 58.

58

Answer these facts.

| | 11 | 11 | 11 | 8 | 9 | 11 | 11 | 11 |
|---|----|----|----|---|---|----|----|----|
| | -6 | -3 | -5 | +3 | +2 | -5 | -3 | -6 |
| | 5  | 8  | 6  | 11 | 11 | 6  | 8  | 5  |

| | 11 | 3  | 11 | 11 | 7  | 11 | 5  | 11 |
|---|----|----|----|----|----|----|----|----|
| | -4 | +8 | -6 | -7 | +4 | -8 | +6 | -9 |
| | 7  | 11 | 5  | 4  | 11 | 3  | 11 | 2  |

| | 11 | 6  | 11 | 11 | 6  | 11 | 11 | 4  |
|---|----|----|----|----|----|----|----|----|
| | -6 | +5 | -4 | -8 | +5 | -7 | -9 | +7 |
| | 5  | 11 | 7  | 3  | 11 | 4  | 2  | 11 |

**Blacklines**

Fact Hives #6

Missing Whole or Parts #4

Fact Form III

Write the time.

12:30   9:30   4:30   1:30   8:30

2:30   11:30   6:30   3:30   10:30

77

---

*After Class*

| | | |
|---|---|---|
| 5 6=11 | 8 2=10 | 9 6=3 |
| 8 3=5 | 11 3=8 | 7 3=10 |
| 4 6=10 | 9 2=11 | 7 4=11 |
| 11 5=6 | 7 4=11 | 11 9=2 |

1. Point to Blossom 11 Chart. **(11) 9 2;**
   **(11) 8 3; (11) 7 4; (11) 6 5 . . .**

2. Stand near the samples. **Can you fill in the missing signs?**

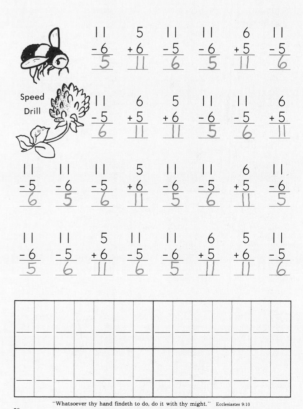

Speed Drill

| 11 | 5  | 11 | 11 | 6  | 11 |
|----|----|----|----|----|----|
| -6 | +6 | -5 | -6 | +5 | -5 |
| 5  | 11 | 6  | 5  | 11 | 6  |

| 11 | 6  | 5  | 11 | 11 | 6  |
|----|----|----|----|----|----|
| -5 | +5 | +6 | -6 | -5 | +5 |
| 6  | 11 | 11 | 5  | 6  | 11 |

| 11 | 11 | 11 | 5  | 11 | 11 | 6  | 11 |
|----|----|----|----|----|----|----|----|
| -5 | -6 | -5 | +6 | -6 | -5 | +5 | -6 |
| 6  | 5  | 6  | 11 | 5  | 6  | 11 | 5  |

| 11 | 11 | 5  | 11 | 11 | 6  | 5  | 11 |
|----|----|----|----|----|----|----|----|
| -6 | -5 | +6 | -5 | -6 | +5 | +6 | -5 |
| 5  | 6  | 11 | 6  | 5  | 11 | 11 | 6  |

**59**

Fill in the whole and parts.

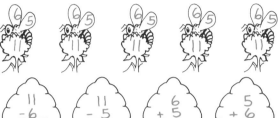

Write the facts.

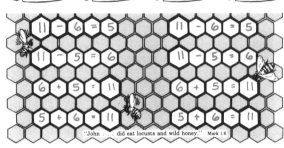

Trace, answer, and write the facts.

"John . . . . did eat locusts and wild honey." Mark 1:6

79

## Before Class

**Materials**

Addition and Subtraction 10 and 11 flash cards

Form C

**Chalkboard**

657
765
576

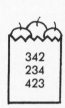

342
234
423

798
987
879

## Class Time

1. Stand near the clover patch.

**In the Bible a hungry man was walking through the woods. How glad he was to see some honeycomb. He took the end of his rod and dipped it in a honeycomb. The honey tasted delicious! Who was the man?**

Jonathan (1 Samuel 14:27)

2.  ⎡(11) 9 2⎤

**The whole number is __.**
**Its parts are __ and __.**
a. **The triplet is (11) 9 2 . . .**
b. **The facts are 11−9, 2; 11−2, 9; 9+2, 11; 2+9, 11.**

3.  ⎡(11) 8 3⎤

**The whole number is __.**
**Its parts are __ and __.**
a. **The triplet is (11) 8 3 . . .**
b. **The facts are 11−8, 3; 11−3, 8; 8+3, 11; 3+8, 11.**

Fill in the missing whole or parts.

| | | |
|---|---|---|
| 11 − 6 = 5 | 6 + 5 = 11 | 11 − 6 = 5 |
| 11 − 5 = 6 | 5 + 6 = 11 | 11 − 5 = 6 |
| 6 + 5 = 11 | 11 − 6 = 5 | 11 − 6 = 5 |
| 5 + 6 = 11 | 11 − 5 = 6 | 11 − 5 = 6 |
| 11 − 5 = 6 | 6 + 5 = 11 | 6 + 5 = 11 |
| 6 + 5 = 11 | 5 + 6 = 11 | 5 + 6 = 11 |

Extra Activity

Answer these problems.

```
  2    4    2    4    3    1    3    6
  3    5    0    2    3    4    4    0
 +6   +2   +8   +5   +5   +6   +3   +5
 11   11   10   11   11   11   10   11

  3    2    2    4    4    5    4    1
  2    4    2    1    5    1    2    5
 +6   +5   +6   +6   +1   +5   +5   +5
 11   11   10   11   10   11   11   11
```
80

4.  | (11)  7  4 |

The whole number is __.
Its parts are __ and __.
a. The triplet is (11) 7 4 . . .
b. The facts are 11−7, 4;  11−4, 7;
7+4, 11;  4+7, 11.

5.  | (11)  6  5 |

The whole number is __.
Its parts are __ and __.
a. The triplet is (11) 6 5 . . .
b. The facts are 11−6, 5;  11−5, 6;
6+5, 11;  5+6, 11.

6. Flash Addition and Subtraction 10 and 11 cards
for 1 minute. **Answer together.**

7. Flash Card Drill: Addition and Subtraction 10
and 11 cards. Use Form C.
**Flower Row: Box 1 . . .**

8. Review place value.
a. **1 apple is __.**  1 one
**1 bag of apples is __.**  1 ten
**1 bushel of apples is __.**  1 hundred
b. Point to the samples. **Which number has
the greatest ones?** (879)
**. . . tens?** (798) **. . . hundreds?** (987)
Continue.

9. Assign Lesson 59.

206

Circle the numeral
in ones' place,
in tens' place,
in hundreds' place.

| ones | 50⑦ | 25⑥ | 1⑧ | 48③ | ③ | 6⑦ |

| tens | 2⑤9 | ⑧3 | 5①2 | ⑨0 | 5⓪0 | ③5 |

| hundreds | ⑤98 | ③06 | 59 | ④89 | 82 | ②12 |

Form C (Class Time)

Fact Hives #7

Missing Whole or Parts #4

Write the time.

9:30   7:30   5:30   3:30   1:30

10:30   8:30   6:30   4:30   2:30

81

## After Class

1. Ask each child to recite the 11's triplets in order.

2. Chalkboard Drill: **Write the number you hear.**

   •**King David had 288 men who liked to sing.**

   (1 Chronicles 25:7)

   •**Aaron the priest lived 123 years.**

   (Number 33:39)

   •**Job had 500 yoke of oxen.**

   (Job 1:3)

   •**The Book of Joshua has 658 verses.**

   •**There were 276 people on a ship.**

   (Acts 27:37)

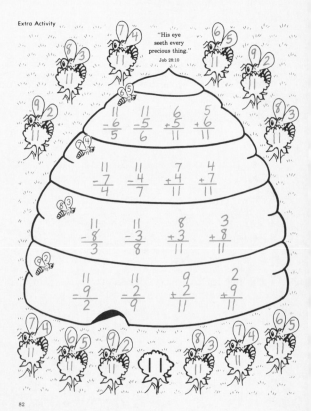

Extra Activity

"His eye
seeth every
precious thing."
Job 28:10

82

Fill in the whole or parts.

Write the facts.

Trace, answer, and write the facts.

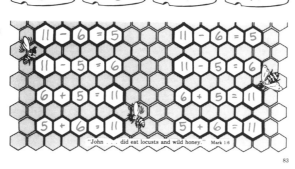

83

## Before Class

**Materials**

11's flash cards
Large coins
*Large clock*

**Chalkboard**

| 53 | 62 | 40 | 61 | 73 | 23 |
|----|----|----|----|----|----|
| 64 | 43 | 73 | 32 | 43 | 92 |
| +2 | +4 | +5 | +5 | +3 | +4 |

## Class Time

1. Flash the 11's cards. **Say the triplet; then say the answer.**

2. **Say the facts as I fill the beehive.**

3. Do the Column Addition samples.

4. Flash the large coins.
   a. **Penny, 1¢; nickel, 5¢; dime, 10¢; quarter, 25¢ . . .**
   b. **Which is less**
      **•2 quarters or 6 dimes?**
      **•3 nickels or 16 pennies?**
      **•3 dimes or 1 quarter?**
      **•3 quarters or 7 dimes?**

5. Review time.
   a. **60 minutes=1 hour. . . .**
      **30 minutes=½ hour. . . .**
   b. **Mother baked the bread for 60 minutes. She baked the buns for 30 minutes. Which did Mother bake longer, the bread or the buns?**

Read the story.
Write the numbers
  in the beehive.
Write the label words
  on the lines.
Answer the problem.

Speed
Drill

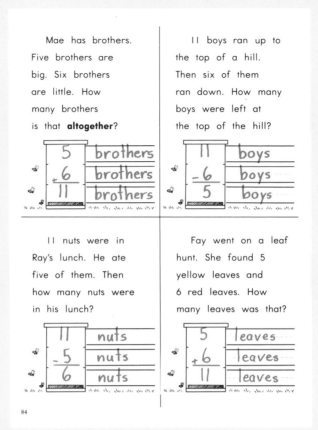

Mae has brothers.
Five brothers are
big. Six brothers
are little. How
many brothers
is that **altogether**?

5
+6
11
brothers
brothers
brothers

11 boys ran up to
the top of a hill.
Then six of them
ran down. How many
boys were left at
the top of the hill?

11
-6
5
boys
boys
boys

11 nuts were in
Ray's lunch. He ate
five of them. Then
how many nuts were
in his lunch?

11
-5
6
nuts
nuts
nuts

Fay went on a leaf
hunt. She found 5
yellow leaves and
6 red leaves. How
many leaves was that?

5
+6
11
leaves
leaves
leaves

84

c. **It takes 30 minutes to drive to Uncle Roy's house. It takes 60 minutes to drive to Grandmother's house. Who lives closer, Uncle Roy or Grandmother?**

6. Do the Speed Drill in Lesson 60.

7. Assign Lesson 60.

60

Answer these facts.

| | | | | | | | | 6 | 7 | | | | |
| -5 | -2 | -8 | -9 | +5 | +4 | -6 | -3 |
| 6 | 9 | 3 | 2 | 11 | 11 | 5 | 8 |

| | | | | | | | 6 | 9 | | | | | | | |
| -8 | -2 | -5 | +5 | +2 | -9 | -3 | -6 |
| 3 | 9 | 6 | 11 | 11 | 2 | 8 | 5 |

| | | 3 | | | | | 5 | | | 8 | | | |
| -4 | +8 | -3 | -7 | +6 | -5 | +3 | -6 |
| 7 | 11 | 8 | 4 | 11 | 6 | 11 | 5 |

**Blacklines**

Fact Hives #7

Missing Whole or Parts #4

Fact Form III

| | | 5 | | | | | 3 | | | | | 4 |
| -3 | +6 | -4 | -5 | +8 | -7 | -6 | +7 |
| 8 | 11 | 7 | 6 | 11 | 4 | 5 | 11 |

Answer these problems.

| 42 | 32 | 33 | 54 | 23 | 15 |
| 23 | 22 | 51 | 12 | 21 | 52 |
| +54 | +63 | +22 | +33 | +72 | +51 |
| 119 | 117 | 106 | 99 | 116 | 118 |

85

## After Class

1. Double Drill: 11's flash cards.

2. Hold the large clock. Ask individuals to set the clock at **1:30, 4:30, 8:30, 11:30, 2:30, 6:30** . . .

3. Point to the Number Line. **Add.**

   | 10+3 | 10+4 | 10+6 |
   | 10+7 | 10+1 | 10+2 |
   | 10+5 | 10+9 | 10+8 |

Speed Drill

| | | | | | | | | | | | | 8 |
| -6 | -8 | -7 | -5 | -9 | +3 |
| 5 | 3 | 4 | 6 | 2 | 11 |

| | | | | 5 | | | 4 | | |
| -3 | -2 | +6 | -8 | +7 | -5 |
| 8 | 9 | 11 | 3 | 11 | 6 |

| | | | | 6 | | | | | | | | | |
| -4 | -6 | +5 | -9 | -5 | -7 | -8 | -6 |
| 7 | 5 | 11 | 2 | 6 | 4 | 3 | 5 |

| | | | | | | 9 | | | 7 | | | | |
| -6 | -4 | -5 | +2 | -8 | +4 | -2 | -3 |
| 5 | 7 | 6 | 11 | 3 | 11 | 9 | 8 |

"Whatsoever thy hand findeth to do, do it with thy might." Ecclesiastes 9:10

86

# Appendix

<u>Patterns</u>

Boat Poster

Number Line Markers

Clover Patch Poster

Blossom Chart

Place Value Chart

These patterns are repeated on loose sheets with the set of blacklines for this course.

Patterns for individual flash cards and *My 1,000 Book* are provided with the blacklines for this course.

**Boat Poster**
See page 12 for instructions.

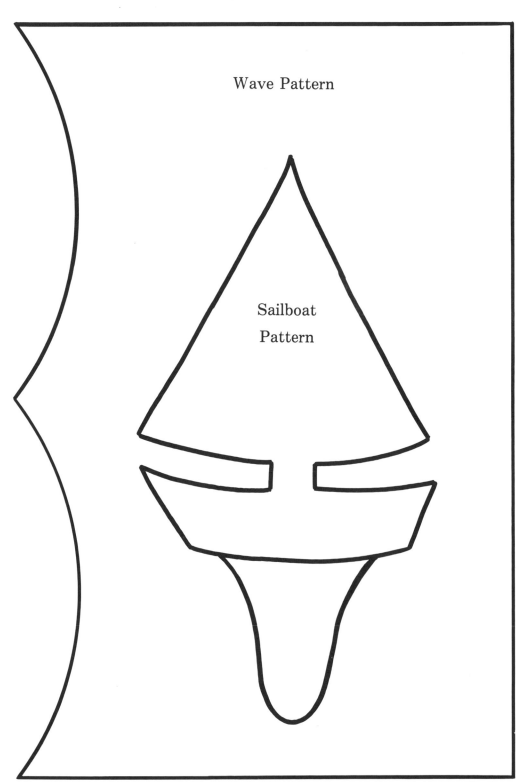

Wave Pattern

Sailboat
Pattern

Boat Poster patterns are repeated on loose sheets with the blacklines.

These patterns are repeated on loose sheets with the blacklines.

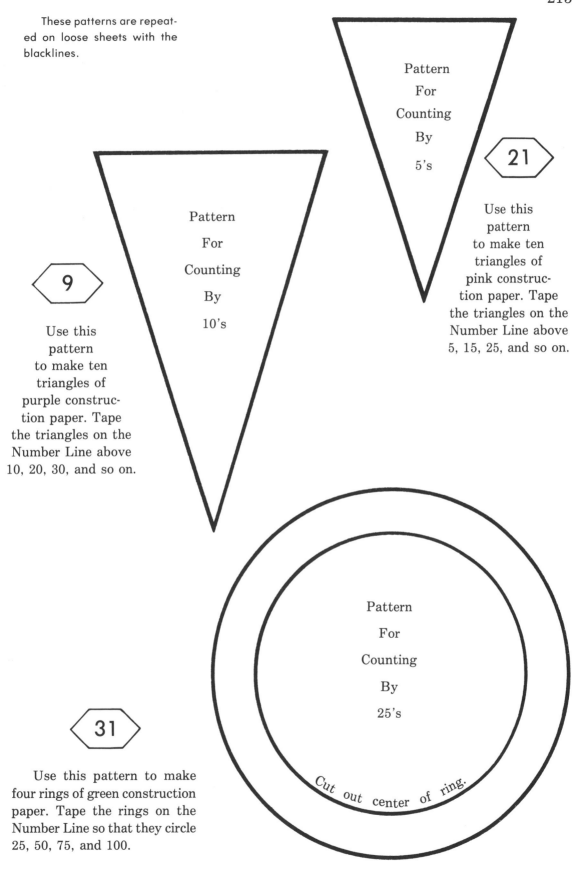

Pattern
For
Counting
By
5's

Pattern
For
Counting
By
10's

21

Use this pattern to make ten triangles of pink construction paper. Tape the triangles on the Number Line above 5, 15, 25, and so on.

9

Use this pattern to make ten triangles of purple construction paper. Tape the triangles on the Number Line above 10, 20, 30, and so on.

Pattern
For
Counting
By
25's

Cut out center of ring.

31

Use this pattern to make four rings of green construction paper. Tape the rings on the Number Line so that they circle 25, 50, 75, and 100.

**Clover Patch Poster**

See page 13 for instructions.

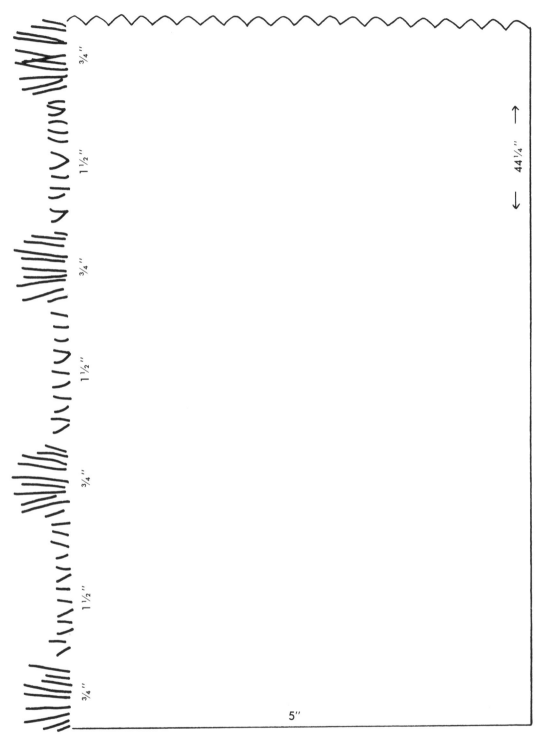

Draw this grass pattern 5″ from the bottom of your poster. The clover blossoms will slip into the slots when the poster is made.

# Clover Patch Poster

Make nine
of this pattern.
Color the clover
blossoms pink.
Color the bees'
body yellow.

Clover Patch Poster patterns are
repeated on loose sheets with the
blacklines.

Make eighteen
of this pattern.
Color ten clover
blossoms pink.
Color eight clover
blossoms red-violet.

**Blossom Chart**

See page 14 for instructions.

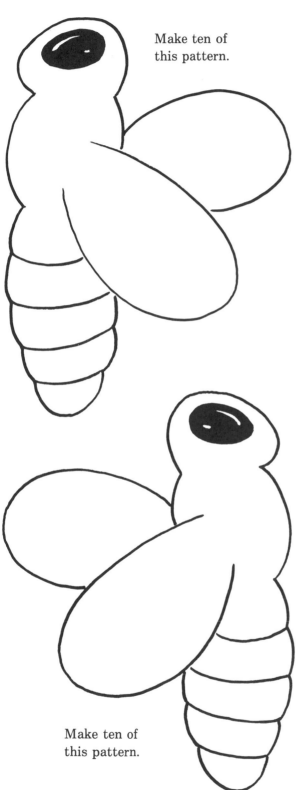

Make ten of
this pattern.

Color the bees yellow and brown.
Do not color the wings.
Write the *2 parts* on the wings
with a broad-tipped green marker.
Make the numbers as large and bold
as possible.

With each new triplet, add another
bee to the chart.
1. Arrange the bees clockwise
   around the clover blossom.
2. Mount the bees with reusable
   adhesive.
3. When the school year closes,
   remove the bees. Store the blossom charts for use next year.

Make ten of
this pattern.

# Blossom Chart

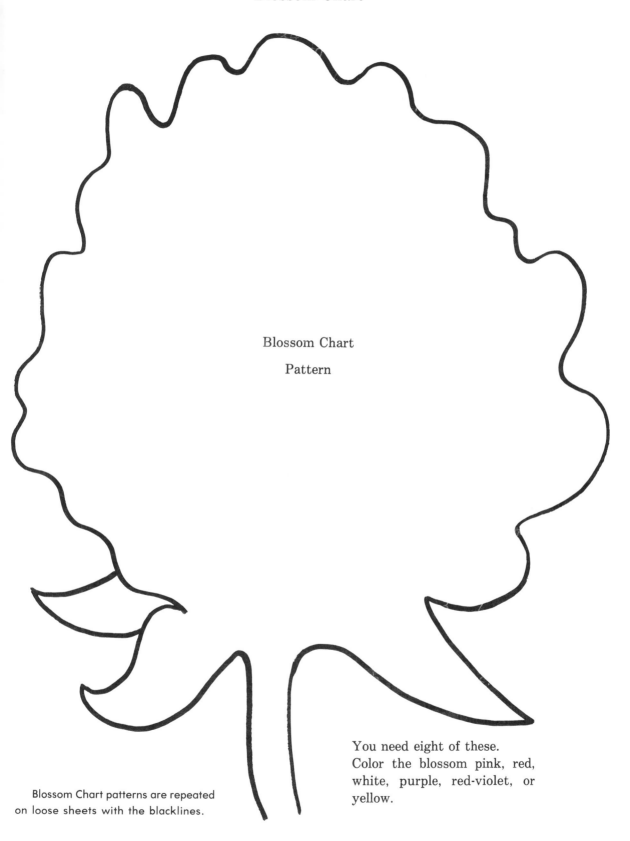

Blossom Chart

Pattern

You need eight of these.
Color the blossom pink, red,
white, purple, red-violet, or
yellow.

Blossom Chart patterns are repeated
on loose sheets with the blacklines.

# Place Value Chart

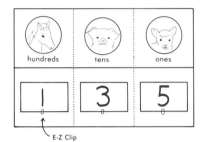

A place value chart can help the children learn and remember the names of the places. Draw a grid on a large white poster board. Reproduce and color the pictures of these three animals. Paste the lamb in ones' place, the pig in tens' place, and the pony in hundreds' place.

Write numerals 0–9 on 3×5 index cards. Make three cards of each numeral for working with numbers like 111.

Press an E-Z Clip at the bottom of each number place to hold the card.

Use the chart for handy reference during seatwork and for working with numbers that switch digits (127 and 172, 105 and 150).

Place Value Chart patterns are repeated on loose sheets with the blacklines.

# Index of New Skills—Where They Are First Introduced

| COMPUTATION | Teacher's Manual Lesson Number | Pupil's Book Lesson Number | Blacklines Lesson Number | Skill Number |
|---|---|---|---|---|
| Addition Families 2 and 3 | 1 | 1 | | |
| Addition Family 4 | 2 | 2 | | |
| Addition Family 5 | 3 | 3 | | |
| Addition Family 6 | 4 | 4 | 5 Number Facts | #1 |
| 2 digits + 2 digits | 6 | 8 | | |
| Addition Family 7 | 7 | 7 | 8 Number Facts | #2 |
| 2 digits + 1 digit | 8 | 10 | 10 Adding 2-Place Nos. | #1 |
| Subtraction Families 2 and 3 | 11 | 11 | | |
| Subtraction Family 4 | 12 | 12 | | |
| Subtraction Family 5 | 13 | 13 | | |
| 2 digits − 2 digits | 13 | 15 | | |
| Subtraction Family 6 | 14 | 14 | 15 Number Facts | #3 |
| 2 digits − 1 digit | 15 | 17 | 18 Subtracting 2-Place Nos. | #2 |

# Index of New Skills—Where They Are First Introduced

| COMPUTATION | Teacher's Manual Lesson Number | Pupil's Book Lesson Number | Blacklines Lesson Number | Skill Number |
|---|---|---|---|---|
| Subtraction Family 7 | 17 | 17 | 18 Number Facts | #4 |
| Addition Family 8 | 21 | 21 | 22 Number Facts | #5 |
| Addition Family 9 | 24 | 24 | 25 Number Facts | #6 |
| 3 digits + 3 digits | 25 | 27 | | |
| Addition Family 10 | 27 | 27 | 28 Fact Form I | |
| 3 digits + 2 digits | 28 | 29 | | |
| Subtraction Family 8 | 31 | 31 | | |
| Subtraction Family 9 | 34 | 34 | 35 Number Facts | #7 |
| 3 digits − 3 digits | 35 | 36 | | |
| Subtraction Family 10 | 37 | 37 | 38 Fact Form II | |
| 3 digits − 2 digits | 37 | 38 | | |
| 1 digit + 1 digit + 1 digit | 38 | 44 | | |
| (11) 9 2 triplet and facts | 41 | 41 | 41 Fact Hives<br>43 Missing Whole or Part | #1<br>#1 |

# Index of New Skills—Where They Are First Introduced

| COMPUTATION | Teacher's Manual<br><br>Lesson Number | Pupil's Book<br><br>Lesson Number | Blacklines |  |
|---|---|---|---|---|
| | | | Lesson Number | Skill Number |
| (11)  8  3  triplet and facts | 46 | 46 | 46  Fact Hives<br>48  Missing Whole or Part | #2<br>#2 |
| (11)  7  4  triplet and facts | 51 | 51 | 51  Fact Hives<br>51  Triplets With Facts<br>53  Missing Whole or Part | #4<br>#1<br>#3 |
| 2 digits + 2 digits + 2 digits | 53 | 55 | | |
| (11)  6  5  triplet and facts | 56 | 56 | 56  Fact Hives<br>56  Triplets With Facts<br>58  Missing Whole or Part<br>64  Fact Form IV | #6<br>#2<br>#4 |
| 2 digits + 2 digits + 1 digit | 56 | 61 | | |
| (12)  9  3  triplet and facts | 61 | 61 | 61  Fact Hives<br>61  Triplets With Facts<br>63  Missing Whole or Part | #8<br>#3<br>#5 |
| Carrying: 2 digits + 2 digits | 65 | 67 | | |
| (12)  8  4  triplet and facts | 66 | 66 | 66  Fact Hives<br>66  Triplets With Facts<br>66  Number Facts<br>68  Missing Whole or Part | #9<br>#4<br>#8<br>#6 |
| (12)  7  5  triplet and facts | 71 | 71 | 71  Fact Hives<br>71  Triplets With Facts<br>72  Number Facts<br>73  Missing Whole or Part | #11<br>#5<br>#9<br>#7 |
| (12)  6  6  triplet and facts | 76 | 76 | 76  Fact Hives<br>76  Missing Whole or Part<br>79  Fact Form V | #13<br>#8 |
| (13)  9  4  triplet and facts | 79 | 79 | 79  Fact Hives<br>81  Missing Whole or Part<br>82  Number Facts<br>84  Triplets With Facts | #14<br>#9<br>#10<br>#6 |
| Column addition—carrying | 84 | 84 | | |

# Index of New Skills—Where They Are First Introduced

| COMPUTATION | Teacher's Manual Lesson Number | Pupil's Book Lesson Number | Blacklines Lesson Number | Skill Number |
|---|---|---|---|---|
| (13) 8 5 triplet and facts | 87 | 87 | 87 Fact Hives<br>88 Number Facts<br>89 Missing Whole or Part<br>92 Triplets With Facts | #15<br>#11<br>#10<br>#7 |
| Borrowing: 2 digits − 2 digits | 88 | 90 | | |
| (13) 7 6 triplet and facts | 95 | 95 | 95 Fact Hives<br>96 Number Facts<br>97 Missing Whole or Part<br>98 Triplets With Facts<br>100 Fact Form VI<br>106 Subtracting 2-Place Nos. | #17<br>#12<br>#11<br>#8<br><br>#7 |
| (14) 9 5 triplet and facts | 103 | 103 | 103 Fact Hives<br>105 Missing Whole or Part<br>106 Triplets With Facts | #19<br>#12<br>#9 |
| (14) 8 6 triplet and facts | 111 | 111 | 111 Fact Hives<br>112 Number Facts<br>113 Missing Whole or Part<br>114 Triplets With Facts | #20<br>#13<br>#13<br>#10 |
| Carrying twice: 3 digits + 3 digits | 114 | 115 | | |
| (14) 7 7 triplet and facts | 119 | 119 | 119 Fact Hives<br>119 Fact Form VII<br>125 Triplets With Facts | #22<br><br>#11 |
| (15) 9 6 triplet and facts | 122 | 122 | 122 Fact Hives<br>123 Number Facts<br>124 Missing Whole or Part | #23<br>#14<br>#14 |
| 2× table (optional) | 124 | | | |
| Divide by 2 (optional) | 130 | | | |
| (15) 8 7 triplet and facts | 130 | 130 | 130 Fact Hives<br>132 Missing Whole or Part<br>132 Number Facts<br>133 Triplets With Facts<br>134 Fact Form VIII | #24<br>#15<br>#15<br>#12 |

# Index of New Skills—Where They Are First Introduced

| COMPUTATION | Teacher's Manual | Pupil's Book | Blacklines | |
|---|---|---|---|---|
| | Lesson Number | Lesson Number | Lesson Number | Skill Number |
| 10× table (optional) | 133 | | | |
| (16) 9 7 triplet and facts | 138 | 138 | 138 Fact Hives<br>140 Missing Whole or Part<br>140 Number Facts<br>141 Triplets With Facts | #26<br>#16<br>#16<br>#13 |
| Divide by 10 (optional) | 139 | | | |
| 5× table (optional) | 142 | | | |
| (16) 8 8 triplet and facts | 146 | 146 | 146 Fact Hives<br>147 Fact Form IX | #28 |
| Divide by 5 (optional) | 148 | | | |
| (17) 9 8 triplet and facts | 149 | 149 | 149 Fact Hives<br>150 Number Facts<br>151 Missing Whole or Part<br>152 Triplets With Facts | #29<br>#17<br>#17<br>#14 |
| 1× table (optional) | 151 | | | |
| (18) 9 9 triplet and facts | 157 | 157 | 157 Fact Hives<br>158 Missing Whole or Part<br>158 Number Facts<br>159 Triplets With Facts<br>161 Fact Form X | #31<br>#18<br>#18<br>#15 |
| | | | | |
| | | | | |
| | | | | |

# Index of New Skills—Where They Are First Introduced

| EQUATIONS | Teacher's Manual Lesson Number | Pupil's Book Lesson Number | Blacklines Lesson Number | Skill Number |
|---|---|---|---|---|
| 60 minutes = 1 hour | 48 | | | |
| 30 minutes = ½ hour | 55 | | | |
| 12 things = 1 dozen | 115 | 117 | | |
| 6 things = ½ dozen | 115 | 117 | | |
| 7 days = 1 week | 117 | | | |
| 12 months = 1 year | 119 | | | |
| 12 inches = 1 foot | 125 | 127 | | |
| 3 feet = 1 yard | 128 | 129 | 141 Equations | #1 |
| 2 cups = 1 pint | 147 | 149 | | |
| 2 pints = 1 quart | 150 | 151 | 155 Equations | #2 |
| 4 quarts = 1 gallon | 153 | 154 | 161 Equations | #3 |
| 16 ounces = 1 pound | 157 | 157 | 165 Equations | #4 |

| FRACTIONS | Teacher's Manual Lesson Number | Pupil's Book Lesson Number | Blacklines Lesson Number | Skill Number |
|---|---|---|---|---|
| 1/2 | 98 | 100 | | |
| 1/4 | 106 | 108 | | |
| 1/2 of a number | 108 | | | |
| 1/3 | 140 | 141 | | |

# Index of New Skills—Where They Are First Introduced

| MONEY | Teacher's Manual Lesson Number | Pupil's Book Lesson Number | Blacklines Lesson Number | Skill Number |
|---|---|---|---|---|
| Penny | 7 | 8 | | |
| Dime | 14 | 16 | 17   Money Identification | #1 |
| Dimes + pennies | 19 | 19 | | |
| Nickel | 22 | 24 | 27   Money Identification | #3 |
| Nickels + pennies | 27 | 29 | | |
| Quarter | 32 | 34 | 41   Money Identification | #5 |
| Quarters + pennies | 36 | 37 | | |
| Dimes + nickels | 49 | 50 | | |
| $ sign and decimal point | 97 | 98 | | |
| Half dollar | 133 | 135 | 138   Money Identification | #7 |
| Half dollar + dimes | 134 | 135 | | |
| Half dollar + pennies | 138 | 138 | | |

| NUMBER COMPARISON | Teacher's Manual Lesson Number | Pupil's Book Lesson Number | Blacklines Lesson Number | Skill Number |
|---|---|---|---|---|
| Largest number | 1 | 3 | | |
| Smallest number | 11 | 13 | | |

| NUMBER ORDER | Teacher's Manual Lesson Number | Pupil's Book Lesson Number | Blacklines Lesson Number | Skill Number |
|---|---|---|---|---|
| After numbers | 3 | 1 | | |
| Before numbers | 4 | 6 | | |
| Before and After numbers | 12 | 21 | | |

# Index of New Skills—Where They Are First Introduced

| PLACE VALUE | Teacher's Manual Lesson Number | Pupil's Book Lesson Number | Blacklines Lesson Number | Skill Number |
|---|---|---|---|---|
| up to 100's place | 5 | 6 | | |
| up to 1000's place | 62 | 64 | | |

| READING PROBLEMS | Teacher's Manual Lesson Number | Pupil's Book Lesson Number | Blacklines Lesson Number | Skill Number |
|---|---|---|---|---|
| Key word: in all | 6 | 8 | 22 | Reading Problems #1 |
| Key word: left | 14 | 19 | 39 | Reading Problems #3 |
| Key word: altogether | 23 | 52 | | |
| Key word: both | 30 | 78 | | |
| No key word | 33 | 50 | | |
| Finding a missing part | 44 | 100 | | |
| 2-digit computation | 64 | 112 | | |
| Using ¢ | 64 | 116 | | |
| Key word: how much more | 100 | | 106 | Reading Problems #4 |
| Key word: less | 113 | | 116 | Reading Problems #6 |
| Using 1 dozen | 117 | 127 | | |
| Key word: sum | 142 | | 143 | Reading Problems #9 |
| Key word: difference | 153 | | 156 | Reading Problems #11 |

# Index of New Skills—Where They Are First Introduced

| SHAPES | Teacher's Manual Lesson Number | Pupil's Book Lesson Number | Blacklines Lesson Number | Skill Number |
|---|---|---|---|---|
| Circle | 83 | 84 | | |
| Square | 83 | 84 | | |
| Triangle | 84 | 85 | | |
| Rectangle | 87 | 87 | | |

| SKIP COUNTING | Teacher's Manual Lesson Number | Pupil's Book Lesson Number | Blacklines Lesson Number | Skill Number |
|---|---|---|---|---|
| Counting by 10's | 9 | 11 | 11 Skip Counting | #1 |
| Counting by 5's | 21 | 23 | 24 Skip Counting | #2 |
| Counting by 25's | 31 | 33 | 33 Skip Counting | #3 |
| Counting by 2's | 39 | 41 | 44 Skip Counting | #4 |
| Counting by 100's | 61 | | | |
| Counting by 50's | 132 | | | |

| TELLING TIME | Teacher's Manual Lesson Number | Pupil's Book Lesson Number | Blacklines Lesson Number | Skill Number |
|---|---|---|---|---|
| :00 | 43 | 44 | | |
| :30 | 56 | 57 | | |
| :15 | 72 | 74 | | |
| :45 | 79 | 81 | | |

# Teaching Aids—Where They Are First Used

| DRILLS | Teacher's Manual Lesson Number |
|---|---|
| Chalkboard Drill | 2 |
| Speed Drill | 6 |
| Double Drill | 9 |
| Flash Card Drill | 26 |
| Circle Drill | 28 |
| Oral Drill | 46 |

| FACT FORMS | Teacher's Manual Lesson Number |
|---|---|
| I | 28 |
| II | 38 |
| III | 46 |
| IV | 64 |
| V | 79 |
| VI | 100 |
| VII | 119 |
| VIII | 134 |
| IX | 147 |
| X | 161 |
| XI | 164 |
| XII | 167 |

| FORMS | Teacher's Manual Lesson Number |
|---|---|
| A | 2 |
| B | 6 |
| C | 26 |
| D | |

| VISUAL AIDS | Teacher's Manual Lesson Number |
|---|---|
| Number line | 1 |
| Boat Poster | 1 |
| My 1,000 Book | 3 |
| Real pennies (one for each child) | 7 |
| Large penny | 9 |
| 10 purple triangles | 9 |
| Real dimes (one for each child) | 14 |
| Large dime | 16 |
| 10 pink triangles | 21 |
| Real nickels (one for each child) | 22 |
| Large nickel | 25 |
| 4 green rings | 31 |
| Real quarters (one for each child) | 32 |
| Large quarter | 34 |
| Clover Patch Poster | 41 |
| Large clock | 43 |

| | |
|---|---|
| Blossom Charts | 47 |
| Large classroom calendar | 117 |
| 12″ ruler | 125 |
| 36″ yardstick | 128 |
| Real half dollar | 133 |
| Large half dollar | 134 |
| Cup | 147 |
| Pint jar | 147 |
| Quart jar | 150 |
| Gallon jar | 153 |
| 1 ounce bundle of 4 new pencils (5 new crayons, 3 sticks of chalk) | 157 |
| 1 pound bundle of 6 boxes of 1 dozen pencils (5 boxes of sixteen crayons, 4 boxes of one dozen chalk sticks) | 158 |
| Place Value Chart | |